LaConner Palates

An Illustrated Cookbook

Patricia Flynn
Patricia McClane

BOOKENDS
PUBLISHING

Bookends Publishing
Oak Harbor, Washington

Printed in the United States of America
1st Printing

Cover photograph, *Tulips* by Patricia Flynn

ISBN 0-9659303-0-0

The nutritional values given in this cookbook were obtained from computer data banks, the U.S. Department of Agriculture, as well as the food industry. Please be aware that seasonal and regional differences may affect the nutritional values in food. The nutritional information in this cookbook is not to be used as a strict guideline for dietary needs.

TABLE OF CONTENTS

ACKNOWLEDGEMENTS

First of all we would like to acknowledge all our friends and family who encouraged us to take on this challenge and supported us through the trials, errors and successes along the journey. It wasn't always easy, but they kept us going! Several of these people provided support above and beyond the call of just "friendship" and to them we owe a special thank you.

Rosemary Toft who put in hour after hour of proofreading and editing and still insisted she was enjoying it!
Louise Deskey who also spent hours of eyestrain to proofread for us.
Laura Moore for her expertise and advice as an already published cookbook co-author with two publications to her name, *Simply Whidbey* and *Seasons on Whidbey*.
Lynette Taylor for providing excellent professional advice on the technical aspects of printing.
John Flynn, who believed in this project from the beginning, offered "technical suggestions" and got the computer back up every time it "crashed."

Of course, we would also like to acknowledge and thank those merchants in LaConner who provided the raw material for this cookbook and await its arrival with anticipation!

PREFACE

Hopefully, *LaConner Palates: An Illustrated Cookbook,* will find a space on a bookshelf somewhere between cookbook and travel guide. The recipes, provided by the merchants featured, range from challenges for experienced cooks to simple, straightforward ones even beginners can try. At the same time, there is plenty of information about this colorful, historic town for the most seasoned visitors, or to entice someone looking for a new travel destination. Even the copy is intended to engage the reader. The illustrations not only help with identifying the places of business, but also give the reader a feel for the unique and quaint atmosphere this town has to offer.

This entire book, except for the illustrations, was formatted and generated on a computer. Though both authors have backgrounds in graphic design, at the start of this project neither of them had put their skills to the test in combination with a computer. The learning curve was HUGE! All recipes were put through a software program, The Cook's Palate (Better Lifestyles), to provide the nutritional values shown. The resulting recipes, copy, scanned photographs and illustrations were then formatted into a publication with the use of Adobe PageMaker® and Adobe Photoshop™. Though the number of hours involved seemed, at times, endless, an undertaking of this proportion would have been impossible to the self-publisher in the past. Thank the age of technology for the end results!

LaConner Palates represents the best LaConner has to offer. The authors have done their best to present the recipes and information provided in its truest form. Recipes will vary according to individual tastes. Wishing you pleasant journeys and sated palates!

Bookends Publishing

Tapestry of Time
A Brief History of LaConner

Picturesque, as well as unique, the small community of LaConner has been voted "Washington's Best Tiny Town." With over 150 buildings and sites listed in The National Register of Historic Places, there is a distinctive sense of history surrounding the oldest town in Skagit county.

Swinomish was the first name given to a small trading post founded by an early settler to the Skagit Valley. Named in honor of the local Native American tribe, it was located on the western shore of the Swinomish Channel. John Conner purchased the trading post in the early 1870's and moved it to the eastern shore of the channel where he had platted a townsite. He renamed the post L. A. Conner in honor of his wife Louisa Ann. This fledgling town was noted on local area maps about 1876.

Other early settlers to the area built dikes which reclaimed farmland taken over by annual flooding of the nearby Skagit River. This created some of the most fertile agricultural land in the world. With its rich farmland producing bountiful crops and the easy accessibility via the Swinomish Channel for steamships to and from Seattle, the town thrived and reached its peak around the turn of the century. During the Depression, local commerce dwindled and remained that way until the mid-1970's when two resident businessmen initiated LaConner's revitalization. Again, the tiny town was a thriving community of distinctive shops, mouth-watering restaurants and charming bed and breakfasts visited by people from all over the world.

Many visitors think of tulips when they think of LaConner, and tulips are certainly the Skagit Valley's most acclaimed crop. Each spring they are celebrated during the Skagit Valley Tulip Festival when people come from near and far to view the tulips' spectacular show of vibrant color that covers the valley like an exquisite patchwork quilt.

Also during this time of year, Skagit Valley witnesses the return of the largest wintering populations of trumpeter swans and snow geese in the United States. Huge flocks blanket the fields with their snowy whiteness and the air clamors with their noisy proclamations. The spectacle of several thousand snow geese feeding in the dormant fields is an experience that will not soon be forgotten.

LaConner has long been the inspiration for many artists. In the late 1930's LaConner attracted the likes of artists Mark Tobey, Morris Graves and Kenneth Callahan, who would later found the "Northwest School" of artistic expression. Today LaConner still has the privilege of a long list of resident artists that likewise call LaConner their inspiration and home.

The first weekend in November is one of the largest events of the year - Art's Alive. LaConner goes all out to stage and play host to a wide variety of demonstrations, exhibitions and events. Local merchants and businesses invite artists, woodworkers, authors, musicians and many other talented individuals to speak about, demonstrate or perform their craft, proving that LaConner is indeed the meeting ground for very diverse talents and tastes.

LaConner has become a town for all seasons, where shops, restaurants and accommodations are open year around. Local merchants and businesses want visitors to feel like welcome guests and enjoy the cornucopia of tangible delights the town has to offer. From a lazy afternoon with a good book at a B & B to strolling down the main streets, LaConner has something to offer everyone. Visitors will find a myriad of shops with everything from steaming lattes and gourmet delights to shops filled with tantilizing treasures for the individual or their home.

It is easy to see why LaConner was voted "Washington's Best Tiny Town." It is a world unto itself that envelopes visitors with a warmth that is remembered long after their stay is over.

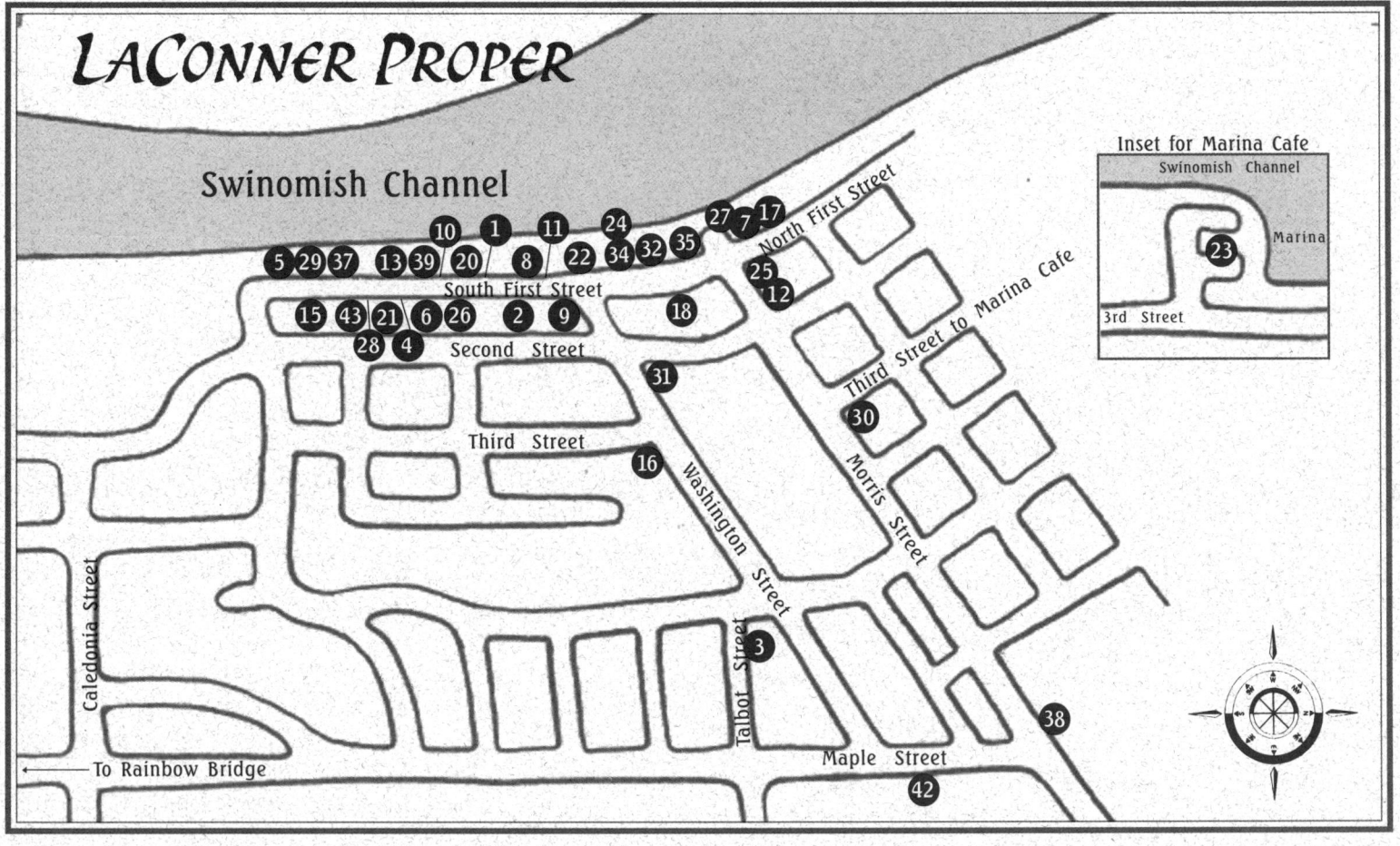

LaConner Proper

Swinomish Channel

South First Street

Second Street

Third Street

North First Street

Washington Street

Talbot Street

Morris Street

Caledonia Street

Maple Street

Third Street to Marina Cafe

← To Rainbow Bridge

Inset for Marina Cafe

Swinomish Channel

Marina

3rd Street

LaConner Proper

1. A Class Act Gallery
2. Andiamo Ristorante Italiano
3. Art's Place Bed and Breakfast
4. Brassy's
5. Calico Cupboard Cafe and Bakery
6. Caravan Gallery
7. Champagne Cove
8. Cottons
9. The Country Lady
10. Dandelion
11. The Ginger Grater
12. Go Outside
13. Homespun Market
14. Hope Island Inn (see page 12)
15. Just Imagine
16. Katy's Inn Bed and Breakfast
17. Kokomo Joe's
18. LaConner Brewing Company
19. LaConner Flats, a garden - The Granary (see page 12)
20. LaConner Seafood and Prime Rib House
21. Legends
22. Lighthouse Inn
23. Marina Cafe
24. Matheson Metal Sculpture
25. Nasty Jack's Antiques
26. O'Leary's Books and Other Comforts
27. The Olive Shoppe
28. Organic Matters
29. The Padilla Bay Store
30. Palace Market Interiors
31. Palmer's Restaurant
32. Rainbow Bridge Shirtworks
33. Rainbow Inn Bed and Breakfast (see page 12)
34. The Scott Collection
35. Serendipity Gallery
36. Skagit Bay Hideaway (see page 12)
37. The Stall
38. Tillinghast Seed Company
39. Two Moon's
40. West Shore Acres (see page 12)
41. The White Swan Guest House (see page 12)
42. The Wild Iris Inn
43. The Wood Merchant

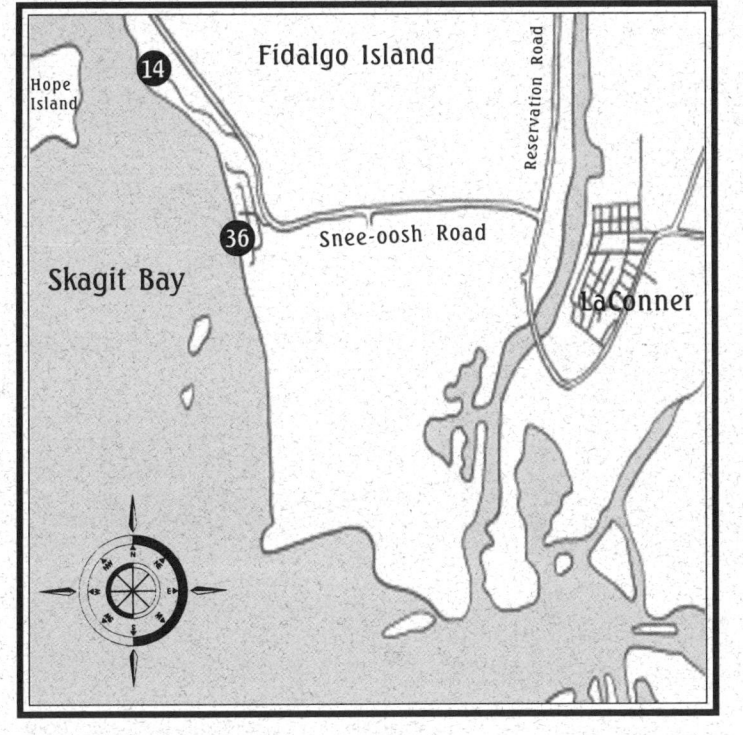

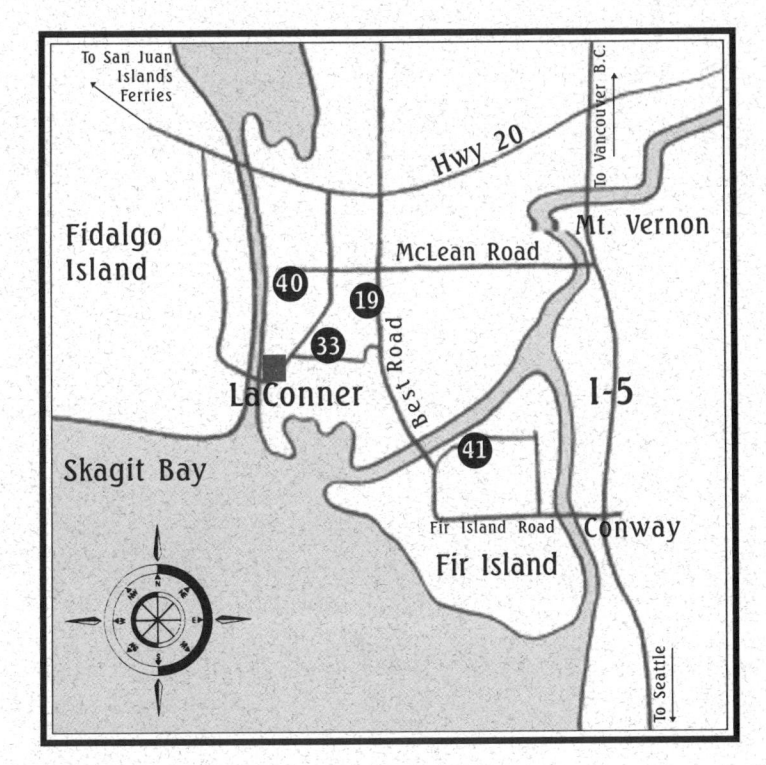

OUTLYING AREA - WEST

14 Hope Island Inn
36 Skagit Bay Hideaway

OUTLYING AREA - EAST

19 LaConner Flats, a garden - The Granary
33 Rainbow Inn Bed and Breakfast
40 West Shore Acres
41 The White Swan Guest House

Useful Kitchen Tips

Chiffonade
When you need ribbon-like pieces of herbs or vegetables, stack several leaves with the largest leaf on the bottom. Roll leaf stack up from one side to the other, then slice roll into ¼" or less increments. Using this fast and easy method the leaves won't get crushed or bruised.

Clarifying Butter
Cube 1 pound unsalted butter and place in saucepan. Melt butter slowly over low heat. As it melts, the water will evaporate and milk solids will sink. Skim foam off top with spoon and discard. Slowly pour the clear, yellow melted butter in to glass jar leaving milk solids in bottom of saucepan. May be refrigerated for several weeks or frozen until needed.

Cleaning and Debearding Mussels
Scrub the outside of shells with stiff brush and scrape off any barnacles with a knife. The beard of the mussel can be cut off with kitchen shears or just pulled off.

Cleaning Leeks
Dirt or sand can get caught between the layers of the leek making them hard to clean. To make this process easier, cut off the coarse parts of the green tops. Split the leek lengthwise and, holding under cold running water, fan the layers to wash away any dirt.

Deveining Prawns
Remove prawn from shell. Holding prawn under cold running water, using a knife, remove black or green vein that runs along the back of prawn.

Dried Mushrooms
If fresh mushrooms aren't readily available, use dried mushrooms. To reconstitute, place mushrooms in a bowl and cover with warm water. After mushrooms have expanded in size, remove individually, being careful not to disturb grit in bottom of bowl. Transfer to a strainer to drain.

GARLIC

To loosen skin on individual garlic cloves for peeling, place the flat side of a large kitchen knife on the clove of garlic and lightly smack with your hand. The skin will peel off easily.

GINGER

Buy ginger that has smooth skin and is firm. To use, cut off and discard exposed ends and peel the amount that you will need. Slice, sliver, mince or grate. Ginger will store well in the refrigerator for up to a week in a plastic bag. Do not freeze.

PROOFING YEAST

Place a pinch of sugar and 1 tablespoon of yeast in warm water (about 110°). Stir and let sit for 5-10 minutes, until yeast and sugar dissolve. If there is a foamy layer on the surface of yeast mixture the yeast is active. If no foamy layer appears your yeast needs to be replaced.

PROPORTIONS WHEN USING FRESH HERBS INSTEAD OF DRIED HERBS

Dried herbs are much stronger than fresh herbs. The general rule of thumb is to use three times as much fresh herbs as you would dried herbs.

STORING FRESH HERBS

Dip herbs in cool water and gently swirl to remove any dirt or insects. Inspect and toss out any bruised, broken or decayed stems or leaves. Gently shake off excess water and place stems of herbs in waterfilled container with leaves above the rim. Place a plastic bag loosely over tops of leaves and refrigerate. Change water periodically and remove any part of the herb that shows signs of decay. This method works well on many different types of green leafy herbs. Of course the quality of the herb affects how well it will keep. Basil may be prepared in the same manner but store it on a countertop instead of the refrigerator. You may find your basil will develop roots. If so, plant the cutting and soon you will have your own basil garden at your fingertips!

TENDERIZING MEAT

Linda Banaszak gave us this great idea for tenderizing meat. Place each piece of meat in an individual freezer bag large enough to accommodate. Tenderize meat with a mallet. Remove meat and discard freezer bag.

TONGS

For turning cuts of meat while cooking, use tongs. Using a fork will pierce the meat and allow juices to escape, drying out the meat.

A CLASS ACT GALLERY

A Class Act Gallery on South First Street began with only a dream. That dream has become three unique galleries including A Class Act II and The Holderby Gallery, both located in the Lime Dock Building.

Artwork that speaks to the individual spirit, not to those who follow the crowd, is A Class Act's key to success. Just watching the sunlight dancing across the blown glass vases in the windows will give you a hint of the pleasures that await you inside.

If a distinctive gift is your mission of the day in LaConner, perhaps a piece of functional or decorative pottery fits the bill. Or perhaps, the find of the day is one of the wind chimes, whose soft, mellow tones soothes the soul. Local artist Randy Van Beek can take you on a trip into the pastoral world of light and space with his original oil paintings. Perhaps it's the magic of the enormous amethyst geodes that mesmerize you.

Take a moment to slow down. Listen to the music. Enjoy a smile and a cup of coffee - always available at A Class Act!

612 SOUTH FIRST STREET   360-466-2000

MORROCCAN MOCHA

East meets West with this delicious meld of espresso and rich chocolate. Easy to make and delicious to sip, it's the perfect answer to one of our gray Northwest mornings.

Recipe contributed by: The Caravan Gallery

Preparation time: 5 minutes   Serves: 2

Ingredients
2 shots espresso
2 1 ounce squares unsweetened chocolate

Preparation
Brew two shots of espresso. Place 1 chocolate square in bottom of each cup and pour freshly brewed espresso over chocolate to melt. Serve with a small spoon to stir.

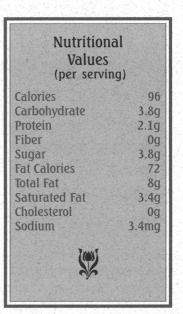

Nutritional Values
(per serving)

Calories	96
Carbohydrate	3.8g
Protein	2.1g
Fiber	0g
Sugar	3.8g
Fat Calories	72
Total Fat	8g
Saturated Fat	3.4g
Cholesterol	0g
Sodium	3.4mg

Scott's Coyote Canyon Margaritas

Your friends are over and it's been the hottest day of the year. Serve up a batch of these 'ritas and you'll have them howling at the moon!

Recipe contributed by: Jan Marie's brother Scott, The Country Lady

Preparation time: 5 minutes   Serves: 4

Ingredients
⅛ cup coarse salt
6 ounces beer
6 ounces tequila
6 ounces limeade, concentrate
4 slices lime

Preparation
Pour 6 ounce can of limeade into blender. Fill limeade can with beer and add to blender. Fill can with tequila and add. Fill blender with ice and blend until ice is slushy, about 1 minute. Rub rims of 4 margarita glasses with lime slices and invert them in the salt until rim is just coated. Pour blended mixture into glasses. Add a lime slice to side of glass and serve. Ola!

Nutritional Values (per serving)	
Calories	76
Carbohydrate	13.4g
Protein	0.6g
Fiber	2g
Sugar	11.4g
Fat Calories	1
Total Fat	0.1g
Saturated Fat	0g
Cholesterol	0g
Sodium	4.4mg

Andiamo Ristorante Italiano

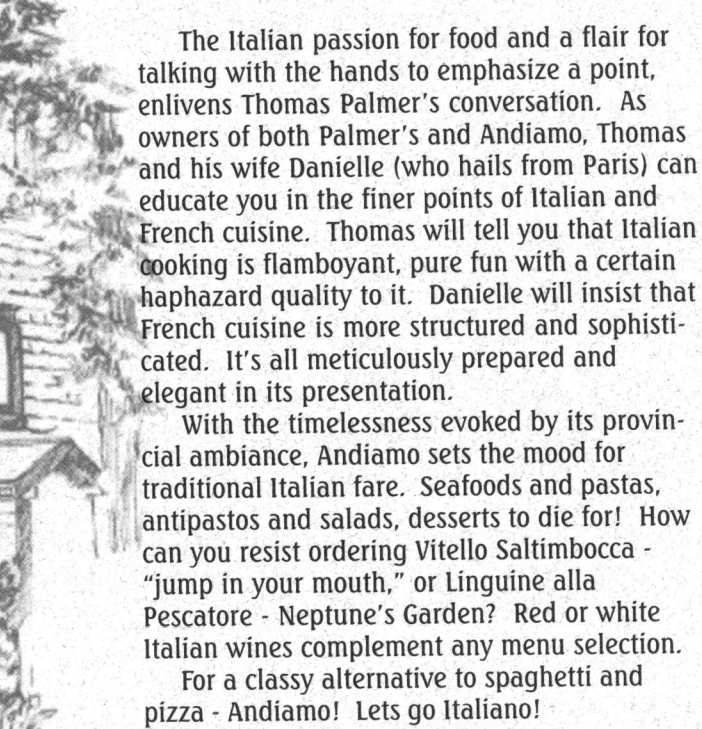

The Italian passion for food and a flair for talking with the hands to emphasize a point, enlivens Thomas Palmer's conversation. As owners of both Palmer's and Andiamo, Thomas and his wife Danielle (who hails from Paris) can educate you in the finer points of Italian and French cuisine. Thomas will tell you that Italian cooking is flamboyant, pure fun with a certain haphazard quality to it. Danielle will insist that French cuisine is more structured and sophisticated. It's all meticulously prepared and elegant in its presentation.

With the timelessness evoked by its provincial ambiance, Andiamo sets the mood for traditional Italian fare. Seafoods and pastas, antipastos and salads, desserts to die for! How can you resist ordering Vitello Saltimbocca - "jump in your mouth," or Linguine alla Pescatore - Neptune's Garden? Red or white Italian wines complement any menu selection.

For a classy alternative to spaghetti and pizza - Andiamo! Lets go Italiano!

505 South First Street   360-466-9111

HOLIDAY HOT MULLED WINE

A snowy starlit night and Christmas carolers are on your doorstep. Join in the Yuletide spirit and invite them in for this warming citrus and spice libation.

Recipe contributed by: Jim and Judi Reeves, Homespun Market

Preparation time: 10 minutes   Cook time: 35 minutes   Serves: 20

Ingredients
1 cup sugar
4 cups water
5 sticks cinnamon
20 whole cloves
¼ cup raisins
juice from 1 orange
peel from 1 orange
juice from 1 lemon
peel from 1 lemon
½ gallon red wine

Preparation
In a large stock pot, mix all ingredients, except red wine, and bring to a boil. Reduce heat and simmer 20 minutes. Strain, then combine with red wine. Heat mixture until steaming hot, not boiling, and serve.

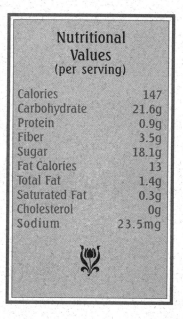

Nutritional Values
(per serving)

Calories	147
Carbohydrate	21.6g
Protein	0.9g
Fiber	3.5g
Sugar	18.1g
Fat Calories	13
Total Fat	1.4g
Saturated Fat	0.3g
Cholesterol	0g
Sodium	23.5mg

CHAMPAGNE COVE SUNSET

It's not another tequila sunrise! This delicious champagne creation adds just the right touch to enjoy the sunset...or sunrise!

Recipe contributed by: Joe and Diane Carter, Champagne Cove

Preparation time: 1 minute   Serves: 1

Ingredients
1 part chilled pineapple juice
3 parts champagne
small splash grenadine

Preparation
In a champagne flute or other exotic glass, pour in pineapple juice followed by champagne. Carefully add splash of grenadine. Let grenadine settle to see the sunset or swirl to enjoy this tropical champagne cooler.

Nutritional Values (per serving)	
Calories	162
Carbohydrate	23.5g
Protein	0.5g
Fiber	0.2g
Sugar	23.3g
Fat Calories	2
Total Fat	0.2g
Saturated Fat	0g
Cholesterol	0g
Sodium	1.7mg

MILK PUNCH

A pleasing non-alcoholic alternative for any celebration you're planning. This velvety smooth punch will please old and young alike.

Recipe contributed by: Marjorie Hart, LaConner Flats, a garden-The Granary

Preparation time: 20 minutes   Serves: 36

Ingredients
12 ounces pink lemonade concentrate, frozen
1 quart strawberry ice cream
1 quart cold water
1 quart milk
1 liter lemon lime soda

Preparation
In a large bowl mix lemonade concentrate, ice cream and water until consistency is like soft ice cream. Stir in milk and lemon lime soda. Transfer to a punch bowl and serve.

Nutritional Values (per serving)	
Calories	90
Carbohydrate	14.6g
Protein	1.6g
Fiber	0g
Sugar	14.6g
Fat Calories	28
Total Fat	3.1g
Saturated Fat	0.6g
Cholesterol	11.1g
Sodium	22.8g

Art's Place Bed and Breakfast

This Bed and Breakfast is so cozy you might decide to make it your home away from home. Art's Place is a private guest house located next to the Hupy's home in a quiet residential section of LaConner.

Skylights, paintings and handmade quilts are the backdrop for this cozy atmosphere featuring a balcony bedroom situated at the top of a spiral staircase. All the family needs for entertainment and food preparation is accommodated downstairs, and there are even pull out beds for extra sleepy heads. A jacuzzi tub can provide the perfect end to a strenuous day of shopping or bicycling.

A family friendly place, this B & B welcomes children and pets, and, yes, you may smoke on the outside deck area.

Long time LaConner residents, Art and Rita Hupy can be counted on to fill you in on all the local history. Not only were they instrumental in the founding of the Museum of Northwest Art, they also opened LaConner's first art gallery in 1977. Rita presently operates the Gaches Mansion as LaConner's only establishment where you may purchase new and antique quilts.

511 Talbot Street   360-466-3033

KOFFEE KRISTINA

This after dinner drink certainly takes its place as a dessert with a medley of flavors that satisfies even the most discerning palate.

Recipe contributed by: The Lighthouse Inn

Preparation time: 10 minutes   Serves: 1

Ingredients
1 cup freshly brewed coffee
½ shot Kahlua liqueur
½ shot Frangelico liqueur
½ shot Bailey's Irish Cream liqueur
3 Tbs. whipped cream

Preparation
Fill a large coffee cup ¾ full with freshly brewed coffee. Add liqueurs and stir. Top generously with whipped cream.

Nutritional Values (per serving)	
Calories	255
Carbohydrate	22.5g
Protein	2g
Fiber	0g
Sugar	22.5g
Fat Calories	106
Total Fat	11.8g
Saturated Fat	7.3g
Cholesterol	34.4g
Sodium	72.9mg

TROPICAL FRUIT SLUSH

The weekend warriors have gathered for the annual "Volleyball Challenge." With this tasty refresher on the sidelines you'll be hard pressed to keep your players on the court!

Recipe contributed by: Craig Reeves, The Marina Cafe

Preparation time: 15 minutes*   Serves: 45

Ingredients
6 cups cold water
5 medium, ripe bananas
2 cups sugar
24 ounces frozen orange juice concentrate, thawed
12 ounces frozen lemonade concentrate, thawed
46 ounces pineapple juice, unsweetened
6 liters lemon lime soda

Preparation
In a blender, process 1 cup water, bananas and sugar until smooth. Pour mixture into large bowl and stir in thawed orange and lemonade concentrates, pineapple juice and remaining water. Cover and freeze. Remove from freezer 2 hours prior to serving and break up and mash mixture. Stir in soda and transfer to punch bowl to serve.

*Make this beverage a day ahead or far enough in advance so it has enough time to freeze.

Nutritional Values (per serving)	
Calories	138
Carbohydrate	35.2g
Protein	0.5g
Fiber	0.7g
Sugars	34.6g
Fat Calories	2
Total Fat	0.2g
Saturated Fat	0.1g
Cholesterol	0g
Sodium	15.5mg

Sarah's Raspberry Liqueur

It's time to indulge yourself. Drizzle this flavorful liqueur over French vanilla ice cream and top with fresh berries or fill a champagne glass half full then pour liqueur down the side and float a few fresh berries. Very pretty.

Recipe contributed by: Earlene Beckes, Skagit Bay Hideaway

Preparation time: 5 minutes*   Serves: 24

Ingredients
4 cups fresh raspberries
3 cups vodka
2 cups sugar

Preparation
Place raspberries, vodka and sugar in a container with a lid. Let sit for 1 week and then stir. Stir again after second week and again after third week. Let stand covered for 3 months! Strain mixture and pour into any fun bottles with tops or corks. This liqueur makes a wonderful gift giving idea.

*This recipe requires 3 months to ferment, so be patient. It's worth the wait!

Nutritional Values (per serving)	
Calories	157
Carbohydrate	23.3g
Protein	0.3g
Fiber	2.6g
Sugar	20.7g
Fat Calories	2
Total Fat	0.2g
Saturated Fat	0g
Cholesterol	0g
Sodium	0.5mg

BRASSY'S

Gary the cat isn't the only animal "proprietor" in LaConner, but he's probably the most notorious. He frequently takes up his station in one of the front windows of First Street's only authentic brick building. He seems to fit quite nicely amongst the brass objects and nautical paraphernalia that abound in Brassy's.

If you didn't happen to come to LaConner to visit Gary, but were looking for "the largest selection of brass in the Pacific Northwest," well then, you've arrived! You may have to circle this emporium of delights to be sure you've seen everything. If you can't find that *special* brass item you *so* desire here, it's probably not available!

Brassy's can also provide you with that elusive picture postcard of LaConner that you've been hunting for all day. Have fun!

701 SOUTH FIRST STREET   360-466-4313

WHITE SWAN FRUIT SMOOTHIE

When the weather is just plain hot, take a tip from the tropics and reward yourself with this soothing mid-day refreshment that revitalizes the spirit and energizes body.

Recipe contributed by: Peter Goldfarb, The White Swan Guest House

Preparation time: 5 minutes   Serves: 6

Ingredients
2 cups cranberry-apricot juice
2 cups pineapple-orange juice
1 banana, peeled
2-3 fresh strawberries

Preparation
Place all ingredients in blender. Blend 10-20 seconds on either the "blend" or "purée" setting. Make sure lid is tight. Serve in 6 small, stemmed wine glasses.

Nutritional Values (per serving)	
Calories	169
Carbohydrate	41.1g
Protein	2.5g
Fiber	4.7g
Sugar	36.4g
Fat Calories	7
Total Fat	0.8g
Saturated Fat	0.1g
Cholesterol	0g
Sodium	5.8mg

WILD IRIS LASSI

You and your two best friend's just got back from that early morning jog. Who's idea was it to make that New Year's resolution anyway?! Reward everyone with this easy to fix blended drink that not only wakes up the taste buds but is good for you too.

Recipe contributed by: Susan Sullivan, Innkeeper, The Wild Iris Inn

Preparation time: 5 minutes   Serves: 4

Ingredients
1 quart vanilla yogurt
2 cups fresh raspberries
½ tsp. rose water

Preparation
Blend yogurt, raspberries and rose water thoroughly in blender until smooth.   Serve in chilled glasses.

Nutritional Values (per serving)	
Calories	197
Carbohydrate	24.1g
Protein	9.1g
Fiber	7.7g
Sugar	16.3g
Fat Calories	75
Total Fat	8.3g
Saturated Fat	4.9g
Cholesterol	30.2g
Sodium	107.6mg

LOYD'S SOUTHWEST SANGRIA

Olé! This sparkling citrus garnished drink makes a nice presentation and tastes as good as it looks. Too much and, well, you'll be showing everyone your version of the Mexican Hat Dance!

Recipe contributed by: Loyd Alt, The Wood Merchant

Preparation Time: 10 minutes   **Chill time: 1 hour**   **Serves: 6**

Ingredients
3½ cups dry red wine
¼ cup brandy
½ fresh lemon juice
½ cup orange juice
½ cup sugar
1¼ cups sparkling water
1 large lemon, thinly sliced
1 orange, thinly sliced
½ cup seedless red grapes

Preparation
In a large serving pitcher, mix red wine, brandy, lemon juice, orange juice and sugar. Chill for 1 hour. Just before serving add sparkling water and fruit.

Nutritional Values (per serving)	
Calories	226
Carbohydrate	32.2g
Protein	1g
Fiber	1g
Sugar	31.2g
Fat Calories	2
Total Fat	0.2g
Saturated Fat	0g
Cholesterol	0g
Sodium	9.6mg

CALICO CUPBOARD CAFE AND BAKERY

How to spot a good restaurant? Look for the crowd outside the door and a waiting list! If you're at LaConner's Calico Cupboard, the wait is more than worth it. Calico opens early for those who need to start the day with a good breakfast, and serves meals to satisfy the heartiest appetite through the afternoon. All the food is prepared from scratch, and the menu selection is varied enough to provide something for everyone - vegetarian, low-fat, heart-wise and just plain hungry!

Calico Cupboard also offers a large variety of the tastiest bakery goods around - breads, scones, coffee cake, pies, danish, cheese cake and more. You can order menu items to go or you can sit back, relax and be served in a comfortable, friendly atmosphere reminiscent of a neighbor's country kitchen filled with antiques.

Linda Freed, proprietress, likes to describe her food as "comfort food," something to make you feel good throughout the day. So next time you're coming to LaConner, get there early, sign up on the waiting list and enjoy "The sweetest buns in town!"

720 SOUTH FIRST STREET   360-466-4451

PRAWNS GENOVESE

Impress your guests with an appetizer that will be remembered long after the evening is over. This easy to make and flavorful dish is a great beginning to a memorable meal.

Recipe contributed by: Thomas and Danielle Palmer, Andiamo Ristorante Italiano

Preparation time: 25 minutes   Cook time: 5 minutes   Serves: 2

Ingredients

3 Tbs. extra virgin olive oil
8 large prawns, shelled and deveined
1 Tbs. shallots, minced
½ tsp. garlic, minced
¼ cup dry white wine
1½ Tbs. capers
3 Tbs. tomatoes, diced
juice of 1 lemon
1 Tbs. parsley, chopped
1 Tbs. butter
salt and pepper to taste

Preparation

In a medium size sauté pan, preheat olive oil over medium high heat. Add prawns and lightly cook both sides. Add shallots and garlic. When garlic begins to brown, deglaze with wine. Add capers, tomatoes, lemon juice and parsley. Cook until prawns lose their translucency. Take pan off heat and whisk in butter. Season to taste with salt and pepper.

Nutritional Values (per serving)	
Calories	394
Carbohydrate	12.5g
Protein	23.6g
Fiber	0g
Sugar	12.5g
Fat Calories	309
Total Fat	34.3g
Saturated Fat	9.3g
Cholesterol	187.5g
Sodium	3,790.mg

PARMESAN FRIED MUSHROOMS

Understandably, Jean has quite the reputation as "the hostess with the mostess!" Her recipe for this mushroom hors d'oeuvre is a real winner.

Recipe contributed by: Jean Tjersland, Just Imagine

Preparation time: 30 minutes   Cook time: 20 minutes   Serves: 20

Ingredients
1 pound fresh mushrooms
⅓ cup all purpose flour
¾ cup seasoned bread crumbs
1 egg, beaten
¼ cup milk
½ cup Parmesan cheese, grated
1 cup vegetable oil

Preparation
Wash mushrooms and trim stems about ¼". Sprinkle flour on a sheet of waxed paper and do the same with the bread crumbs on a second sheet. In a small, deep bowl, beat together egg and milk. Roll each mushroom in flour to coat lightly. Dip floured mushroom into egg mixture. Roll in bread crumbs coating evenly. Preheat oil in heavy pan to 375°. Drop a few mushrooms at a time into hot oil and fry until golden brown, about 30 seconds on each side. Remove mushrooms from pan and drain on paper towels. Dip into grated cheese while still warm. Keep mushrooms warm until ready to serve.

Yield: Approximately 40

Nutritional Values (per serving)	
Calories	182
Carbohydrate	10.4g
Protein	5.8g
Fiber	0.4g
Sugar	10g
Fat Calories	122
Total Fat	13.5g
Saturated Fat	2.8g
Cholesterol	5g
Sodium	351.9mg

Beer Cheese

This makes a great hostess gift when rolled in chopped nuts and presented in an attractive serving dish festively wrapped.

Recipe contributed by: Kathie Hubbard, Katy's Inn Bed and Breakfast

Preparation time: 10 minutes   Chill time: Overnight   Serves: 8

Ingredients
½ pound sharp cheddar cheese, grated
½ pound medium cheddar cheese, grated
2 tsp. Worcestershire sauce
2 Tbs. catsup
½ can beer
1 tsp. seasoning salt
½ tsp. garlic salt
1 pound cream cheese, softened

Preparation
In a medium size glass bowl, combine all ingredients except cream cheese. Mix until thoroughly blended. Drain off any liquid that may have separated from mixture. Add softened cream cheese and any additional seasoning that may be needed for individual tastes.

Cover and chill cheese mixture overnight or longer. It gets better with age. Spoon mixture into a small bowl or crock and serve at room temperature. Another option is to form mixture into a ball and roll in chopped nuts or chopped fresh parsley.

This recipe makes one large cheese ball that could be served at a party, or two cheese balls that are a nice size for gift giving.

Nutritional Values (per serving)	
Calories	417
Carbohydrate	5.1g
Protein	19.6g
Fiber	0.1g
Sugar	5g
Fat Calories	318
Total Fat	35.3g
Saturated Fat	21.5g
Cholesterol	112.4g
Sodium	636.5mg

CARAVAN GALLERY

The Silk Road. The sand dunes of the Sahara. Fragrant, tropical jungles on the island of Bali. All destinations we desire, but ones not always accessible to us. A walk into the grotto-like courtyard of Caravan Gallery will have you convinced that you are on your way to one of them!

A world of treasures from far and near awaits your perusal. Exotic and wonderful crafts from Turkey, China, India and places you only dream of are right here. Quality silver and gold jewelry, along with just the fun "stuff," is in abundance.

African masks and ethnographic display pieces, each with a story of its own, are arranged amongst batiks and Chinese mosaic boxes that delight the eye. Stay too long and you may think that you've been transported to "the Casbah."

619 SOUTH FIRST STREET   360-466-4808

HAWAIIAN HAM BALLS

So your friends and neighbors are throwing a luau? Forget the poi and bring something everyone will enjoy. They'll all be asking where you came up with such a delicious recipe!

Recipe contributed by: Joe and Diane Carter, Kokomo Joe's

Preparation time: 20 minutes   Cook time: 45 minutes   Serves: 12

Ingredients

½ pound cooked ham, ground
½ pound ground beef
1 egg, beaten
1 Tbs. onion, minced
1 can evaporated milk
1 cup raisin bran cereal
⅛ tsp. pepper
⅛ tsp. thyme

Glaze
¼ cup brown sugar
1 Tbs. apple cider vinegar
¼ cup dark corn syrup
½ tsp. dry mustard
1 small can pineapple chunks

Preparation

Preheat oven to 350°. In a large bowl combine, and thoroughly mix cooked ham, ground beef, egg, onion, evaporated milk, raisin bran, pepper and thyme. Shape into balls using approximately 1 tablespoon per ball. Place in single layer on oven proof dish and bake uncovered for 15 minutes in preheated oven. Meanwhile, in a small saucepan, combine brown sugar, vinegar, corn syrup, dry mustard and bring to a boil. Pour sauce over ham balls and bake 10 more minutes. Baste hamballs again and cook 10 additional minutes. Remove from oven, baste once more. Then skewer each with a chunk of pineapple using toothpicks. Serve warm.

Nutritional Values (per serving)	
Calories	222
Carbohydrate	28.1g
Protein	13.4g
Fiber	2.2g
Sugar	25.8g
Fat Calories	66
Total Fat	7.3g
Saturated Fat	2.8g
Cholesterol	37.6g
Sodium	152.9mg

KUNG PAO STEAMER CLAMS

Serve these clams as a first course or add a big tossed green salad, warm crusty bread and your favorite beer or wine. And don't be shy about dunking your bread in that clam nectar!

Recipe contributed by: LaConner Seafood and Prime Rib House

Preparation time: 20 minutes   Cook Time: 12 minutes   Serves: 4

Ingredients

3 Tbs. garlic, minced
3 Tbs. ginger, minced
3 Tbs. jalapeno peppers-seeds removed, minced
1 tsp. dried chile flakes (optional)
¼ cup soy sauce
2 Tbs. brown sugar
3 Tbs. balsamic vinegar

6-7 pounds fresh Puget Sound steamer clams
3 Tbs. sesame oil
1½ cups onions, sliced
4 Tbs. butter (optional)
3 Tbs. fresh cilantro leaves, roughly chopped
½ cup roasted, skinless peanuts or cashews

Preparation

In a small bowl, combine garlic, ginger, jalapeno pepper and chile flakes. Set aside. In another bowl, combine soy sauce, brown sugar and balsamic vinegar. Set this aside, also. Scrub clams thoroughly and discard any empty shells or open clams.

In a large heavy skillet or kettle with lid, heat sesame oil until sizzling. Add garlic mixture and fry for 1 minute to release flavors. Toss in scrubbed clams, onions, optional butter and soy mixture. Cover and bring to a boil. Shake pan to assist cooking. Cook just until all clams are open. Remove from heat and serve in large bowls. Pour "nectar" from pan over clams and sprinkle with cilantro and chopped nuts.

Nutritional Values (per serving)	
Calories	1677
Carbohydrate	77.2g
Protein	212.3g
Fiber	5.6g
Sugar	71.6g
Fat Calories	479
Total Fat	53.2g
Saturated Fat	26.4g
Cholesterol	564.9g
Sodium	2175.9mg

SALMON PATÉ

For an added flair when serving this delicious appetizer, form this paté into a salmon shape and serve with Indian fry bread.

Recipe contributed by: Nancy Wilbur Foster, Legends

Preparation time: 30 minutes   Chill time: 4 hours   Serves: 30

Ingredients
3 pounds cream cheese, softened
1 cup mayonnaise
¼ - ½ cup fresh dill, chopped*
¼ - ½ cup garlic, minced*
¼ - ½ cup onion, finely chopped*
3 cups smoked salmon or fresh alder cooked salmon

Preparation
In a bowl, stir softened cream cheese until smooth. Add mayonnaise and blend. Add dill, garlic and onion and mix well. Make sure salmon has all bones removed. Incorporate into cream cheese mixture. Chill 4 hours or overnight in a covered container. Serve with crackers, bread or veggies.

*Amounts of dill, garlic and onion may be adjusted to suit personal taste.

Fry Bread recipe on page 99

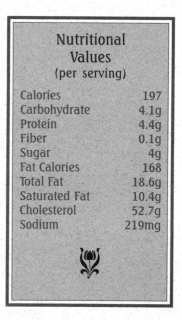

Nutritional Values (per serving)	
Calories	197
Carbohydrate	4.1g
Protein	4.4g
Fiber	0.1g
Sugar	4g
Fat Calories	168
Total Fat	18.6g
Saturated Fat	10.4g
Cholesterol	52.7g
Sodium	219mg

CHAMPAGNE COVE

Champagne Cove could be a tiny tropical village on the southern tip of Hawaii's Big Island. But this Champagne Cove is your first port-of-call in "North LaConner". Watch for the sign posted on the telephone pole!

Tranquility warms the air in this little cove where the flavor of the old world rises to the surface. A wide array of graceful sailing ships evokes images of long sea journeys and newly discovered lands. Lighthouses so familiar to our Northwest coastline, are reinterpreted in beautiful luminescent stained glass. Cards, puzzles and gift wrap with beach themes are all reminders of pleasant days spent at the seashore.

Champagne Cove is filled with treasures from the oceans of the world making this little hideaway a haven for those with champagne taste and a passion for the sea.

"I must go down to the seas again, to the lonely sea and sky,
And all I ask is a tall ship and a star to steer her by..."
    SEA FEVER by John Masefield

101 NORTH FIRST STREET   360-466-2085

SHRIMP AND CRAB SPREAD

This appetizer is a crowd pleaser and the first to disappear at any gathering. Pair up with crackers or toasted baguette slices. A tasty treat.

Recipe contributed by: Bill Matheson, Matheson Metal Sculpture

Preparation time: 25 minutes*   Serves: 24

Ingredients
18 slices white bread
6 Tbs. butter
6 hard boiled eggs, chopped
1 bunch green onions, chopped
8½ ounces canned shrimp, drained
4¼ ounces canned crab, drained
1 cup celery, chopped
2-3 cups mayonnaise

Preparation
Lightly butter bread slices. Trim off crusts and cube. In a large bowl, mix bread cubes, eggs and green onions. Cover bowl with plastic wrap and place in refrigerator overnight. The next day add shrimp, crab, celery and mayonnaise and mix well. Return to refrigerator and let stand 3-4 hours. Transfer a portion to a smaller bowl for serving.

* Make this recipe the day before serving.

Nutritional Values (per serving)	
Calories	239
Carbohydrate	18.6g
Protein	11.1g
Fiber	0.7g
Sugar	17.9g
Fat Calories	120
Total Fat	13.3g
Saturated Fat	3.4g
Cholesterol	34.8g
Sodium	487.1mg

Spicy Crab Stuffed Avocados

An impressive presentation as a first course. The unique combination of ingredients complement one another and please the palate as well.

Recipe contributed by: Marlo Frank, Nasty Jack's Antiques

Preparation time: 15 minutes　　　**Chill time: 1 hour**　　　**Serves: 4**

Ingredients

½ cup mayonnaise
½ cup celery, minced
¼ cup pickled hot peppers, minced
¼ cup fresh parsley, finely chopped
1 Tbs. prepared mustard
3 drops Tabasco sauce
4 drops Worcestershire sauce

1 pinch salt
juice of half a lemon
6 ounces canned crab, drained
2 ripe avocados
1 bunch watercress
8 cherry tomatoes
4 black olives

Preparation

In a bowl, mix mayonnaise, celery, pickled hot peppers, parsley, mustard, Tabasco, Worcestershire, salt and 2 tablespoons lemon juice. Cover and chill mixture for 1 hour. Flake crab meat into bowl, cover and refrigerate. Rinse watercress, pat dry and refrigerate as well.

Just before serving, peel avocados and slice into half lengthwise. Remove pits and dip cut sides into remaining lemon juice. Arrange watercress on 4 salad plates and place avocado half in center. Stuff with crab meat and spoon spicy mayonnaise over top of each. Garnish with cherry tomatoes and black olives.

Nutritional Values (per serving)	
Calories	419
Carbohydrate	23.2g
Protein	12.1g
Fiber	8.9g
Sugar	14.4g
Fat Calories	300
Total Fat	33.3g
Saturated Fat	5g
Cholesterol	45.4g
Sodium	2172.8mg

BERTOLLI CROSTINI DI POLENTA

Polenta has long been a staple of Northern Italy. This colorful variation makes a savory appetizer for a summer's evening dining, al fresco!

Recipe contributed by: Stephanie Banaszak, Organic Matters

Preparation time: 20 minutes   Cook time: 30 minutes   Chill time: 2 hours   Serves: 8

Ingredients

¼ cup onion, finely chopped
2 Tbs. olive oil
1½ cups chicken broth
1 cup water
⅔ cup yellow corn meal

1 Tbs. Parmesan cheese, grated
2 roasted red peppers
1 Tbs. fresh basil, chopped
salt to taste

Preparation

In a saucepan, cook onion in olive oil over low heat until tender, about 5 minutes. Stir in chicken broth. In a bowl, combine water and cornmeal. Stir mixture into chicken broth. Cook, stirring, until cornmeal begins to boil. Add Parmesan, stirring constantly, and allow cornmeal mixture to continue boiling until it thickens.

Line a 9x13x2" pan with tin foil and coat with 1 tablespoon of olive oil. Add polenta and spread into a smooth layer with spatula. Refrigerate until cold, at least 2 hours.

Preheat oven to 425°. Turn polenta out of pan, peel off foil and cut into triangles. Place on cookie sheet and bake on bottom rack of oven. Turn often, until browned and crisp, about 15 minutes. Meanwhile, cut peppers into even portions. Drizzle with remaining olive oil and sprinkle with basil. Arrange on top of each triangle.

Nutritional Values (per serving)	
Calories	119
Carbohydrate	16.9g
Protein	2.9g
Fiber	2g
Sugar	14.9g
Fat Calories	43
Total Fat	4.7g
Saturated Fat	0.9g
Cholesterol	1.5g
Sodium	1123mg

Cottons

Cossetting, cushy and comforting. Just a few of the words you might use to describe the kind of clothing Tia can show you at Cottons. To be at her best, whether at work or at play, today's woman needs clothing that is, at once, versatile and timeless. These classic clothes define who you are through their simplicity and substance...no fluff here.

Intriguing textures and colors beg to be mixed in unabashed combinations called...STYLE! Cotton (of course!), linen and wool. Go ahead. Mix and match. You can't go wrong because everything here works together. To make it even easier, most of the clothing is "low maintenance."

Of course, you'll need shoes to provide the same comfort and quality for your feet. Several lines of European shoes are available to make you forget you just went on that marathon shopping trip or that tomorrow you get to spend eight hours on your feet waiting tables.

Need to accessorize? An inspired collection of leather bags, belts, hats and socks are just a shelf away. An eclectic selection of jewelry helps you round out the look.

Though small in size, Cottons can help you create a thousand different looks!

608 South First Street   360-466-5825

CURRY MUSSELS WITH LEMON GRASS

Available in the speciality produce section of your grocery store, lemon grass adds a delicate touch to this seafood appetizer. Combined with curry, it imparts a Southeast Asian flavor to these mussels.

Recipe contributed by: Thomas and Danielle Palmer, Palmer's

Preparation time: 20 minutes   Cook time: 8-10 minutes   Serves: 2

Ingredients

2 pounds mussels, debearded and scrubbed
2 Tbs. shallots, chopped
1 tsp. fresh ginger, shredded
1 stalk lemon grass, ¼" bias cut
⅓ cup heavy cream
¼ cup dry white wine
1 Tbs. curry powder
salt and pepper to taste

Preparation

Preheat a skillet and add all ingredients. Stir thoroughly, cover with lid and turn heat to medium. Simmer until all mussels are completely open, being sure not to overcook. Salt and pepper to taste.

Nutritional Values (per serving)	
Calories	240
Carbohydrate	11.6g
Protein	9g
Fiber	2.6g
Sugar	8.9g
Fat Calories	146
Total Fat	16.2g
Saturated Fat	9.1g
Cholesterol	67.8g
Sodium	3650mg

ARTICHOKE SQUARES

Charlotte's son Scott Bishop, proprietor of Serendipity Gallery, says these artichoke squares are a favorite at all their family gatherings.

Recipe contributed by: Charlotte Von Moos, Serendipity Gallery

Preparation time: 15 minutes   Cook time: 30 minutes   Serves: 18

20 ounces marinated artichoke hearts, drained, finely chopped-reserve oil from 1 jar
1 clove garlic, crushed
¼ cup onion, finely chopped
4 eggs, beaten
½ cup unseasoned bread crumbs
½ pound cheddar cheese, grated
⅛ tsp. oregano
2 Tbs. fresh parsley, chopped
⅛ tsp. Tabasco sauce
¼ tsp. salt
¼ tsp. pepper

Nutritional Values (per serving)	
Calories	116
Carbohydrate	6g
Protein	9.7g
Fiber	0.5g
Sugar	5.5g
Fat Calories	42
Total Fat	4.6g
Saturated Fat	2.7g
Cholesterol	13.2g
Sodium	274.1mg

Preparation

Preheat oven to 350°. Grease 9" baking dish. In a skillet, sauté garlic and onion in reserved artichoke oil until translucent and set aside. In a medium bowl, combine eggs, bread crumbs, cheddar cheese, oregano, parsley, Tabasco, salt and pepper. Mix well. Add onion mixture and blend. Incorporate artichoke hearts. Pour into prepared baking dish and bake in preheated oven for 30 minutes or until mixture is firm to touch in center. Serve warm or at room temperature.

GOAT CHEESE AND SUN-DRIED TOMATO TORTE

A culinary delight with classic flavor combinations. This delightful torte is as mouthwatering to look at as it is to indulge in.

Recipe contributed by: Kay Trelstad, The Stall

Preparation time: 30 minutes   **Chill time: 1 hour**   **Serves: 16**

Ingredients
8 ounces cream cheese, softened
8 ounces Montrachet cheese
1½ cups butter, softened
1 cup prepared pesto*
1 cup sun-dried tomatoes in oil, drained and minced

Preparation
In a bowl, beat cheeses and butter together until well blended and fluffy. Line a round cake pan with damp cheese cloth, making sure cloth is large enough to fold over top of pan. Fill pan with ⅓ of cheese mixture followed by ½ of pesto. Repeat layering process. Cover last ⅓ of cheese mixture with sun-dried tomatoes. Fold cheese cloth over top of torte. Refrigerate at least 1 hour.

To prepare for serving, fold cheese cloth back, lift torte out and remove cheese cloth from bottom. Place, tomato side up, onto a serving plate. Serve with crackers.

*Pesto recipe on page 128

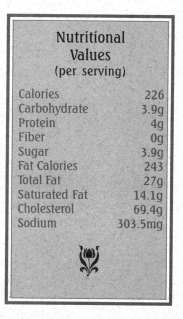

Nutritional Values (per serving)	
Calories	226
Carbohydrate	3.9g
Protein	4g
Fiber	0g
Sugar	3.9g
Fat Calories	243
Total Fat	27g
Saturated Fat	14.1g
Cholesterol	69.4g
Sodium	303.5mg

THE COUNTRY LADY

City women. Country women. All women who enjoy a definitive style that expresses them as individuals, visit the Country Lady when looking for that special something to add to their wardrobe. Unique clothing is truly the theme here. With an emphasis on all natural fabrics, the clothing is as comfortable as it is easy to care for.

Set in a warm atmosphere designed to make the shopper feel welcome, Jan Marie and her staff can help tailor your style with wonderful separates and accessories, or put together a whole new look for you.

Stop in and browse through the wonderful armoires, trunks and cupboards filled with beautiful clothes where, "A Lady is a lady...is a lady...is a lady..."

501 SOUTH FIRST STREET   360-466-4833

Smoked Salmon Spread

Sitting by a roaring fire on a rainy night, you're enjoying that 'most wonderful' glass of wine. What better way to complement it than with a bit of smoked salmon spread and a few crackers.

Recipe contributed by: Peter Goldfarb, The White Swan Guest House

Preparation time: 10 minutes   Chill time: 1 hour   Serves: 6

Ingredients
6 ounces cream cheese, softened
2 Tbs. sour cream
1 Tbs. fresh chives, chopped
½ cup smoked Chinook salmon, flaked
½ tsp. horseradish (optional)

Preparation
In a medium size bowl, mix all ingredients until well blended. Spoon into crock or serving bowl and chill. Serve with toasted, sliced mini bagels, crackers or melba rounds.

Nutritional Values (per serving)	
Calories	132
Carbohydrate	1.1g
Protein	5.8g
Fiber	0.1g
Sugar	1g
Fat Calories	106
Total Fat	11.7g
Saturated Fat	7g
Cholesterol	37.6g
Sodium	236.9mg

BUTTERNUT POTSTICKERS WITH RASPBERRY SZECHUAN SAUCE

Susan Sullivan, Innkeeper at the Wild Iris Inn, says that the aroma and presentation of this appetizer is so enticing that if one of their guests orders it, soon the whole dining room has included it in their evening meal.

Recipe contributed by: Susan Sullivan, Innkeeper, The Wild Iris Inn

Preparation time: 25 minutes　　　**Cook time: 30 minutes**　　　**Serves: 12**

Ingredients
1 onion, diced
4 Tbs. olive oil
1 Tbs. fresh sage, minced
4 cups butternut squash, peeled and diced
1 cup hazelnuts, chopped
1 pkg. wonton wrappers
1½ cups canola oil - approximate
½ cup Madeira
salt and freshly ground pepper to taste

Sauce
½ cup soy sauce
⅔ cup Dona Flora raspberry vinegar
½ cup raspberry syrup
2 Tbs. toasted sesame oil
4 cloves garlic, pressed
2 tsp. fresh ginger, minced
1 whole scallion, minced
½ tsp. dried red chili flakes
½ cup fresh raspberries

Preparation
In a large skillet, sauté onions in olive oil until translucent. Add sage and squash and cook over medium heat until squash tests tender. Add hazelnuts and stir thoroughly. Place a spoonful of squash mixture in middle of wonton wrap, moisten edge of wrap with water and use a potsticker press to seal or hand pleat. Heat canola oil in separate skillet and fry small batches of potstickers in ½" of oil. When potstickers are half cooked, about 3 minutes, add Madiera to caramelize wrap. Cover briefly. Lift potstickers from pan and serve upside down with Raspberry Szechuan Sauce and garnish with fresh raspberries and bamboo leaves.

Raspberry Szechuan Sauce: In a medium size bowl, combine all ingredients and whisk gently. Yields about 2 cups of sauce. Pour a portion in small bowl and place in center of serving plate with potstickers.

Nutritional Values (per serving)	
Calories	348
Carbohydrate	21g
Protein	3.9g
Fiber	1.4g
Sugar	19.6g
Fat Calories	265
Total Fat	29.4g
Saturated Fat	2.6g
Cholesterol	0.2g
Sodium	579.5mg

GINGER CHICKEN WINGS

It's fall, the air is cold and brisk and football season is here. These yummy marinated wings will help you root your team to that winning score!

Recipe contributed by: Laurie Hutt, The Wood Merchant

Preparation time: 15 minutes   **Chill time:** 4 hours   **Cook time:** 1 hour   **Serves:** 12

Ingredients
1 Tbs. fresh ginger, grated
1½ cups sugar
2 cups soy sauce
1 cup sherry
3 pounds chicken wings

Preparation
Rinse chicken, pat dry, place in bowl and refrigerate. In a saucepan, combine ginger, sugar, soy sauce and sherry and bring to boil, stirring constantly. Remove from heat and cool. Pour over chicken wings and marinate in refrigerator for 4 hours. Preheat oven to 350°. Place marinated wings in lightly greased baking dish and bake uncovered for 1 hour.

Nutritional Values (per serving)	
Calories	210
Carbohydrate	33.6g
Protein	36.6g
Fiber	0g
Sugar	33.5g
Fat Calories	83
Total Fat	9.2g
Saturated Fat	2.6g
Cholesterol	96.4g
Sodium	775mg

Roasted Garlic

Roasted garlic has a deliciously mild flavor. Many recipes now call for this savory ingredient, but the easiest way to enjoy freshly roasted garlic is to spread a clove onto a fresh Italian bread roll and enjoy along with a glass of your favorite wine.

Earlene Beckes, proprietor of Skagit Bay Hideaway shared an easy way to roast garlic.
Preheat oven to 325°. Cut ½" to ¾" off top of whole garlic bulb. Remove some of the loose outer skin, leaving bulb intact. Place in garlic roaster and pour 1 tablespoon olive oil over cut bulb. Roast in preheated oven for 50-60 minutes. If you don't have a garlic roaster, place garlic bulb, cut side down, on a non-stick baking dish with ½" of water and roast until soft at 450°.

To remove garlic from head after baking, hold upside down, squeezing pulp out. Remove any garlic skin that might have mixed into soft garlic.

Roasted Peppers

Roasted peppers can be a delicious addition to many recipes. You'll find that they are so easy to prepare that you'll be incorporating them into your culinary repetoire.

To roast, slice peppers in half lengthwise. Remove core and seeds. Place peppers, cut side down on a preheated broiler rack. Broil for about 5 minutes, or until skin blisters. Remove peppers from broiler rack and place in paper or plastic bag and allow to sweat, about 10-15 minutes. When cool, remove from bag and the charred skins will peel off easily.

TASTEFUL HARMONIES

DANDELION

Step into Dandelion and you could be stepping into the pages of your favorite children's book. Lindas' delightful sense of whimsy prevails here, and the appeal of country cottage accessories for casual living is evident.

A happy gathering of creatures and faeries, teacups and dolls sit on the shelves, stairs and cupboards. There are buttons and bows, laces and doilies, braided rag rugs and clothing to charm you. Birdhouses provide gracious country living for the avian population at your residence.

Several lines of enchanting greeting cards can solve your correspondence dilemmas. No Hallmark verses to confuse the issue...you get to write your own salutation! Recipe cards, notepads and calendars with country themes round out your choices.

Artwork to fill the walls of your country home is plentiful at Dandelion. Maybe a unique handcrafted wooden sign or dried flower swag would be the answer to the "hole" on the kitchen wall.

Just remember, Dandelion is not a weed. It's a beautiful shop!

618 SOUTH FIRST STREET   360-466-2033

LUNCHEON SALAD

Having the ladies over for an afternoon of bridge? Serve this light and distinctive salad and they will be lauding kudos to you for such an enjoyable beginning to their afternoon.

Recipe contributed by: Robyn Eisses, Brassy's

Preparation time: 25 minutes   **Serves:** 6

Ingredients

1 bunch bibb lettuce
1 bunch romaine
1 bunch leaf lettuce
1 cup fresh mushrooms
1 papaya, peeled and seeded
1 apple, cored
1 avocado, peeled and pitted

Dressing
½ cup sugar
1 cup vegetable oil
½ cup apple cider vinegar
2 Tbs. poppy seeds
½ tsp. pepper
1 Tbs. dry onion flakes
1 tsp. dry mustard
1 tsp. salt

Preparation

Rinse and dry lettuce. Tear into bite size pieces and place enough for 6 servings in large bowl. Thinly slice mushrooms, papaya, apple and avocado. Add to lettuce. In small bowl, combine all dressing ingredients and whisk well to combine. Pour dressing over salad and toss. Serve immediately.

Nutritional Values (per serving)	
Calories	548
Carbohydrate	152g
Protein	4.5g
Fiber	7.3g
Sugar	144.7g
Fat Calories	418
Total Fat	46.4g
Saturated Fat	6.6g
Cholesterol	0g
Sodium	326.4mg

Javanese Veggie Salad

An ethnic salad of Indonesian origin will add variety to your entertainment menu. Forewarn your guests! This dish is not for the faint of heart. Hot and spicy enough to make your taste buds tingle!

Recipe contributed by: Caravan Gallery

Preparation time: 30 minutes   Cook time: 12 minutes   Chill time: 20 minutes   Serves: 6

Ingredients

1 bunch fresh spinach, washed and stemmed
½ pound green beans, 2" bias cut
¾ pound mung bean sprouts

Marinade
6 Tbs. fresh lime juice
2 cloves garlic, minced
½ tsp. salt
3 Tbs. sugar
2 Tbs. crushed red pepper flakes
2 tsp. dried mint
1-2 tsp. fresh ginger, minced
1 cup unsweetened lightly toasted coconut, shredded

Preparation

In a small bowl, combine all marinade ingredients and stir until well blended. Set aside. Place spinach in heavy skillet and cook quickly without water until wilted. Immediately add to marinade mixture. Bring a saucepan of water to boil, add green beans and cook for 5 minutes. Take saucepan off the boil and using a slotted spoon remove beans and place them in bowl of ice water. Drain and then add to spinach mixture. Place saucepan of water back on heat and bring back to boil. Add mung bean sprouts and cook 2 minutes. Drain and add to spinach mixture as well. Toss, cover and chill.

Nutritional Values (per serving)	
Calories	310
Carbohydrate	35.4g
Protein	6.1g
Fiber	3.1g
Sugar	32.3g
Fat Calories	166
Total Fat	18.4g
Saturated Fat	18.8g
Cholesterol	0g
Sodium	210.4mg

The Ginger Grater

Every meal should be a celebration. You don't have to match recipes with Julia Child, but be ready to be inspired to get the best out of your preparations *and* presentation.

Specialty food items are the norm here. The shelves are so full of delectable jars, bottles, bags and boxes of goodies, you'll have to grab a basket to hold them all. The kitchen and serving utensils, table linens and enchanting collection of whimsical pottery will leave you wishing you entertained every week!

The perfect furnishings for that hard-to-fit eating space can also be found here, serving both form and function.

Located in the historic Wiggin's mercantile, an ornate false-fronted red building so perfectly suited to its name, the Ginger Grater is unmistakable on First Street.

604 South First Street   360-466-4161

Sweet and Sour Three Bean Salad

A summer's day and a picnic is planned. This chilled salad is the perfect accompaniment to the day and the occasion.

Recipe contributed by: Tia Kurtz, Cottons

Preparation time: 30 minutes   Marinate time: 30 minutes - 2 hours   Serves: 6

Ingredients
1 cup fresh green beans
15 ounces chick peas, rinsed and drained
15 ounces kidney beans, rinsed and drained
1 small Bermuda onion, thinly sliced

Dressing
½ cup wine vinegar
½ cup olive oil
2 Tbs. honey

Preparation
Rinse and cut green beans into 2" pieces and steam for 5 minutes until just barely tender. Plunge into bowl of ice water to stop cooking. Drain thoroughly. In a large bowl, mix green beans, chick peas, kidney beans and onion. In a small bowl, combine dressing ingredients and beat together until honey "melts". Pour dressing over bean mixture and allow to marinate at room temperature from 30 minutes to 2 hours. This salad will keep for several days in the refrigerator.

Nutritional Values (per serving)	
Calories	377
Carbohydrate	4.2g
Protein	10.6g
Fiber	4g
Sugar	36.2g
Fat Calories	181
Total Fat	20.1g
Saturated Fat	2.8g
Cholesterol	0g
Sodium	382.2mg

Seviche

This healthy and flavorful dish could be South America's answer to sushi. If you love scallops and the flavor of cilantro this is the ultimate in unique seafood accompaniments.

Recipe contributed by: Jim and Judi Reeves, Homespun Market

Preparation time: 20 minutes   Marinate: 4 hours   Serves: 8

Ingredients
¾ pounds scallops
juice from 1 lime
¼ cup white onion, chopped
¼ cup fresh cilantro, chopped
¼ cup fresh green chiles, chopped
1 large tomato, chopped
3 tsp. olive oil
salt and pepper to taste

Preparation
Rinse scallops. If scallops are large, cut into thirds. Place scallops in glass bowl with lime juice and marinate in refrigerator for 4 hours or overnight. Drain scallops, add remaining ingredients and toss. Serve garnished with sprig of fresh cilantro.

Nutritional Values (per serving)	
Calories	72
Carbohydrate	4.9g
Protein	7.9g
Fiber	0.6g
Sugar	4.3g
Fat Calories	18
Total Fat	2g
Saturated Fat	0.6g
Cholesterol	14.2g
Sodium	1017.7mg

BROCCOLI SALAD

Margie says that this salad is best if you allow it to chill overnight. Crunchy, chewy, tangy and delicious, this is one salad that you won't have any trouble getting the kids to eat. It'll be gone in the wink of an eye!

Contributed by: Marjorie Hart, LaConner Flats, a garden-The Granary

Preparation time: 25 minutes   **Cook time:** 15   **Chill time:** 3 hours   **Serves:** 10-12

Ingredients

1 pound bacon
3 bunches broccoli
½ cup raisins
½ cup sunflower seeds, unsalted
1 medium red onion, finely chopped

Dressing
½ cup mayonnaise
½ cup sugar
2 Tbs. apple cider vinegar

Preparation

In a skillet, fry bacon until crisp. Drain on paper towels until cool. Crumble and set aside. Rinse broccoli and break or cut into small flowerettes. In a large bowl, combine broccoli, raisins, sunflower seeds and red onion. Set aside. In a small bowl, whisk together mayonnaise, sugar and vinegar. Pour dressing over broccoli mixture and toss. Transfer salad to serving bowl and sprinkle with crumbled bacon. Cover with plastic wrap and refrigerate 3 hours or overnight.

Nutritional Values (per serving)	
Calories	343
Carbohydrate	48.5g
Protein	9.3g
Fiber	4.6g
Sugar	43.9g
Fat Calories	207
Total Fat	23g
Saturated Fat	3.3g
Cholesterol	2.9g
Sodium	761mg

Go Outside

LaConner's own Smith and Hawken... ...without the catalogue! This could be the ultimate gardeners "pleasure emporium" From mud gloves and shiny, black polished rocks to birdhouses of architectural craft-manship, gardening parphernalia fills this tiny shop of outdoor living experiences.

Mark and Heidi have managed to accomplish their goal - to bring the "outside in and the inside out." This theme is even followed through when you take a stroll around their outside sculpture garden. Art in the yard!

A wonderful selection of gardening books can advise you on the best ways to achieve the garden of your dreams. A tasteful assortment of garden theme gift wraps and silk ribbons can make that special gift memorable just in its presentation.

As you walk down Morris Street, there's no mistaking Go Outside...just look for the "best windows" in town!

111 Morris Street   360-466-4836

Peter's Curried Rice Salad

Flavors from the East are served up in this delicious salad that could be used as an entreé. Be sure to include fresh fruit and a tall glass of iced mint tea.

Recipe contributed by: *LaConner Seafood and Prime Rib House*

Preparation time: 15 minutes   Cook time: 30 minutes   Chill time: 1 hour   Serves: 8

Ingredients

¼ cup olive oil
2 cups vermicelli noodles, broken
1 cup celery, chopped
1 cup onion, chopped
1 Tbs. dried thyme
1 Tbs. dried basil
2 Tbs. curry powder
3 cups rice
6 cups chicken broth
1 cup golden raisins
1 cup celery, finely chopped

1 cup onion, finely chopped
1 cup large cooked cocktail shrimp
   or 1 cup cooked chicken, cubed

Dressing
½ cup lemon juice
1 cup olive oil
1 Tbs. sugar
1 tsp. curry powder
½ cup fresh cilantro, chopped
½ tsp. salt

Nutritional Values (per serving)	
Calories	795
Carbohydrate	97.4g
Protein	18g
Fiber	6.9g
Sugar	90.6g
Fat Calories	344
Total Fat	38.2g
Saturated Fat	6.1g
Cholesterol	55.9g
Sodium	1108.3mg

Preparation

In a large skillet, over medium heat, brown vermicelli in olive oil, stirring frequently. When browned, add 1 cup chopped celery, 1 cup chopped onion, thyme, basil and curry powder. Cook 1 minute to toast seasonings. Pour in rice and cook 2 minutes to coat rice and brown slightly. Add chicken broth and stir well. Bring to boil, stir again and reduce heat. Cover pan and simmer 20-25 minutes or until rice is done. Remove skillet from heat and stir in raisins. Turn rice mixture out into a large pyrex baking dish and spread as thin as possible. Refrigerate. When rice is cold, stir in 1 cup finely chopped celery, 1 cup finely chopped onion and either cocktail shrimp or chicken. In a small bowl, whisk together all dressing ingredients. Pour over salad. Stir to combine and let sit at room temperature for 1 hour to meld flavors.

HOT SEAFOOD SALAD

A gastronomic extravaganza of seafoods served in a distinctive combination is one of the most frequently ordered dishes at the Lighthouse. Crustacean lovers, this is the consummate recipe!

Recipe contributed by: Lighthouse Inn

Preparation time: 20 minutes   **Cook time:** 3-4 minutes   **Serves:** 2

Ingredients

6 ounces shrimp
6 scallops
6 smoked mussels
12 Dungeness crab legs, shelled
4 pieces bacon, chopped
½ cup white wine
2 cloves garlic, minced
4 cups mixed salad greens
2 eggs, hard-boiled
8 tomato wedges
2 lemon wedges

Hot Seafood Salad Dressing
4 egg yolks
1 cup olive oil
½ cup fresh lemon juice
1 tsp. Worcestershire sauce
1 clove garlic, minced
1 tsp. oregano
½ tsp. dill
2 dashes Tabasco sauce
¼ cup Parmesan cheese, grated
1 tsp. dried mustard

Nutritional Values (per serving)	
Calories	2318
Carbohydrates	63.6g
Protein	296.4g
Fiber	0.4g
Sugar	63.2g
Fat Calories	687
Total Fat	76.3g
Saturated Fat	28.9g
Cholesterol	1093g
Sodium	4226.1mg

Preparation

Prepare dressing by whipping egg yolks for 10 minutes. Add olive oil and blend well. Whip in rest of dressing ingredients. Set aside. In a skillet, sauté seafood and bacon in wine and garlic until scallops and shrimp lose their translucency. Add 4 ounces of dressing to sautéed mixture and stir in. Arrange salad greens on 2 plates. Spoon hot seafood over top. Garnish with hard-boiled egg, tomato and lemon wedges.

Spicy Beef Salad

Because of its low sugar content, this is an excellent recipe for those who are trying to diet or who need to watch their sugar intake. Those looking for low-fat menu items can use this as an entrée.

Recipe contributed by: Craig Reeves, Marina Cafe

Preparation time: 25 minutes   Cook time: 6 minutes   Serves: 4

Ingredients

½ pound boneless sirloin steak
⅓ cup fresh lime juice
1 Tbs. brown sugar
1 Tbs. soy sauce
1 Tbs. fresh basil, minced
2 tsp. fresh mint, minced

1 jalapeno pepper, minced
2-3 cloves garlic, minced
1 tsp. ginger root, grated
1 large sweet red pepper, julienned
½ medium cucumber, peeled and chopped
6 cups mixed salad greens, torn

Preparation

Partially freeze beef as it makes it easier to cut. Slice across the grain into thin strips and set aside. In a small bowl combine lime juice, brown sugar, soy sauce, basil and mint adjusting, if needed, to suit personal taste and set aside. Coat a medium non-stick skillet with cooking spray and sauté jalapeno, garlic and ginger for 30 seconds. Add beef strips and stir fry until cooked as desired. Remove beef from skillet and gently toss with red pepper and cucumber. Place greens on individual salad plates and top with beef mixture. Add soy mixture to skillet and bring to boil then remove from heat and drizzle proportionately over each salad. Serve immediately.

Nutritional Values (per serving)	
Calories	217
Carbohydrate	23.1g
Protein	23.1g
Fiber	7.2g
Sugar	15.9g
Fat Calories	47
Total Fat	5.2g
Saturated Fat	1.7g
Cholesterol	50.5g
Sodium	772.3mg

Homespun Market

A classic, 100 year old waterfront building sets the stage for a delightful array of clothing and accessories for the home. The only remaining clues to the past life of this speciality store are the slight tilt to the building (appropriate to the tavern it once was) and the aging storefront sign proclaiming it to be a meat market!

In spite of its intriquing past, Homespun Market is definitely a store for today's shopper. The beautiful old world curtain and table lace, woven afghans and table linens may make you feel a little nostalgic for those days spent at the beach in your summer cottage.

A winsome collection of apparel by April Cornell will make you feel pampered and feminine. Lovely earrings or a brooch to complete the ensemble are just waiting to be chosen.

With scented candles, a charming picture frame holding that special photograph or any other accessory from Homespun Market, any place you toss your hat will feel like home.

622 South First Street   360-466-4441

LaConner Slough Salad

This is a definite pleaser for pasta lovers. In combination with sun-dried tomatoes, Greek olives and Feta cheese, this salad is mouthwatering. Fourth of July celebrations aren't complete without this crowd-pleaser.

Recipe contributed by: Linda Banaszak, The Padilla Bay Store

Preparation time: 25 minutes*   Cook time: 12 minutes   Serves: 10-12

Ingredients
16 ounces rotini pasta, uncooked
10 ounces Greek olives, pitted and chopped; reserve brine
8 ½ ounces sun-dried tomatoes in oil, drained and chopped; reserve oil
1 large red onion, chopped
3 cups large shrimp, fresh cooked and chilled
8 ounces Feta cheese, crumbled
3 Tbs. red wine vinegar
1¼ - 1½ cups mayonnaise
2 Tbs. fresh basil leaves, chopped
2 Tbs. fresh oregano, chopped
2 Tbs. fresh parsley, chopped
2 cloves garlic, minced
salt and pepper to taste

Nutritional Values (per serving)	
Calories	306
Carbohydrate	20.2g
Protein	16.7g
Fiber	0.9g
Sugar	19.4g
Fat Calories	175
Total Fat	19.4g
Saturated Fat	4.8g
Cholesterol	135.1g
Sodium	1305.5mg

Preparation
Cook pasta according to package directions and cool. In a large bowl, combine olives, tomatoes and onion. Add pasta and mix together. In a separate bowl, whisk together red wine vinegar, mayonnaise, reserved liquids, garlic, herbs, salt and pepper. Mix into salad. Before serving, add Feta cheese and shrimp and toss.
May substitute chicken for shrimp if desired.

*This salad is best if made the day before.

Becky's Tortellini Salad

A light lunch al fresco? This chilled pasta salad with its mix of delicious summer vegetables and herbs served with a nice crusty bread and chilled bottle of wine make it a meal to linger over.

Recipe contributed by: Becky Fiveash, Rainbow Bridge Shirtworks

Preparation time: 30 minutes   **Cook time:** 10 minutes   **Chill time:** 2-4 hours   **Serves:** 4

Ingredients

18 ounces cheese tortellini, uncooked
1 cup asparagus tips
2 Tbs. olive oil
1 red pepper, julienned
½ yellow pepper, julienned
3 ounces black olives, sliced
2 green onions, finely chopped

1 clove garlic, minced
½ tsp. celery seed
1 tsp. fresh basil, finely chopped
1 tsp. fresh rosemary, finely chopped
1 cup prepared Caesar dressing
¼ cup Parmesan cheese, grated

Preparation

Cook tortellini according to package directions and cool. In a skillet, sauté asparagus tips in 1 tablespoon olive oil. In a large bowl, combine all ingredients and chill for 2-4 hours. Serve chilled.

Nutritional Values (per serving)	
Calories	407
Carbohydrate	38.9g
Protein	16.8g
Fiber	3.9g
Sugar	35g
Fat Calories	194
Total Fat	21.5g
Saturated Fat	19.1g
Cholesterol	47.5g
Sodium	551.8mg

Smoked Turkey, Pecan and Blue Cheese Salad

The surprising meld of flavors in this salad will have your guests asking for extra servings and the recipe, of course!

Recipe contributed by: Kay Trelstad, The Stall

Preparation time: 20 minutes   Serves: 4

Ingredients

½ cup vegetable oil
¼ cup white wine vinegar
¼ cup honey
½ cup onion, chopped
4 tsp. Tabasco sauce
6 cups assorted salad greens, bite
   size pieces

2 cups curly endive, bite size pieces
8 ounces smoked turkey, diced
⅔ cup blue cheese, crumbled
⅔ cup pecans, toasted and chopped
1 avocado, peeled, pitted and diced
salt and pepper to taste

Preparation

In a blender, combine oil, vinegar, honey, onion, Tabasco and purée. Season dressing to taste with salt and pepper. Rinse and dry greens in salad spinner. Greens have to be as dry as possible for dressing to adhere. In a large bowl, combine greens and endive and toss with enough dressing to coat. Add remaining ingredients and drizzle with more dressing. Toss gently. May be made up to 4 hours ahead.

Nutritional Values (per serving)	
Calories	880
Carbohydrate	42.1g
Protein	22.2g
Fiber	10.3g
Sugar	31.8g
Fat Calories	666
Total Fat	74g
Saturated Fat	14.6g
Cholesterol	34.6g
Sodium	807.6mg

Hope Island Inn

Follow in the legendary footsteps of John Wayne, Bob Hope, Bill Cosby, Eddie Bauer and Duncan Hines to Hope Island Inn by the sea. Where culture complements cuisine in a restaurant filled with an eclectic collection of art, antiques and rare books. The menu fulfills every expectation set by this aura of comfort and eloquence. A select wine list complements the food and atmosphere.

Garden wedding in your future? Or maybe a special anniversary? Make it one to remember with this unique setting offered at Hope Island Inn. Spectacular westerly views and gardens, that even "Martha" would be jealous of, will never disappoint you.

Join the the list of celebs and find out what makes this inn-by-the-sea a place to return to in years to come.

1686 Chilberg Avenue   360-466-3221

DOMINIQUE'S TOMATO AND FETA SALAD

France is, of course, noted for its many fine wines. But, for those who have lived or travelled there, no other tomatoes quite compare with those grown in France. Dominique Darcy, owner of Two Moons and a native of France, says that the tomatoes available at Hedlin's Greenhouse in LaConner, when in season, are as succulent as any she has tasted since leaving her native country.

Recipe contributed by: Dominique Darcy, Two Moons

Preparation: 10 minutes*   Serves: 2

Ingredients
2 large tomatoes
3 ounces Feta cheese, crumbled
1 bunch fresh basil leaves, coarsely chopped
2 Tbs. olive oil

Preparation
Cut tomatoes into thick slices and arrange attractively on two salad plates. Crumble half of Feta cheese over each serving. Sprinkle liberally with basil. Drizzle olive oil over each portion to accommodate individual tastes. Serve at room temperature.

*Though simple to prepare, this salad's success depends on the use of the freshest and most flavorful ingredients available.

Nutritional Values
(per serving)

Calories	308
Carbohydrate	17g
Protein	8.7g
Fiber	0.4g
Sugar	16.6g
Fat Calories	218
Total Fat	24.2g
Saturated Fat	8.4g
Cholesterol	37.8g
Sodium	1067.4mg

SPINACH SALAD WITH STRAWBERRIES

You've just picked the first strawberries of the season. Plump, sweet and deliciously juicy. This simple salad will feature them in all their glory.

Recipe contributed by: Marilyn Gardner, West Shore Acres

Preparation time: 15 minutes   Serves: 4

Ingredients

6 ounces fresh spinach
1 cup fresh strawberries, rinsed and stems removed
1 small red onion, thinly sliced
1 Tbs. sesame seeds, toasted

Dressing
2 Tbs. balsamic vinegar
2 Tbs. rice vinegar
1 Tbs. + 1 tsp. honey
2 tsp. Dijon mustard
salt and freshly ground pepper to taste

Preparation

Rinse spinach in several cold water baths to clean thoroughly and pat dry. Tear leaves into bite size pieces. In a small bowl, whisk vinegars, honey and mustard together until well blended. Place spinach leaves in a large bowl, add dressing and toss to coat leaves. Cut strawberries in half. Add strawberries, red onion and sesame seeds to dressed spinach and lightly toss.

Nutritional Values (per serving)	
Calories	71
Carbohydrate	12g
Protein	2.7g
Fiber	2.8g
Sugar	9.2g
Fat Calories	22
Total Fat	2.4g
Saturated Fat	0.3g
Cholesterol	0g
Sodium	35.9mg

CHILLED SUMMER BERRY SOUP

Not all soups need to be hot. The bounty of fresh berries in the Skagit Valley should inspire the chef to be daring and different. The season defines the soup!

Recipe contributed by: Shawna Powell, A Class Act Gallery

Preparation time: 15 minutes   Serves: 8

Ingredients
3 cups orange juice
3 cups yogurt, plain or vanilla
2 Tbs. lemon or lime juice
2 Tbs. honey (optional)
3 cups fresh strawberries*
4 Tbs. granola
mint sprigs for garnish

Preparation
Combine orange juice, yogurt, lemon or lime juice, optional honey and berries in blender. Purée until smooth. Serve in individual bowls with a sprinkling of granola. Garnish with a sprig of mint and a sprinkling of nutmeg or cinnamon.

*You may substitute your favorite summer berries.

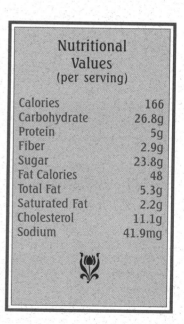

Nutritional Values (per serving)	
Calories	166
Carbohydrate	26.8g
Protein	5g
Fiber	2.9g
Sugar	23.8g
Fat Calories	48
Total Fat	5.3g
Saturated Fat	2.2g
Cholesterol	11.1g
Sodium	41.9mg

Just Imagine

Just imagine...you're looking for something comfortable and casual to wear to the family picnic at the beach. Just imagine...you really want something fresh and fun for the cruise you and your best friend are going on next week. Just imagine...all you want is something soft and cuddly to throw on when you sit by the fire after a long day at work.

Imagine no more. Clothing for all these occasions and more can be found in this tiny store located in one of LaConner's historic buildings. You won't find a gown for the Inaugural Ball, but you will find cottons and corduroys, knits and denim with the perfect accessories in jewelry and scarves to complete the look. Just imagine...

715 South First Street   360-466-3003

BLACK BEAN SOUP

Add a Caesar salad, Parmesan Rolls and you'll have a complete meal. This soup also freezes well and can be easily doubled or tripled.

Recipe contributed by: Tia Kurtz, Cottons

Preparation time: 30 minutes*   Cook time: 1 hour 15 minutes   Serves: 4

Ingredients

1 cup black beans
3½ cups water
1 bay leaf
1 clove garlic, minced
1 small onion, chopped

½ green pepper, chopped
1 tsp. fresh oregano, finely chopped
2 tsp. salt
2 Tbs. wine vinegar
½ tsp. Tabasco sauce

Preparation

In a bowl, cover beans with water and soak overnight. In the morning, drain beans and transfer to saucepan. Add 3½ cups water, bay leaf, garlic, onion, green pepper and oregano. Bring to boil over medium heat. Cover and simmer on low heat for 1 hour or until beans are tender. Add salt, wine vinegar, Tabasco and cook 5 more minutes. Remove about half of beans from saucepan, place in blender and purée. Stir puréed beans back into soup. Serve in individual bowls garnished with chopped onions or yogurt with a sprinkle of fresh chopped cilantro.

*Beans need to soak overnight.

Parmesan Rolls recipe on page 101

Nutritional Values (per serving)

Calories	93
Carbohydrate	17.3g
Protein	5.6g
Fiber	0.7g
Sugar	16.6g
Fat Calories	7
Total Fat	0.8g
Saturated Fat	0.1g
Cholesterol	0g
Sodium	1077mg

CREAMY POTATO AND LEEK BISQUE

Sally says that when her boys were younger they were convinced that mom said they were eating potato and "leech" soup. A soup that Indiana Jones would have loved. Sally recommends that you serve Calico Cupboard whole wheat bread with this tasty soup, sans the leeches, of course!

Recipe contributed by: Sally Cram, O'Leary's Books and Other Comforts

Preparation Time: 20 minutes   **Cook time:** 45 minutes   **Serves:** 8

Ingredients
½ cup butter
3 leeks, including some of the tops, thinly sliced
1 cup celery, including some of the tops, thinly sliced
4 cups potatoes, peeled and diced into ½" cubes
¼ cup parsley, finely chopped
½ tsp. salt
¼ tsp. pepper
4 cups chicken broth
4 cups milk
3 Tbs. cornstarch
¼ cup water
1½ cups cooked ham, cubed

Nutritional Values (per serving)	
Calories	372
Carbohydrate	42.5g
Protein	17.7g
Fiber	2.4g
Sugar	40.1g
Fat Calories	164
Total Fat	18.2g
Saturated Fat	10.5g
Cholesterol	70.6g
Sodium	1522.5mg

Preparation
In a large stockpot, melt butter over medium heat. Add leeks and celery. Cook, stirring often, for about 10 minutes. Add potatoes, parsley, salt, pepper and chicken broth. Cover and cook until potatoes are tender, about 20 minutes. Stir in milk and cook, covered, until soup is thoroughly hot but NOT boiling. In a small bowl, blend cornstarch and water until smooth. Add to soup and continue cooking until soup boils and thickens, about 5 minutes. Adjust seasoning to taste. Add ham and cook 10 minutes longer. Top with butter and parsley to serve.

GREEN OLIVE SOUP

An elegant soup that will delight green olive lovers and convert the rest! It's easy to make and will impress the most discrimnating guests. (But make them guess what's in it!)

Recipe contributed by: Vernee Neff, The Olive Shoppe

Preparation time: 1 hour   Cook Time: 40 minutes   Serves: 4

Ingredients

2 cups green olives, pitted
6 Tbs. olive oil
½ medium yellow onion, sliced
2 cloves garlic, crushed
4 cups chicken stock
1 cup whipping cream

6 Tbs. all purpose flour
freshly ground pepper to taste
4 dashes Tabasco sauce
⅓ cup sherry
4 pimiento green olives, sliced
1 cup garlic croutons

Preparation

Soak green olives in cold water for 1 hour. Drain and coarsely chop. Heat 3 tablespoons olive oil in skillet. Sauté onion, garlic and ⅔ of green olives until onion is translucent. Transfer mixture to food processor and purée with 1 cup chicken stock.

In a 4 quart saucepan, combine puréed mixture with remaining chicken stock. Simmer for 20 minutes. Stir in whipping cream.

In small skillet, combine remaining 3 tablespoons olive oil and flour, stirring and cooking to form a roux. Whisk roux into soup and simmer, stirring constantly until thickened. Pepper to taste. Add remaining chopped olives, Tabasco and sherry. Heat to serving temperature and serve in individual bowls garnished with sliced pimiento olives and garlic croutons.

Nutritional Values (per serving)	
Calories	753
Carbohydrate	60.7g
Protein	11.6g
Fiber	7.6g
Sugar	53g
Fat Calories	460
Total Fat	51.1g
Saturated Fat	6.3g
Cholesterol	5.7g
Sodium	2908.3mg

KATY'S INN BED AND BREAKFAST

Katy's Inn is nestled against the hillside two blocks up from the main street of LaConner. One of the oldest Victorian homes in LaConner, it was built by Captain John Peck in 1876.

The guest rooms are decorated with exquisite Victorian detail and attention to comfort. Sweeping views of the town and Swinomish Channel invite guests in the upstairs rooms to step out the French doors onto the wrap around porch. Private baths are available, and a sheltering gazebo makes the hot tub an all weather destination!

The suite on the main floor has a sitting area that looks out onto the perfectly cultivated gardens, sparkling pond and waterfall. On cool Northwest evenings, a gas log stove provides atmosphere.

Your stay includes fresh cookies in the evening and breakfast served in the dining room or on a silver tray at your door. Come and feel pampered!

503 SOUTH THIRD STREET   800-914-7767

NONI'S MINESTRONE SOUP

Any fresh vegetables may be added to this soup such as broccoli, eggplant, cauliflower or summer squash. Other kinds of cabbage may be substiuted as well. Use shell beans or other meaty beans, the more the better.

Recipe contributed by: Stephanie Banaszak, Organic Matters

Preparation time: 30 minutes   Cook time: 6 hours   Serves: 12

Ingredients

4 quarts water
2 tsp. salt
½ tsp. pepper
6 ounces salt pork, finely chopped
1 large carrot, finely chopped
5 medium potatoes, cubed
½ head cabbage, shredded
1 large tomato, cored
1-2 cans green beans, drained
2 small zucchini, cubed

½ onion, chopped
3 cups dry navy beans
1 cup frozen peas
1 package pasta, your choice

Pesto
2 cups fresh basil
3-4 cloves garlic
½ cup Parmesan, grated

Preparation

Fill stock pot with water, salt and pepper. Add salt pork, carrot, potatoes, cabbage, tomato, green beans, zucchini, onion, dry beans and peas. Bring ingredients to a boil, reduce heat and simmer, stirring occasionally, for at least 6 hours. When cabbage is cooked to where it's not noticeable and soup begins to reduce in volume, add package of pasta: elbows, small shells, etc. Stir soup often at this point as it will scorch easily. While pasta is cooking make your pesto. In a blender, add basil, garlic, Parmesan and a couple of ladles of soup mixture and blend well. Add to soup and cook briefly. Remove soup from heat and add salt to taste.

Nutritional Values (per serving)	
Calories	343
Carbohydrate	38.9g
Protein	15g
Fiber	3.8g
Sugar	35.1g
Fat Calories	137
Total Fat	15.2g
Saturated Fat	6.2g
Cholesterol	19.7g
Sodium	893.3mg

OLD FASHIONED CREAM OF TOMATO SOUP

Once you make this tomato soup from scratch, your family will never eat Campbells again! This is an old family recipe handed down from Sharons' grandmother.

Recipe contributed by: Sharon Scott, The Scott Collection

Preparation time: 10 minutes　　Cook time: 1 hour　　Serves: 8

Ingredients
32 ounces canned tomatoes, diced
9 ounces chicken broth
1 ounce butter
2 Tbs. sugar
1 Tbs. onion, finely chopped
1 pinch baking soda
2 cups milk

Preparation
In a large saucepan, combine tomatoes, chicken broth, butter, sugar, onions and baking soda. Simmer for 1 hour. Heat milk in double boiler. Add to hot tomato mixture and stir. Serve in individual bowls or pour in a tureen and serve at the table.

Nutritional Values (per serving)	
Calories	106
Carbohydrate	13g
Protein	3.2g
Fiber	1.2g
Sugar	11.8g
Fat Calories	48
Total Fat	5.3g
Saturated Fat	3.1g
Cholesterol	15.8g
Sodium	362.4mg

HARVEST PUMPKIN SOUP

Roasted garlic is the quintessential ingredient in this soup. Earlene makes this recipe easier by roasting a whole small pumpkin and garlic at the same time in a 325° oven for about 1 hour.

Recipe contributed by: Earlene Beckes, Skagit Bay Hideaway

Preparation time: 1 hour   Cook time: 1 hour 20 minutes   Serves: 10-12

Ingredients

1 large onion, chopped
2 cloves garlic, chopped
3 Tbs. olive oil
2 tsp. allspice
1 Tbs. coriander, ground

1 cup sherry
4 cups pumpkin, cooked and skin removed
2 quarts low salt chicken stock
2 heads roasted garlic*
salt and pepper to taste

Preparation

In a large saucepan over medium heat, sauté onion and raw garlic in olive oil until onion is translucent, adding more oil if needed. Do not allow garlic to brown or it will become bitter. Add allspice and coriander. Stir frequently for about 5 minutes. Add sherry and cook 10 more minutes. Add pumpkin, chicken stock and roasted garlic, mixing well and bringing to a boil over medium high heat. Reduce heat and simmer uncovered for about 30 minutes, stirring occasionally. Butter may be added for flavor, but cream isn't necessary as the roasted garlic will act as a thickener.

Pour batches of soup in blender and purée until smooth, returning them to saucepan when processed. Bring soup to boil, reduce heat to simmer again, cooking an additional 15 minutes. Season to taste. Serve in individual bowls garnished with nuts for a festive touch.

*Instructions for roasting garlic on page 50

Nutritional Values (per serving)	
Calories	124
Carbohydrate	12.4g
Protein	2.7g
Fiber	2.1g
Sugar	10.3g
Fat Calories	49
Total Fat	5.4g
Saturated Fat	0.8g
Cholesterol	0g
Sodium	1133.7mg

Kokomo Joe's

Kokomo Joe's is so alive with color, variety and the feel of the tropics, it makes you want to break out your Hawaiian lei and grass skirt and do a hula!

As you dance through the jungle of kites and windsocks descending on you from above, make sure to stop and play with a few of the nostalgic toys, brain teasers and pick up a pair of pink flamingoes for your yard!

Joe and his wife Diane are so friendly they'll even rent you some bicycles to ride around on and discover the rest of LaConner. Of course, he'll want to see your bicycle-riding license. (Just kidding!) The old deck chairs out front can be sat upon in exchange for your best joke or, possibly, for free if you're in a really good mood.

So, come on in and say hello to resident parrot Mangler, and get a little sun. You're guaranteed not to get a sunburn but always a warm feeling and lots of fun.

101 North First Street   360-466-2085

Easy Crab Bisque

New England has its clam chowder, but here in the Pacific Northwest, any excuse to use fresh crab is a good one. A quick stop at the store, and this a great recipe for that unexpected, last minute company.

Recipe contributed by: Arberta Lammers, Tillinghast Seed Company

Preparation time: 5 minutes   Cook time: 10 minutes   Serves: 8

Ingredients
1 can tomato soup
1 can split pea soup (no ham)
1 can consommé
1 cup half and half cream
1 cup fresh Dungeness crab, cooked and shelled
sherry to taste
8 Tbs. sour cream
4 tsp. chives, chopped

Preparation
In a food processor, purée soups and consommé. Transfer mixture to saucepan and heat to boiling point. Add crab. You may substitute canned crab, just make sure that you drain it. Heat through. Add sherry to taste. Serve immediately in individual bowls and garnish with a dollop of sour cream sprinkled with chives.

Nutritional Values (per serving)	
Calories	188
Carbohydrate	16.1g
Protein	11.9g
Fiber	1.1g
Sugar	15g
Fat Calories	72
Total Fat	8g
Saturated Fat	4.8g
Cholesterol	42.1g
Sodium	790mg

BARLEY AND LENTIL SOUP

This soup will warm you up on those rainy winter days. For variation add cooked, shredded turkey or left-over ham and other favorite vegetables.

Recipe contributed by: Marilyn Gardner, West Shore Acres

Preparation time: 15 minutes   Cook time: 1 hour   Serves: 6

Ingredients
½ cup barley
½ cup lentils
5 cups chicken or vegetable broth
¾ cup carrot, peeled and diced
¾ cup celery, diced
1 medium onion, chopped
1 bay leaf
1 tsp. cumin, ground
⅓ tsp. pepper

Preparation
Rinse and drain barley and lentils well. In a large stock pot, combine barley and lentils with chicken broth, carrot, celery, onion, bay leaf, cumin and pepper. Simmer over medium low heat for about 1 hour, or until barley and lentils are tender. Add seasoning to accommodate personal taste. Variations include finely chopped Polish sausage or ham. Soup is best when topped with a spoonful of plain yogurt and peeled chopped cucumber.

Nutritional Values (per serving)	
Calories	132
Carbohydrate	24.6g
Protein	6.1g
Fiber	4.9g
Sugar	19.7g
Fat Calories	18g
Total Fat	2g
Saturated Fat	0.3g
Cholesterol	0g
Sodium	1231.7mg

ON THE SIDE

LaConner Brewing Company

The warm aromas of basil, roasted peppers, mushrooms and cheese greet you the minute you open the door at the LaConner Brewing Company. The cozy fire in the corner invites you to take some time out for freshly baked pizza from the wood-fired oven, a cold brewski and leisurely conversation. As you sit watching people pass by on First Street, you feel a little more content to be just where you are! During a lull in the conversation there's always a fresh batch of local artwork to discover on the walls, or a new display of brew pub paraphernalia to contemplate.

For the adventurous micro-brew buffs, the LaConner Brewing Company's wheat and stout beers are always available. Their Pale Ale and other draught beers change seasonally. Mouth-watering pizzas, soups, salads and desserts complete the menu.

Known to locals as "the brew house", the LaConner Brewing Company also provides a respite for the die-hard shopper. The good beer and trendy ambiance expected at today's micro-breweries is second nature here.

117 South First Street   360-466-1415

GRACE'S COFFEE CAKE

The aroma of this cake right out of the oven is heavenly, reminiscent of Grandma's kitchen, perhaps? Art and Rita Hupy, owner's of Art's Place Bed and Breakfast, treat their guests to a taste that will truly remind them of their Grandma's kitchen.

Recipe contributed by: Rita Hupy, Art's Place Bed and Breakfast

Preparation time: 30 Minutes   Bake time: 1 hour   Serves: 12

Ingredients

1¼ cups butter
1½ cups sugar
3 eggs
1½ cups sour cream
2¼ cups flour, sifted
2¼ tsp. baking powder
1½ tsp. baking soda
1½ tsp. vanilla extract

Topping
½ cup brown sugar
1 Tbs. cinnamon
½ cup walnuts, chopped

Preparation

Preheat oven to 350°. In a small bowl, combine brown sugar, cinnamon and walnuts and set aside. In a large bowl, cream butter and sugar together. Beat in eggs one at a time. Add sour cream, flour, baking powder, baking soda and vanilla. Mix well. Pour half the batter into a greased and flour dusted angel food cake springform pan and sprinkle half of topping over batter. Pour in remaining cake batter and sprinkle on remaining topping. Bake in preheated oven for 1 hour. Remove from oven and cool right side up in pan.

Nutritional Values (per serving)	
Calories	529
Carbohydrate	73.8g
Protein	.1g
Fiber	2.1g
Sugar	71.8g
Fat Calories	188
Total Fat	20.9g
Saturated Fat	11.1g
Cholesterol	43.5g
Sodium	400.3mg

KATY'S INN BLUEBERRY MUFFIN CAKES

Big, fat, juicy blueberries picked right here in Skagit Valley are the featured ingredient for these delectable muffin cakes. Kathie Hubbard, owner of Katy's Inn, says these muffins are a big favorite of her guests.

Recipe contributed by: Kathie Hubbard, Katy's Inn

Preparation time: 15 minutes　　　Bake time: 25 minutes　　　Serves: 18

Ingredients

½ cup butter
¾ cup sugar
2 eggs
2⅓ cups flour
2½ tsp. baking powder
½ tsp. salt
½ tsp. nutmeg, ground
¾ cup milk
1½ cups fresh blueberries

Topping
¼ cup butter, melted
¼ cup sugar
¼ tsp. cinnamon

Preparation

Preheat oven to 350°. Grease muffin tin or line with paper muffin cups. In a large bowl, cream butter and sugar together. Add eggs and beat well. In a separate bowl, sift together flour, baking powder, salt and nutmeg. Add sifted ingredients to creamed mixture in small amounts, alternating with milk. Making sure all ingredients are well blended, gently fold in blueberries. Fill prepared muffin cups approximately ⅔ full and bake in preheated oven 20-25 minutes. While muffins are baking, prepare topping. In a small, deep bowl melt butter. In another bowl, combine sugar and cinnamon. When muffins are baked and still warm, carefully remove from muffin tins. Dip tops into melted butter and then in cinnamon mixture. This not only enhances the richness of the muffin cakes but also helps to keep them moist.

Nutritional Values (per serving)	
Calories	255
Carbohydrate	38.8g
Protein	6.4g
Fiber	1.4g
Sugar	37.4g
Fat Calories	76
Total Fat	8.4g
Saturated Fat	5.1g
Cholesterol	22g
Sodium	176.2mg

LaConner Flats, a Garden... The Granary

Discover the beauty and tranquility of an English country garden. Sheltered and encircled by stately stands of poplar, this country garden, vibrant with color, is waiting to welcome and refresh you.

Stroll the winding green pathways of LaConner Flats. Rediscover the nuances of nature; a lilting birdsong, rustling leaves and breeze-stirred boughs. Pause and inhale a rose's sweet perfume, the crisp cinnamon scent of nodding carnations. Luxuriant beds of brilliant blooming flowers surround you.

Any of life's milestones, weddings, anniversaries, birthdays or reunions, can be a little more special when celebrated at LaConner Flats and the Granary. Treat a group of your friends to High Tea. But remember it's by reservation only.

The gardens are open year around and donations are accepted to view the gardens and help maintain them.

1598 Best Road   360-466-3190

Orange Cinnamon Waffles

It's the first snow of the season and the morning fire is crackling in the hearth. What better way to start off your week-end than with waffles that "Martha" would be proud to serve at her table.

Recipe contributed by: Rainbow Inn Bed and Breakfast

Preparation time: 10 minutes   Cook time: 4-5 minutes each   Serves: 6

Ingredients

2 cups flour
2 tsp. baking soda
1 tsp. baking powder
1 tsp. salt
3 Tbs. butter, melted
1½ cups buttermilk

2 eggs
½ cup vegetable oil
½ cup orange juice
1 Tbs. orange zest
1 tsp. cinnamon

Preparation

Preheat waffle iron. For light and crispy waffles, use a Belgian waffle iron. In a large bowl, combine all ingredients and blend well. Pour ½ cup batter in preheated waffle iron and cook until done. Serve sprinkled with powdered sugar and an assortment of goodies to top with.

Nutritional Values (per serving)	
Calories	536
Carbohydrate	65.1g
Protein	18.4g
Fiber	2.6g
Sugar	62.5g
Fat Calories	234
Total Fat	26g
Saturated Fat	6.7g
Cholesterol	17.8g
Sodium	993.6mg

APPLE BROWN BETTY MUFFINS

The kids want something different for breakfast and you want something to enjoy with that first morning cup of Starbucks. Apples, cinnamon, nutmeg, allspice and brown sugar all wrapped up in satisfying little cakes, the perfect solution.

Recipe contributed by: Rainbow Inn Bed and Breakfast

Preparation time: 15 minutes   Bake time: 35 minutes   Serves: 12

Ingredients

1 cup flour
½ cup sugar
1½ Tbs. baking powder
½ tsp. salt
2½ Tbs. canola oil
½ cup milk
1 egg
1 Tbs. cinnamon
1 tsp. allspice, ground

1 tsp. nutmeg, ground
4 large apples, cored and chopped with skins

Streusel Topping
2 Tbs. butter
¼ cup flour
¼ cup brown sugar
½ tsp. cinnamon

Preparation

Preheat oven to 350°. Grease muffin tins. In a small bowl, cut together streusel topping ingredients and set aside. In a large bowl, mix flour, sugar, baking powder, salt, oil, milk, egg, cinnamon, allspice, nutmeg and apples. Mix well. Fill prepared muffin cups ⅔ full and sprinkle streusel mixture over tops of muffin batter. Bake in preheated oven 30-35 minutes. Let cool 5 minutes before serving.

Nutritional Values (per serving)	
Calories	457
Carbohydrate	81.1g
Protein	10.1g
Fiber	5g
Sugar	76.1g
Fat Calories	105
Total Fat	11.6g
Saturated Fat	3.6g
Cholesterol	13g
Sodium	268.5mg

Pumpkin Waffles à la Skagit Bay

It's the autumn harvest and pumpkins abound. Why not include these delicious pumpkin waffles in a harvest themed brunch? Top with maple syrup or whipped cream with a dash of ginger for flavor and freshly grated nutmeg.

Recipe contributed by: Earlene Beckes, Skagit Bay Hideaway

Preparation time: 10 minutes   Cook time: 20 minutes   Serves: 8

Ingredients

1 cup pumpkin, cooked
1½ cups milk
3 eggs
2 Tbs. butter, melted
1 cup all purpose flour
⅓ cup whole wheat flour

2 tsp. baking powder
½ tsp. salt
2 Tbs. sugar
⅛ tsp. nutmeg, ground
⅛ tsp. pumpkin pie spice

Preparation

In a large bowl, stir together pumpkin, milk, eggs and butter. In a separate bowl, sift together flours, baking powder, salt, sugar, nutmeg and pumpkin pie spice. Add sifted ingredients to pumpkin mixture, stirring thoroughly until combined. Preheat waffle iron (Belgian waffle iron is preferrable), spoon in batter and bake till golden.

Nutritional Values (per serving)	
Calories	255
Carbohydrate	37.3g
Protein	15.4g
Fiber	2.5g
Sugar	34.9g
Fat Calories	44
Total Fat	4.9g
Saturated Fat	2.8g
Cholesterol	13.7g
Sodium	297.3mg

LaConner Seafood and Prime Rib House

On a hot July afternoon, with a breeze blowing across the Channel, it's hard to beat a cold beer and a seafood salad while sitting on the deck of the LaConner Seafood and Prime Rib House. Of course you can also eat inside, in the dark of winter and be just as well sated by the food and atmosphere. Why else would they be voted the "Best Seafood Restaurant in Skagit Valley" year after year?

Like the mythical phoenix rising from the ashes, the restaurant became even better after a fire ravaged the building in 1992. The Swinomish Channel provides a panoramic backdrop for the dining room, bar and deck with the Rainbow Bridge spanning the water in the distance.

Seafood is, of course, the specialty here, but soups, salads, pasta and steak are all just as deliciously prepared. Beverages and appetizers are a must.

The hard part of your meal is getting up to leave...but you can always come back.

614 South First Street   360-466-4014

WHITE SWAN GINGER CARROT MUFFINS

The air is crisp and your dogs, faithful companions, have been patiently waiting for their morning jaunt. After you've taken that brisk stroll and the dogs are ready for a snooze by the fire, reward yourself with fresh baked ginger carrot muffins.

Recipe contributed by: Peter Goldfarb, The White Swan Guest House

Preparation time: 15 minutes   **Bake time:** 20 minutes   **Serves:** 6

Ingredients

¾ cup milk
½ cup vegetable oil
1 egg
1 carrot, grated
½ cup brown sugar
½ cup raisins

1 tsp. fresh ginger root, grated
2 cups flour
1 tsp. salt
1 tsp. cinnamon
1 Tbs. baking powder

Preparation

Preheat oven to 400°. Grease muffin tin or line with paper muffin cups. In a medium bowl, mix milk, egg, carrot, brown sugar, raisins and ginger. In a separate bowl, combine flour, salt, cinnamon and baking powder. Add to carrot mixture and stir until just mixed and batter is lumpy. Fill prepared muffin cups ¾ full. Bake in preheated oven for about 20 minutes or until muffins are golden brown on top and a knife inserted in center of muffin comes out clean. Peter says to be sure and allow two muffins per person because no one can eat just one!

Nutritional Values (per serving)	
Calories	612
Carbohydrate	95.6g
Protein	13.6g
Fiber	4.2g
Sugar	91.6g
Fat Calories	187
Total Fat	20.8g
Saturated Fat	3.4g
Cholesterol	4g
Sodium	394.8mg

PICTURE PERFECT PEA PODS WITH ALMONDS

Craving a tasty alternative to the same round robin of vegetables? This crunchy and flavorful side dish will perk up the taste buds and add interest to any meal.

Recipe contributed by: Shawna Powell, A Class Act Gallery

Preparation time: 10 minutes   Cook time: 6 minutes   Serves: 2

Ingredients

½ cup water (must be cool)
1 Tbs. soy sauce
1½ tsp. cornstarch
1 tsp. vegetable boullion

2 Tbs. butter
2 Tbs. almonds, slivered
6 ounces frozen pea pods, thawed
½ cup fresh mushrooms, sliced

Preparation

In a small bowl, combine water, soy sauce, cornstarch and boullion and set aside. In a 10" skillet, melt butter. Add almonds and stir fry 2 minutes or until almonds are lightly browned. Add pea pods and stir fry 2 minutes more. Stir in mushrooms. Add cornstarch mixture and cook until thickened and bubbly, about 1-2 additional minutes.

Nutritional Values (per serving)	
Calories	255
Carbohydrate	15.1g
Protein	6.4g
Fiber	2.3g
Sugar	12.8g
Fat Calories	177
Total Fat	19.7g
Saturated Fat	8g
Cholesterol	31g
Sodium	656.2mg

SAGE ROASTED NEW POTATOES

Your garden has just produced the most wonderful harvest of red potatoes and the herbs potted on the sill are waiting to flavor your next culinary creation. The only requirement for this dish is your garden fresh new potatoes and savory herbs.

Recipe contributed by: Mark Epstein, Go Outside

Preparation Time: 10 minutes   **Bake time:** 1 hour   **Serves:** 6

Ingredients
12-15 new potatoes, 1½" diameter
½ cup olive oil
1 tsp. salt
2 tsp. pepper, freshly ground
10 sprigs fresh sage

Preparation
Preheat oven to 350°. Wash potatoes, pat dry and rub with olive oil and 2 sage clusters. Place potatoes and all sage clusters in baking dish just large enough so potatoes can be arranged in single layer. Sprinkle with salt and pepper. Bake in preheated oven for 1 hour or until potato skins are crispy and centers are tender when pierced with a fork.

Nutritional Values (per serving)	
Calories	270
Carbohydrate	48.8g
Protein	5.3g
Fiber	1g
Sugar	40.8g
Fat Calories	89
Total Fat	9.9g
Saturated Fat	1.5g
Cholesterol	0g
Sodium	313.9mg

Legends

Whether you are a collector of Native American artwork or just looking to enhance your knowledge of America's first occupants, Legends is a necessary stop for you when in LaConner.

Nancy Wilbur Foster has gathered the finest collection of old and new artwork produced by artisans from many tribes, from the far reaches of Alaska to the sun-drenched plains of the Southwest.

Strong, powerful carvings and totems seem to blend effortlessly with traditional silver jewelry and fragile beadwork, all part of a heritage that is being revived and encouraged. Blankets, kachinas, moccasins and brightly designed clothing make it difficult to choose just one thing!

If the spirituality and tradition of Native American life hold your interest, add to your knowledge with a selection from their video or music offerings. Legends evokes a quiet sense of spirituality all its own.

705 South First Street   360-466-5240

CARROTS MARSALA

Not only a simple and elegant vegetable dish to compliment chicken or fish, but one that Skagit Bay Hideaways' proprietress Earlene Beckes says is requested by friends, family and guests alike.

Recipe contributed by: Earlene Beckes, Skagit Bay Hideaway

Preparation time: 10 minutes   Cook time: 10 minutes   Serves: 8

Ingredients
14 carrots, sliced ⅛" diagonal slices
3 Tbs. butter
¾ cup Marsala wine
2 Tbs. fresh parsley, chopped

Preparation
In a skillet, sauté carrot slices in butter until well coated, about 2-3 minutes. Add marsala and cover. Cook over medium low heat until carrots are tender, about 5-7 minutes. Liquid will reduce so check half way through cooking and add small amount of water, if needed, to complete cooking. Sprinkle with parsley before serving.

Nutritional Values (per serving)	
Calories	132
Carbohydrate	24.9g
Protein	3.1g
Fiber	0g
Sugar	24.9g
Fat Calories	41
Total Fat	4.6g
Saturated Fat	2.7g
Cholesterol	11.6g
Sodium	821.5mg

Artichoke Soufflé

Searching the cupboards for inspiration, you spy two jars of marinated artichoke hearts. Not wanting to cook the ordinary, you face your fear and decide to go for it, "SOUFFLÉ!"

Recipe contributed by: Arberta Lammers, Tillinghast Seed Company

Preparation Time: 20 minutes   Bake time: 30 minutes   Serves: 8

Ingredients

2 small jars marinated artichoke hearts
1 small onion, chopped
2 cloves garlic, finely chopped
4 eggs
⅛ tsp. oregano
¼ tsp. salt

⅛ tsp. pepper
⅛ tsp. Tabasco sauce
2 cups sharp cheddar cheese, shredded
2 Tbs. parsley, chopped
¼ cup bread crumbs

Preparation

Preheat oven to 325°. Drain artichoke hearts reserving marinade from one jar. Coarsely chop artichokes and set aside. In a small skillet, sauté onion and garlic in reserved marinade. In a bowl, beat eggs. Mix in artichoke hearts, onion mixture, oregano, salt, pepper, Tabasco and cheese. Pour mixture into soufflé dish or 7x10" pan. Sprinkle top with parsley and bread crumbs. Bake in preheated oven 30 minutes or until lightly browned on top. This dish can be made ahead and reheated before serving.

Nutritional Values (per serving)	
Calories	373
Carbohydrate	16.2g
Protein	28.3g
Fiber	1.1g
Sugar	15.2g
Fat Calories	206
Total Fat	22.9g
Saturated Fat	12.1g
Cholesterol	59.5g
Sodium	787.8mg

New Mexico Cornbread

So it's not Cinco de Mayo, but who needs a reason to create a little bit of the Southwest? Make a festive meal with New Mexico Cornbread, Turkey Chili and Loyd's Southwest Sangria. Don't forget the piñata!

Recipe contributed by: Fredi Alt, Just Imagine

Preparation time: 20 minutes   Bake time: 1 hour   Serves: 9

Ingredients

1 cup yellow cornmeal
1 Tbs. baking powder
¾ tsp. salt
1 cup cream style corn
1 cup sour cream

⅔ cup butter, melted
2 eggs
4 ounces cheddar cheese, grated
4 ounces canned green chilies, diced

Preparation

Preheat oven to 350°. Grease a 9″ square baking pan. In a bowl, combine cornmeal, baking powder and salt. In a separate bowl, combine cream style corn, sour cream, butter, eggs, cheese and chilies. Add chile mixture to dry ingredients and stir until thoroughly blended. Pour mixture into prepared pan. Bake in preheated oven 1 hour or until knife inserted into center comes out clean.

Recipe for Turkey Chili on page 152
Recipe for Loyd's Southwest Sangria on page 29

Nutritional Values (per serving)	
Calories	364
Carbohydrate	26.7g
Protein	12.2g
Fiber	2.1g
Sugar	24.6g
Fat Calories	217
Total Fat	24.1g
Saturated Fat	14.6g
Cholesterol	61.1g
Sodium	562.3mg

Lighthouse Inn

Relax and dine in a restaurant that combines a sense of history with a variety of fine seafoods complemented with daily specials and exquisite desserts. Enjoy lunch, deckside, on a lazy summer afternoon, or a romantic dinner by candlelight. A friendly and professional waitstaff will serve your every need.

Once the Bellingham Yacht Club, the Lighthouse Inn was shipped to its present location in the late 1950's by Dunlap Towing. Since then much has been added and changed. Dining areas have been expanded that are capable of serving large party's or the individual, along with a deck for dining "al fresco" in the summer. Plan on stopping in the next time you're in LaConner. Just look for the "lighthouse" and you're there!

512 South First Street   360-466-3147

HERB CHEESE BREAD

It's Sunday. It's football. It's half time and you want something crunchy-chewy-cheesy. The answer, herb cheese bread. Linda Banaszak, co-owner of The Padilla Bay Store, says she can't even get this one out of the oven before it's gone!

Recipe contributed by: Linda Banaszak, The Padilla Bay Store

Preparation time: 15 minutes   Bake time: 12 minutes   Serves: 8

Ingredients
1 loaf French bread, sliced lengthwise
½ cup butter, melted
1 cup mayonnaise
2 cups cheddar cheese, grated
1 cup Parmesan cheese, grated
4 Tbs. oregano*

Preparation
Preheat oven to 350°. In a bowl, combine butter, mayonnaise and cheddar cheese. Place bread halves on baking tray face up and spread butter mixture over top of each piece. Sprinkle on Parmesan and oregano. Bake until golden brown, about 12 minutes. Remove from oven and slice into serving size portions.

*May substitute basil for oregano or other favorite herbs.

Nutritional Values (per serving)	
Calories	687
Carbohydrate	34.6g
Protein	29.1g
Fiber	2.1g
Sugar	32.5g
Fat Calories	440
Total Fat	48.9g
Saturated Fat	25.6g
Cholesterol	117.1g
Sodium	1382.9mg

FABULOUS SOFT ROLLS

Make any occasion special with these melt in your mouth crescent rolls. Phil Perry, owner of Palace Market Interiors, says that this recipe doesn't make nearly enough rolls to last long. They're also great to freeze for your next holiday dinner or buffet.

Recipe contributed by: Phil Perry, Palace Market Interiors

Preparation time: 2 hours 30 minutes   Bake time: 10-12 minutes   Serves: 16

Ingredients

1 cup milk
¾ cup butter
¼ cup sugar
½ tsp. salt
1 package yeast

¼ cup water, very warm
4 cups unbleached flour
2 eggs, room temperature
1 Tbs. vegetable oil
3 Tbs. butter, melted

Preparation

In saucepan heat milk, ¼ cup butter, sugar and salt until butter melts; move saucepan off heat and cool slightly. In large mixer bowl, dissolve yeast in ¼ cup warm water. When milk mixture is lukewarm, beat into yeast. Add 2 cups flour and beat for 2 minutes. Beat in eggs. Slowly add 1 cup flour, beating 2 minutes again. Stir in ¾ cup flour and beat with dough hook until dough is smooth and elastic. Oil a large bowl, place dough in it and brush with melted butter. Cover bowl with plastic wrap and towel and set in warm place to rise. Let dough double in bulk. After dough has risen, remove wrap and punch dough down, kneading out all air bubbles. Sprinkle remaining flour on work surface, place dough on it and divide into 4 equal portions. Roll out each portion into circle ⅛" thick. Brush with melted butter. Cut dough circle into wedges and roll each wedge from wide end to narrow end to form crescent rolls. Arrange on baking sheets, cover with plastic wrap and let rise 1 more hour. Preheat oven to 400°. Bake rolls 10-12 minutes. Makes 32 rolls. Refrigerate leftover rolls or freeze and reheat for later use.

Nutritional Values (per serving)	
Calories	242
Carbohydrate	26.2g
Protein	6.9g
Fiber	0g
Sugar	26.2g
Fat Calories	112
Total Fat	12.4g
Saturated Fat	7.1g
Cholesterol	31.1g
Sodium	218.3mg

FRY BREAD

This tasty quick bread can be served in a variety of ways. For those with a sweet tooth, drizzle bread with corn syrup or serve as an appetizer, spread with a savory Salmon Paté.

Recipe contributed by: Liz Borgen's grandma, Carole Sullivan, Rainbow Bridge Shirtworks

Preparation time: 10 minutes   Fry time: 10 minutes   Serves: 4

Ingredients
2 cups flour
5 tsp. sugar
4 tsp. baking soda
pinch of salt
½ cup water
2 cups shortening

Preparation
In a large bowl, combine flour, sugar, baking soda, salt and water and knead or stir like biscuit dough. Turn dough out on floured work surface and divide into 4 or 5 equal portions. Pat each portion into a round semi-flat piece. With a sharp knife, score each piece down the middle 3 times. Melt shortening in skillet and heat until very hot but not smoking. Gently place each dough portion into skillet and fry, turning with knife until golden brown. Remove from skillet and drain on paper toweling. When serving, divided sections may be pulled apart.

Recipe for Salmon Paté on page 37

Nutritional Values (per serving)	
Calories	561
Carbohydrate	92.5g
Protein	11.7g
Fiber	3.1g
Sugar	89.4g
Fat Calories	138
Total Fat	15.3g
Saturated Fat	4.5g
Cholesterol	0g
Sodium	3046.9mg

Marina Cafe

After a long day at sea, in not so good weather, there's nothing more comforting than to set foot on dry land. Add to that a chance to let someone else do the work while you contemplate a steaming mug of hot coffee and the smell of your food cooking.

Sea air always makes for hearty appetites, and this local cafe always delivers the goods for the breakfast and lunch crowd.

Famous for their Northwest Clam Chowder and Red Texas Chili, the Marina Cafe can get the tired sailor ship-shape again and ready to sail to distant ports.

One of the few restaurants where breakfast is always available. You'll probably find some of the locals there well past noon indulging in a hearty breakfast dish with Country Cream Gravy!

611 North Second Street   **360-466-4242**

PARMESAN ROLLS

You've just phoned up a few friends and invited them over for pasta. Round out the meal with a tossed green salad, a couple bottles of your favorite wine and these savory rolls.

Recipe contributed by: Jolene Berry, Rainbow Bridge Shirtworks

Preparation time: 2 hours 10 minutes   Bake time: 20 minutes   Serves: 8

Ingredients

1 cup warm water
1 Tbs. olive oil
1 tsp. garlic salt
1 tsp. sugar

1 tsp. dry yeast
3 cups unbleached all purpose flour
¼ cup Parmesan cheese, grated
1½ tsp. dried rosemary, crumbled

Preparation

In a large bowl, combine water, oil, garlic salt and sugar. Sprinkle in yeast and stir to dissolve. Gradually mix in enough flour to form moderately firm dough. Turn out on lightly floured surface and knead until smooth and elastic, about 8-10 minutes, adding more flour if dough is too sticky. Grease a large bowl, add dough, turning to coat surface. Cover bowl with a towel and let dough rise in a warm place until it doubles in bulk, about 1 hour. Grease a baking sheet. Punch down dough and knead until smooth. Divide into 8 portions and shape into 3" domed rounds and place on baking sheet 2" apart. Brush tops with oil and sprinkle with Parmesan and rosemary and let rise 45 minutes. Preheat oven to 400°. Bake rolls until golden brown, about 15-20 minutes. These rolls may be prepared a day in advance and be reheated.

Nutritional Values (per serving)	
Calories	205
Carbohydrate	34g
Protein	7.8g
Fiber	0g
Sugar	34g
Fat Calories	40
Total Fat	4.4g
Saturated Fat	1.6g
Cholesterol	5.6g
Sodium	233mg

SOUR CREAM NOODLES

A great pasta side dish. With the addition of cooked chicken and slivered almonds it becomes a hearty entrée, good after a hectic work day and you want a quick and satisfying meal.

Recipe contributed by: Phil Perry, Palace Market Interiors

Preparation time: 15 minutes   Cook time: 12 minutes   Serves: 4-6

Ingredients
6 ounces extra wide egg noodles
1 cup sour cream, room temperature
1 green onion, sliced
1 Tbs. chicken boullion extract
¼ cup butter
1 pound fresh mushrooms, thinly sliced

Preparation
Prepare noodles according to package directions. In a large skillet, sauté mushrooms in butter. Add onion, boullion and small amount of water. Heat through then stir in sour cream. Add noodles. Reheat but do not boil. To make an entrée, mix in 1 ½ cups cooked chicken and top with slivered almonds.

Nutritional Values (per serving)	
Calories	325
Carbohydrate	22.2g
Protein	8g
Fiber	1.7g
Sugar	20.5g
Fat Calories	216
Total Fat	24g
Saturated Fat	14.6g
Cholesterol	56g
Sodium	177.6mg

SILK ROAD PASTA WITH ROSEMARY GREMOLATA

An unusual pasta dish from the Wild Iris Inn. Chef Casey Schanen claims the fragrance of this dish is "awesome!" He suggests the addition of a simple grilled chicken breast for heartier appetites.

Recipe contributed by: Chef Casey Schanen, The Wild Iris Inn

Preparation time: 25 minutes   **Cook time:** 15 minutes   **Serves:** 4*

Ingredients

¼ cup garlic, shaved (about 8 cloves)
¼ cup olive oil
½ cup dried apricots, thinly sliced
½ cup dried sour cherries
½ cup medium to dry white wine
8 ounces cappellini pasta
salt and pepper to taste
Parmesan for garnish

Rosemary Gremolata
¼ cup fresh parsley
4 cloves garlic
2 tsp. fresh rosemary needles
zest from 1 lemon
dash of salt and pepper

Preparation

Cook cappellini according to package directions. It should be slightly chewy, al denté. In a pan, sauté ¼ cup shaved garlic in olive oil until golden. Add apricots, cherries and wine. Reduce liquid in pan by half. While liquid is reducing, combine parsley, garlic cloves, rosemary and lemon zest on cutting board and mince together finely. When liquid in pan is reduced, swirl cappellini in sauce, plate up and sprinkle generously with gremolata. Garnish with Parmesan and serve.

*This serves eight as a first course for formal entertaining.

Nutritional Values (per serving)	
Calories	504
Carbohydrate	92.2g
Protein	10.2g
Fiber	4.1g
Sugar	88.1g
Fat Calories	142
Total Fat	15.8g
Saturated Fat	2g
Cholesterol	0g
Sodium	1756.4mg

MATHESON METAL SCULPTURE

Influenced by the beauty of the Skagit Valley and San Juan Islands, Bill Matheson fabricates metal sculptures in a combination of welded steel, brass and bronze. Whether your interest is a perfect wall piece for over the mantle or one of Bill's free standing sculptures, there are many from which to make your selection.

If you would like a piece designed specifically for a particular place, Bill does many commissioned works and is happy to accommodate your needs. While birds of the region are his specialty, he is also well known for his boat replicas and sailboat trophies. Just ask to see his portfolio.

Bill's working studio and display area are at the end of Pier 7 on the Channel. Just look for the bronze heron on the roof, taking flight, and you know you've arrived!

ON THE DOCK AT PIER 7   360-446-3341

Barley and Pine Nut Pilaf

Patti Dynes, co-proprietress of The Ginger Grater says this wonderful pilaf is the perfect accompaniment to her tasty Lamb Shanks entrée.

Recipe contributed by: Patti Dynes, The Ginger Grater

Preparation time: 20 minutes   Bake time: 1 hour 10 minutes   Serves: 4

Ingredients
1 cup pearl barley
6 Tbs. butter
⅓ cup pine nuts
1 cup green onions, chopped
½ cup fresh parsley, chopped
¼ tsp. salt
¼ tsp. ground pepper
3⅓ cups chicken broth

Preparation
Preheat oven to 350°. Rinse barley in cold water and drain. In a skillet, heat butter and brown pine nuts. Remove with a slotted spoon and reserve. In the same skillet, sauté onions and barley until barley is lightly toasted. Remove skillet from heat and stir in reserved pine nuts, parsley, salt and pepper. Spoon barley mixture into 2 quart ungreased casserole dish. In a saucepan, bring chicken broth to boil. Pour over barley mixture and stir. Bake uncovered in preheated oven for 1 hour 10 minutes.

Lamb Shanks recipe on page 122

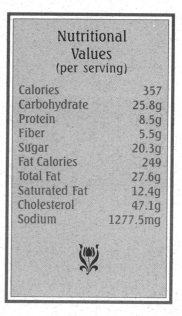

Nutritional Values (per serving)	
Calories	357
Carbohydrate	25.8g
Protein	8.5g
Fiber	5.5g
Sugar	20.3g
Fat Calories	249
Total Fat	27.6g
Saturated Fat	12.4g
Cholesterol	47.1g
Sodium	1277.5mg

Oriental Fried Rice

All the family is home for once and everyone agrees on "Chinese" for dinner. Pull out all the stops and the chop sticks and treat everyone to this yummy side dish that also doubles as a light supper.

Recipe contributed by: Marilyn Gardner, West Shore Acres

Preparation time: 15 minutes   **Cook time:** 15 minutes   **Serves:** 8

Ingredients

6 Tbs. butter
4 cups cooked rice
½ cup green onion, sliced diagonally
10 slices bacon, diced and cooked
2 Tbs. sesame seeds, toasted

1 Tbs. soy sauce
1 tsp. sugar
1 tsp. salt
1 egg, slightly beaten

Preparation

In a large skillet, over medium heat, melt butter and sauté rice until golden brown, about 5-10 minutes. Stir in onion, bacon, sesame seeds, soy sauce, sugar and salt. Heat for 5 minutes. Pour egg over rice and cook about 1 more minute or until egg is set.

Nutritional Values (per serving)	
Calories	517
Carbohydrate	36.9g
Protein	17.4g
Fiber	2.1g
Sugar	34.9g
Fat Calories	298
Total Fat	33.1g
Saturated Fat	14.2g
Cholesterol	63.2g
Sodium	1188.9mg

Mint Meringue Pears

These delectably dressed pears would compliment many meat entrées'. Arberta Lammers, owner of Tillinghast Seed Company, has paired them up with her Crusted Rack of Lamb with Garlic and Rosemary.

Recipe contributed by: Arberta Lammers, Tillinghast Seed Company

Preparation time: 10 minutes   Broil time: 1 minute   Serves: 6

Ingredients
1 egg white
¼ cup mint jelly*
6 canned pear halves

Preparation
Beat egg whites until stiff. Add jelly and beat until well mixed. Drain pear halves, pat dry and arrange on baking tray. Place scoop of mint mixture in hollow of each pear. Preheat broiler to 500°. Place pears under broiler until meringue is lightly browned.

*Currant jelly may be substituted for mint.

Crusted Rack of Lamb with Rosemary and Garlic recipe on page 147

Nutritional Values (per serving)	
Calories	49
Carbohydrate	12g
Protein	0.8g
Fiber	1.5g
Sugar	10.4g
Fat Calories	1
Total Fat	0.1g
Saturated Fat	0g
Cholesterol	0g
Sodium	13.8mg

NOTES

HEART OF THE MEAL

NASTY JACK'S ANTIQUES

The wonderful, old building on the corner of First and Morris makes no secret of what kind of business it is. Nasty Jack's great signage can be seen for several blocks down the street.

Room after room of antique tables, chairs, armoires, beds, furnishings of every shape and size, all in perfectly restored condition, are an antique shoppers fantasy come true. Gary and his staff are experts at restoration and refinishing of even the most difficult projects.

Antiques are not the only "old things" you'll find here. You could get lost for hours looking through their exceptional collection of Life magazines, Harley-Davidson tin advertising signs, turn-of-the-century collectibles and other rarities.

Slow the pace a little, relax your mind and take a step back in time when you cross the threshold of Nasty Jack's.

!ST AND MORRIS STREET   360-466-3209

Vegetarian Tamale Pie

It's a potluck and you can't decide what to take. There's just enough "heat" in this casserole to satisfy tried and true chili lovers and the bread is built in.

Recipe contributed by: Shawna Powell, A Class Act Gallery

Preparation time: 25 minutes   Bake time: 30 minutes   Serves: 8

Ingredients

1 tsp. canola oil
1½ cups onions, finely chopped
1½ cups green peppers or green chili, chopped
1 cup frozen corn
3 cups tomato sauce
⅛ tsp. cayenne pepper
½ cup black olives, pitted and drained
1 Tbs. chili powder
3 cups kidney beans, cooked

Cornbread Topping
¾ cup yellow cornmeal
½ cup flour
1½ tsp. baking powder
½ tsp. baking soda
2 Tbs. light corn syrup
¾ cup buttermilk
2 egg whites
1 tsp. canola oil

Preparation

Preheat oven to 350°. In a heavy saucepan, sauté onions and pepper in 1 teaspoon oil until softened. Add corn, tomato sauce, cayenne pepper, black olives and chili powder. Cook mixture, stirring occasionally for 5-7 minutes or until slightly thickened. Stir in beans. Spread bean mixture in 9x13x2" casserole dish. In a bowl, combine cornmeal topping ingredients and blend. Drizzle cornmeal mixture over top of beans. Bake in preheated oven 30 minutes or until toothpick inserted in cornbread comes out clean.

Nutritional Values (per serving)	
Calories	391
Carbohydrate	72.3g
Protein	15.2g
Fiber	5.5g
Sugar	66.8g
Fat Calories	53
Total Fat	5.9g
Saturated Fat	0.4g
Cholesterol	0.9g
Sodium	368.1mg

LINGUINE PUTTENESCA

You want to impress that certain someone. The secret? Memorize this recipe then throw it all together while entertaining him or her with a little before dinner conversation. One bite of this pasta and, an impression made!

Recipe contributed by: *Thomas and Danielle Palmer, Andiamo Ristorante Italiano*

Preparation time: 15 minutes   Cook time: 10 minutes   Serves: 2

Ingredients

16 ounces linguine pasta
¼ cup sweet red cherry peppers,
   destemmed and quartered
3 Tbs. capers
¼ cup roasted garlic*
4 Tbs. basil leaves, chiffonade

3 Tbs. Kalamata olives, pitted
4 anchovies, diced
¼ cup tomatoes, diced
2 tsp. crushed red pepper
⅓ cup extra virgin olive oil
¼ cup Parmesan cheese, grated

Preparation

Cook linguine according to package directions until al denté. Preheat olive oil in sauté pan. Add cherry peppers, capers, garlic, olives, anchovies, tomatoes and crushed red pepper. Heat thoroughly. Add warm linguine and basil and toss. Serve on a large platter. Buon gusto!

*Instructions for roasting garlic on page 50

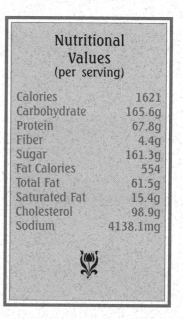

Nutritional Values (per serving)	
Calories	1621
Carbohydrate	165.6g
Protein	67.8g
Fiber	4.4g
Sugar	161.3g
Fat Calories	554
Total Fat	61.5g
Saturated Fat	15.4g
Cholesterol	98.9g
Sodium	4138.1mg

O'Leary's Books and Other Comforts

Having always been a place to sharpen your wit, engage your brain or otherwise indulge in mind-boggling reparté, O'Leary's Books is metamorphosing into an elegant butterfly. One can still count on engaging and stimulating conversation from Sally and Amy while perusing a shop full of books and other wonders.

Aside from being the only shop in LaConner to boast its own waterfall, O'Leary's now represents several Northwest fiber and craft artisans. Books on quilting, basketry, weaving, cooking, etc. are snuggled up between sumptuous hand-woven wool/mohair blankets and pillows. One-of-a-kind baskets seem to become bookends on the shelves and the jewel-toned quilts on the walls complement the antique displays holding books on "How to... ." The bright, colorful space created for children cannot help but make them want to read a book of their own.

Many more delights await the visitor to LaConner who steps inside the new "old" building that Sally Cram built in 1993 to become O'Leary's Books and Other Comforts.

609 South First Street   360-466-1305

Nancy Tobie's Chicken Marinade

Rita Hupy, owner of Art's Place Bed and Breakfast, says this recipe is good for guest dinners. You may keep it warm after cooking, with the oven turned off, while you're busy with other dinner preparations.

Recipe contributed by: Rita Hupy, Art's Place Bed and Breakfast

Preparation time: 15 minutes   Marinate time: 2+ hours   Bake time: 1 hour 30 minutes   Serves: 8

Ingredients
12 pieces chicken, rinsed and patted dry
1 cup white wine
½ cup soy sauce
1 clove garlic, minced
1 Tbs. brown sugar
1 tsp. ginger
1 tsp. oregano
3 Tbs. cornstarch
¼ cup water

Preparation
Using a casserole dish with lid, combine all marinade ingredients and mix well. Place chicken in marinade, coating all pieces. Marinate 2 or more hours, turning chicken occasionally. After chicken has marinated desired time, preheat oven to 350°. Place covered casserole dish of chicken in preheated oven and bake for 1 hour. Meanwhile, in a small bowl, mix cornstarch with water. After chicken has baked for 1 hour, pour cornstarch mixture into chicken dish and mix well into marinade. Bake, uncovered, for an additional 15-20 minutes to thicken sauce.

Nutritional Values (per serving)	
Calories	350
Carbohydrate	11g
Protein	20.8g
Fiber	0.2g
Sugar	10.7g
Fat Calories	200
Total Fat	22.2g
Saturated Fat	6.2g
Cholesterol	98.4g
Sodium	893.6mg

Sweet and Sour Meatloaf

Meatloaf lover's unite! This variation of an old stand by will convert the biggest hold-outs to meatloaf. In fact, it will probably be a top request once it's tried.

Recipe contributed by: Marlys Rodgers, Brassy's

Preparation time: 15 minutes   **Bake time:** 1 hour   **Serves:** 8

Ingredients

1½ pounds lean hamburger
1 cup dry bread crumbs
1 tsp. pepper
2 eggs
1 tsp. onion flakes
7½ ounces tomato sauce

Sauce
7½ ounces tomato sauce
2 Tbs. brown sugar
2 tsp. prepared mustard
2 Tbs. apple cider vinegar

Preparation

Preheat oven to 350°. In a large bowl, mix hamburger, bread crumbs, pepper, onion flakes and 7 ½ ounces tomato sauce. Form into loaf in 9x5x3" pan. Bake in preheated oven for 50 minutes. Meanwhile, prepare sauce. In a saucepan, combine 7½ ounces tomato sauce, sugars, mustard and vinegar and heat to boiling. Remove meatloaf from oven after 50 minutes and pour hot sauce over top. Return to oven for an additional 10 minutes. Remove from oven and let meatloaf stand for 10 minutes. Remove from pan and slice into servings. May also leave sauce off and serve on the side at the table.

Nutritional Values (per serving)	
Calories	525
Carbohydrate	87.1g
Protein	26.4g
Fiber	1.3g
Sugar	85.8g
Fat Calories	158
Total Fat	17.6g
Saturated Fat	6.3g
Cholesterol	49.1g
Sodium	696mg

SANTA FE QUICHE

You spent a wonderful day in LaConner beginning with breakfast at Calico Cupboard. Now you have the recipe for that delicious quiche you enjoyed to share with friends at a weekend brunch.

Reciped contributed by: Calico Cupboard Cafe and Bakery

Preparation time: 30 minutes   **Bake time:** 45 minutes   **Serves:** 8

Ingredients

1 small onion, finely chopped
1 Tbs. vegetable oil
7 eggs
2 Tbs. flour
1 tsp. salt
1 cup half & half
1 cup whipping cream
1 dash cayenne pepper

½ cup cheddar cheese, grated
½ cup Swiss cheese, grated
1 cup salsa
¾ cup green chilies, diced
¾ cup black olives, sliced
¾ cup frozen corn
1 large tomato, sliced
1 prepared pie crust, uncooked

Preparation

Preheat oven to 350°. In a skillet, sauté onion in vegetable oil until soft and set aside. In a large bowl, combine eggs, flour, salt, half and half, whipping cream, cayenne pepper and mix well. Line a 10" pie dish with uncooked pastry shell. Layer in cheddar cheese, Swiss cheese, salsa, green chilies, olives, corn, tomato and reserved onion. Pour egg mixture evenly over layered ingredients and bake in preheated oven 45 minutes or until knife inserted in center comes out clean.

Nutritional Values (per serving)	
Calories	476
Carbohydrate	20g
Protein	35g
Fiber	1.5g
Sugar	18.6g
Fat Calories	281
Total Fat	31.2g
Saturated Fat	16.6g
Cholesterol	79.3g
Sodium	852mg

The Olive Shoppe and More

U.biq.ui.tous (ū-bik'wə-təs) *adj. present, or seeming to be present everywhere, at the same time.* Certainly the appropriate word to use for olives when you step over the threshold of the Olive Shoppe.

You'll find green olives, Jamaican Jerk olives, hot, spicy olives, black olives, olives stuffed with pimientos, olives stuffed with onions and olives stuffed with almonds! Olives to put in your martini, olives to put in a salad, olives to add to your pasta. Just to name a few.

You'll also find olive oil (dozens of varieties), olive tapenade (yummy!), olive relish and our own personal favorite, Ma's Olives (you gotta try 'em!).

You say you want to give them as a gift but don't know what they taste like? Try samples at the tasting bar. Then, when you've made your selection, find some great serving dishes or pressed glass bottles to put them in, mix and match with salsa, pickled garlic, chutney, peppers, pastas or marinated vegetables and...voilà!

101 North First Street   360-466-4101

LYNN'S LASAGNE

You've been "nominated" to have your daughter's soccer team over to your house after the game. What to feed a bunch of hungry girls but a big pan of home made lasagne. But watch out. After they taste this pasta you'll be the nominee every game!

Recipe contributed by: Lynn Moore, The Country Lady

Preparation time: 1 hour 15 minutes   Bake time: 45-55 minutes   Serves: 10

Ingredients

1½ pounds ground beef
1 pound ground pork
1 cup onion, chopped
1 clove garlic, crushed
28 ounces canned crushed tomatoes
15 ounces tomato sauce
1½ Tbs. parsley flakes
1½ Tbs. sugar
1 tsp. basil, crushed

1 tsp. salt
32 ounces cottage cheese, large curd
1 cup Parmesan cheese, grated
1 Tbs. parsley flakes
1 tsp. salt
1 tsp. oregano, crushed
8 ounces lasagne pasta, cooked and drained
1 pound Mozzarella, shredded

Preparation

In a skillet, brown ground beef, ground pork, onion and garlic. Drain off fat. Add crushed tomatoes, tomato sauce, 1½ tablespoons parsley flakes, sugar, basil and 1 teaspoon salt. Simmer until sauce is thick as a good spaghetti sauce would be, stirring occasionally, for 1 hour. Preheat oven to 350°.

In a bowl, mix cottage cheese, ½ cup Parmesan cheese, 1 tablespoon parsley, 1 teaspoon salt and oregano. In a rectangular baking dish (13x9x2") layer half each of pasta, tomato sauce, Mozzarella and cottage cheese mixture. Repeat another layer of same. Reserve enough tomato sauce to pour thin layer over top. Sprinkle top with ½ cup Parmesan cheese. Bake uncovered in preheated oven for 45-55 minutes, or until cheese is bubbly in center. Remove from oven and let stand for 15 minutes before serving to allow lasagne to set.

Nutritional Values (per serving)	
Calories	816
Carbohydrate	35g
Protein	63.3g
Fiber	1.4g
Sugar	33.7g
Fat Calories	420
Total Fat	46.7g
Saturated Fat	22.5g
Cholesterol	170.1g
Sodium	1447.2mg

BLACK BEANS WITH COUCOUS

Jan Marie, owner of the Country Lady, says that although this recipe appears time consuming, it's worth every minute! Beans may be prepared ahead of time and marinated for two days. But if time is an issue, canned beans may be used.

Recipe contributed by: Jan Marie McGehee, The Country Lady

Preparation time: 3 hours   Cook time: 1 hour 15 minutes   Serves: 8-10

Ingredients

Black Beans
1¼ cups dry black beans, rinsed
2 cloves garlic, peeled
1 bay leaf

Black Bean Marinade
⅓ cup olive oil
1½ ounces sherry wine vinegar
½ Tbs. Worchestershire sauce
1 tsp. salt
¼ tsp. pepper, freshly cracked
1 clove garlic, peeled and pressed
1 tsp. cumin

Coucous Dressing
3 Tbs. sherry wine vinegar
½ cup olive oil
1 clove garlic, peeled & pressed
½ tsp. oregano
½ tsp. cumin
½ tsp. salt
⅛ tsp. pepper
juice of 1 lemon
1½ cups chicken stock

Coucous
1½ cups chicken stock
2 Tbs. olive oil
1 cup instant coucous

Veggie Topping
½ cup red pepper, diced
½ cup green pepper, diced
½ cup yellow pepper, diced
¾ cup fresh parsley, finely chopped
½ cup green onions, sliced diagonally ⅛"
¼ cup fresh cilantro, coarsely chopped

Preparation instructions begin on following page.

BLACK BEANS WITH COUCOUS...CONTINUED

Preparation

Instructions for Cooking Beans
Place beans in saucepan large enough to accommodate them after they've cooked as they expand in size 4 to 1. Add enough warm water to cover, place lid on saucepan and bring to boil over low heat. Boil 1 minute, remove from heat and let beans sit, covered, for 1 hour. Drain, then cover beans with enough chicken stock so beans are covered by 1 inch of stock. Add 2 garlic cloves and bay leaf. With lid slightly ajar, bring to boil over medium heat and cook 1 hour. Check liquid level periodically, maintaining original level. After 45 minutes, add 1¼ tablespoons salt and continue cooking. Taste beans periodically during cooking and adjust seasoning if necessary. The beans should feel creamy on your tongue and a few in the pot will begin to split before the batch is done. When beans have finished cooking, drain well and rinse in cold water.

Instructions for Black Bean Marinade
Assemble black bean marinade and coucous dressing at the same time in separate bowls, as it cuts down on prep time. While beans are cooking in a large bowl, combine all black bean marinade ingredients and whisk together. As soon as beans are cooked, drained and rinsed, toss with marinade and set aside.

Instructions for Coucous Dressing and Coucous
In a large bowl, combine all coucous dressing ingredients and whisk together. In a 1 quart saucepan, heat chicken stock and olive oil until simmering. Stir in coucous, cover and remove from heat. Let stand for 3 minutes. Stir well with fork to remove any lumps. Fold coucous into dressing and let cool to room temperature.

Final Assembly
Toss marinated beans with coucous and veggies, reserving ⅓ of veggies. Transfer bean mixture to serving bowl and top with with reserved veggies. Serve at room temperature.

Nutritional Values (per serving)	
Calories	356
Carbohydrate	42.7g
Protein	5.7g
Fiber	1.1g
Sugar	41.6g
Fat Calories	253
Total Fat	28.1g
Saturated Fat	4.3g
Cholesterol	0g
Sodium	1574.9mg

ORGANIC MATTERS

The soothing blend of natural fragrances greets you upon entering LaConner's only store devoted entirely to earth-friendly products.

Organic Matters is a store in which you can find premium quality organic wool and cotton bedding; all made and produced right here in the United States. A restful night awaits you! Custom orders are encouraged and never a problem at Organic Matters.

Several lines of clothing made from organic cotton to Tencel® and hemp are a delight to the eye and feel so good next to your skin. No allergies here! The fashions from Fir Street are even produced right here in Skagit Valley.

A myriad of other products from all natural Egyptian cotton throws and bedspreads to soothing aromatherapy oils, recycled glass chimes, hemp twine and lip balm, and bamboo kitchen utensils are imaginatively displayed throughout the store. Half the pleasure is in the viewing.

707 SOUTH FIRST STREET   360-466-4012

Chicken Enchiladas

Looking for a dish that can be pulled out of the freezer on those nights you come home late from work and there's no time to cook? The family will never want to order pizza again once you treat them to this casserole with its spicy Mexican flair.

Recipe contributed by: Linda Morris, Dandelion

Preparation time: 35 minutes   Bake time: 20 minutes   Serves: 6

Ingredients

2 Tbs. butter
¼ cup flour
10 ounces chicken broth
16 ounces green chile salsa
4 cups chicken, white meat, cooked

1 large onion, diced
12 corn tortillas
1 cup cheddar cheese, shredded
1 cup Monterey jack cheese, shredded
½ cup sour cream

Preparation

Preheat oven to 325°. In a saucepan, melt butter. Add flour and chicken broth. Simmer over low heat until mixture thickens. Remove from heat and mix in sour cream and green chile salsa. Set aside. Cube or shred chicken into ½" pieces and cook in skillet over medium heat for 5 minutes. Add onions and cook another 2-3 minutes. Warm tortillas in oven to soften. Fill tortilla with chicken mixture and cheeses. Roll tortilla up loosely and place in a 13x9x2" glass baking dish. Repeat process until all tortillas are filled and in baking dish. Pour sour cream mixture over rolled up enchiladas and bake in preheated oven for 20 minutes or until cheese melts and mixture begins to bubble.

Nutritional Values (per serving)	
Calories	844
Carbohydrate	23.5g
Protein	47.4g
Fiber	0.7g
Sugar	22.8g
Fat Calories	555
Total Fat	61.7g
Saturated Fat	28.4g
Cholesterol	223.2g
Sodium	1915mg

LAMB SHANKS

You're welcoming the new neighbors by having them over to dinner. Thumbing through a fabulous new cookbook you find every course taken care of. You're serving a tasty entrée of Lamb Shanks with Barley and Pine Nut Pilaf, Carrots Marsala, Spinach Salad with Strawberries, and, don't forget the Dilettante Chocolate Mousse!

Recipe contributed by: Patti Dynes, The Ginger Grater

Preparation time: 15 minutes   Bake time: 3 hours 30 minutes   Serves: 4

Ingredients
4 large onions, sliced
3½ pounds lamb shanks, cracked
¾ cup dry vermouth
¼ cup soy sauce
¼ cup lemon juice
4 cloves garlic, minced
½ tsp. fresh ground pepper

Preparation
Preheat oven to 350°. Arrange onions in bottom of 5-6 quart oven-proof pan and top with lamb shanks. Pour vermouth over onions and meat. In a small bowl, stir together soy sauce, lemon juice, garlic and pepper. Pour mixture over lamb. Cover with tight fitting lid and bake in preheated oven for 3½ to 4 hours.

Barley and Pine Nut Pilaf recipe on page 105
Carrots Marsala recipe on page 93
Spinach Salad with Strawberries recipe on page 68
Dilettante Chocolate Mousse recipe on page 175

Nutritional Values (per serving)	
Calories	840
Carbohydrate	12.7g
Protein	125.4g
Fiber	1.8g
Sugar	10.8g
Fat Calories	217
Total Fat	24.1g
Saturated Fat	8.6g
Cholesterol	412.8g
Sodium	1108.1mg

ADOBO WITH COCONUT SAUCE

Popularly regarded as the national dish of the Philippine's, there are many variations of Adobo. Aficionados will tell you that it's best when cooked the day before and refrigerated. Doing so allows the flavors to mix and age. Just reheat before serving.

Recipe contributed by: Chef Tom Clay, Hope Island Inn

Preparation time: 20 minutes   **Cook time:** 35 minutes   **Serves:** 6

Ingredients
1 chicken, rinsed, patted dry and cut into serving pieces
1 pound pork loin, cut into cubes
1 head garlic, peeled and diced
½ cup apple cider vinegar
1 cup water
1 cup coconut milk
salt and pepper to taste

Preparation
In a large lidded skillet over medium heat simmer chicken, pork, garlic, vinegar and water until tender, about 30 minutes. Add coconut milk and simmer 5 more minutes. Serve over bed of freshly cooked rice.

Nutritional Values (per serving)	
Calories	601
Carbohydrate	3g
Protein	47.3g
Fiber	0g
Sugar	2.9g
Fat Calories	395
Total Fat	43.8g
Saturated Fat	17.7g
Cholesterol	192.5g
Sodium	148.4mg

KATY'S INN CRUSTLESS SPINACH AND CHEESE QUICHE

If you love quiche but are too intimidated by pie crusts, this recipe is your answer. It has all the flavor and pizzazz of traditional quiche but bakes its own crust.

Recipe contributed by: Kathie Hubbard, Katy's Inn Bed and Breakfast

Preparation time: 20 minutes   Cook time: 40-50 minutes   Serves: 6

Ingredients

4 eggs
½ tsp. onion powder
1 cup sour cream
1 cup cottage cheese, small curd
¼ cup Bisquick baking mix

1 cup Mozzarella cheese, shredded
2 cups Monterey jack cheese, shredded
3½ ounces frozen spinach, thawed, drained and chopped
6 Tbs. sour cream
sprigs of parsley for garnish

Preparation

Preheat oven to 350°. Spray 6 individual custard cups with vegetable cooking spray. In large bowl, beat eggs thoroughly. Add onion powder, 1 cup sour cream, cottage cheese, Bisquick, cheeses and spinach. Stir all ingredients together until well blended. Divide egg mixture between prepared custard cups. Bake in preheated oven 40-50 minutes. Remove from oven and cool. Invert onto a serving dish arranged in a ring and top with dollops of sour cream and sprigs of parsley.

This quiche can be baked in a single quiche dish but baking time will vary depending on the size and shape of the dish used. Allow 40 minutes baking time. If more time is needed, continue baking, checking every few minutes until middle of quiche feels firm.

Nutritional Values (per serving)	
Calories	600
Carbohydrate	12.1g
Protein	36.9g
Fiber	0.7g
Sugar	11.4g
Fat Calories	406
Total Fat	45.1g
Saturated Fat	27.6g
Cholesterol	125.3g
Sodium	910.4mg

Mrs. Kokomo's Sunburnt Seashells

For those whose tonsils don't fair well in the tropical heat, a little less cayenne will take the edge off your tonsil sunburn. For those who enjoy the sun and whose innards tan well, sprinkle on the cayenne and let out a Kokomo yell!

Recipe contributed by: Joe and Diane Carter, Kokomo Joe's

Preparation time: 10 minutes   **Cook time: 30 minutes**   **Serves: 6**

Ingredients

1-1¼ pounds ground turkey
1 medium onion, coarsely chopped
8 ounces tomato sauce
15 ounces canned tomatoes, diced
2-2½ cups large shell pasta, uncooked

14 ounces canned green chilies, diced
1 tsp. cayenne pepper
1 tsp. garlic salt
3-4 cups Tillamook cheddar cheese, shredded

Preparation

Brown turkey and onion in large deep frying pan in the hot, tropical sun (or on the stove top if the sun is not available). Add all other ingredients, except cheese, and mix well. Cover and increase heat, bringing to a boil. Reduce heat and simmer on low, stirring often, for 25 minutes (for that deep rich tan) or until pasta is done. Cover top of pasta with a boatload of cheese and let sit sizzling in the sand until the cheese washes over the golden seashells (covered about 5 minutes.)

Nutritional Values (per serving)	
Calories	664
Carbohydrate	18.4g
Protein	48.7g
Fiber	1.4g
Sugar	17g
Fat Calories	397
Total Fat	44.1g
Saturated Fat	25.7g
Cholesterol	171.2g
Sodium	1686.6mg

Pesto Pizza with Oven Roasted Peppers

Chef Mark Abrahamson says this pizza makes a wonderful and eye pleasing winter meal for two. Consider it single servings, though, for the men at the table!

Recipe contributed by: Chef Mark Abrahamson, LaConner Brewing Company

Preparation time: 20 minutes   Cook time: 6 minutes   Serves: 2

Ingredients

1 prepared pizza dough ball*
½ Tbs. olive oil
1 pinch garlic, minced
1 Tbs. prepared pesto sauce*
2 sun-dried tomatoes, julienned

1½ ounces goat cheese, crumbled
4 artichoke hearts, quartered
½ roasted red pepper, julienned
½ roasted yellow pepper, julienned

Preparation

Preheat oven to 500°. Place prepared dough ball onto floured surface and form crust by pushing down on the center of dough ball and flattening until dough is bowl shaped. Pick up dough and with thumb and forefinger begin stretching around edges until dough is 8-10 inches in diameter. Dough may also be rolled out with a rolling pin which makes for a thinner, more crunchy crust. The more adventurous may try throwing the dough until round.

Place crust on perforated pan and rub with olive oil and garlic. Spoon pesto sauce onto center of crust and distribute in a circle with the back of the spoon. Cover evenly with sun-dried tomatoes and goat cheese. Place roasted red and yellow peppers and artichoke hearts evenly over pizza as well. Cook in preheated oven 6 minutes or until crust edges and bottom are golden brown.

*LaConner Brewing Company Pizza Dough recipe on page 128
*LaConner Brewing Company Pesto Sauce recipe on page 128

Nutritional Values (per serving)	
Calories	419
Carbohydrate	62.9g
Protein	15.7g
Fiber	1.6g
Sugar	61.3g
Fat Calories	135
Total Fat	15g
Saturated Fat	1.4g
Cholesterol	11.2g
Sodium	1145.6mg

LaConner Brewing Company Pizza Dough

Preparation time: 1 hour 30 minutes   Serves: 4

Ingredients

2½ tsp. active dry yeast
¼ cup warm water
¾ cup water
2 tsp. salt

3 Tbs. olive oil
2 Tbs. honey
3¼ cups unbleached flour

Preparation

Dissolve yeast in ¼ cup warm water (100°) and let stand 10 minutes to proof. While yeast is proofing, mix together ¾ cup water, salt, olive oil and honey. Pour mixture into mixer and add flour. Mix for 2 minutes. Add yeast and continue mixing for 7-8 minutes longer until dough is smooth. Remove dough from mixer onto floured surface and divide into 4 equal portions. Roll dough into balls and let rise at room temperature or overnight, in refrigerator, covered with a damp towel.

Nutritional Values (per serving)	
Calories	463
Carbohydrate	78.6g
Protein	12.7g
Fiber	2.1g
Sugar	76.4g
Fat Calories	106
Total Fat	11.8g
Saturated Fat	1.5g
Cholesterol	0g
Sodium	926.3mg

LaConner Brewing Company Pesto Sauce

Preparation time: 10 minutes   Serves: 8

Ingredients

2 cups fresh basil
⅛ cup olive oil
3 cloves garlic
3 sprigs parsley
⅛ cup pine nuts, minced

¼ cup Parmesan cheese, shredded
¼ tsp. salt
¼ tsp. pepper
1 tsp. anchovy paste
1 Tbs. lemon juice

Preparation

Place all ingredients in food processor and mix thoroughly.

Nutritional Values (per serving)	
Calories	106
Carbohydrate	5.3g
Protein	5.5g
Fiber	0.6g
Sugar	4.6g
Fat Calories	70
Total Fat	7.8g
Saturated Fat	2g
Cholesterol	5.1g
Sodium	187.1mg

Three Mushroom and Herb Pizza

From the desk of Chef Mark: "If you are a mushroom lover this should tempt your palate, all others beware. Enough to share or bring a B-I-G appetite." We agree! Serve piping hot with a chilled bottle of your favorite wine.

Recipe contributed by: Chef Mark Abrahamson, LaConner Brewing Company

Preparation time: 25 minutes   Cook time: 6 minutes   Serves: 2

Ingredients

1 prepared pizza dough ball*
2 large Portabello mushrooms, chopped
6 Shitake mushrooms, chopped
½ cup Oyster mushrooms, chopped
¼ cup olive oil
4 large cloves garlic, peeled and minced

1 Tbs. fresh rosemary needles, chopped
2 Tbs. fresh thyme, chopped
½ cup white wine
½ cup Mozzarella, shredded
2 Tbs. fresh Italian parsley, chopped

Preparation

Preheat oven to 500°. In a pan, sauté mushrooms, olive oil, garlic, rosemary, thyme and wine until mushrooms are soft yet firm. Set aside. Roll out pizza dough according to instructions for Pesto Pizza on page 127 and place crust on perforated pan. Rub crust with olive oil and a little minced garlic. Cover crust with Mozzarella cheese. Spoon on sautéed mushroom mixture and arrange evenly over crust. Cook 6 minutes in preheated oven until crust edges and bottom are golden brown. Sprinkle with Italian parsley and serve.

*LaConner Brewing Company Pizza Dough recipe on page 128

Nutritional Values (per serving)	
Calories	870
Carbohydrates	88.3g
Protein	22.7g
Fiber	2.3g
Sugar	86g
Fat Calories	424
Total Fat	47.1g
Saturated Fat	12.2g
Cholesterol	44.2g
Sodium	1103.2mg

STUFFED SALMON IN PUFF PASTRY

Tired of barbequeing salmon? Try this elegant and impressive way of preparing it. Pernod lends a distinctive flavor to the sauce. Any accompaniments to this dish should be spare and uncomplicated as the servings are quite large and rich.

Recipe contributed by: Lighthouse Inn

Preparation time: 30 minutes   **Cook time:** 20 minutes   **Serves:** 2

Ingredients

2 5 ounce fresh salmon fillets
4 Tbs. butter
½ onion, chopped
2 cup fresh spinach
4 ounces Pernod apertif

4 ounces cream cheese
4 5" squares prepared puff pastry sheet
2 tsp. olive oil
salt and pepper to taste

Preparation

Preheat oven to 350°. In a small skillet, sauté onion in butter until soft. Add spinach and sauté until wilted. Add Pernod and cream cheese, blend thoroughly. Set aside to cool.

Slice each salmon fillet in half and place one half fillet on piece of puff pastry. Trim pastry to ½" of fillet. Divide sauce in half and spoon over top of fillet. Add another layer of salmon then place piece of puff pastry for the top. Moisten edge of bottom piece of pastry and seal edges by folding and crimping the two pieces of pastry together. Repeat process with remaining puff pastry, sauce and salmon.

Place salmon stuffed pastry in oven proof dish and baste lightly with olive oil. Bake for 20 minutes in preheated oven. Serve immediately. The Lighthouse also includes Hollandaise sauce, but it is optional as the dish is quite rich in itself.

Nutritional Values
(per serving)

Calories	856
Carbohydrate	16.7g
Protein	27.5g
Fiber	6.5g
Sugar	10.2g
Fat Calories	633
Total Fat	70.3g
Saturated Fat	31.8g
Cholesterol	159.4g
Sodium	680.6mg

CHICKEN WITH CRACKED OLIVES AND PRESERVED LEMON PEEL

Preserved lemon peel, pungent and delicious. Added to this recipe it's an ingredient that gives a unique and enjoyable flavor to the entire dish.

Recipe contributed by: LaConner Seafood and Prime Rib House

Preparation time: 3 hours 15 minutes   Cook time: 1 hour 10 minutes   Serves: 12

Ingredients

4 chicken breasts, with skin
8 chicken thighs, with skin
3 cups onion, minced
6 cloves garlic, minced
2 tsp. paprika
1 tsp. dark chile powder
1½ tsp. ground ginger
1½ tsp. tumeric
1 tsp. cumin
4 Tbs. dried onion flakes
1 tsp. salt

½ tsp. pepper
4 Tbs. olive oil
4 Tbs. butter
1 cup cilantro, chopped
1 cup flat leaf parsley, chopped
6 cups chicken broth
2 potatoes, cut into ¾" cubes
4 preserved lemons*, rinsed, cut open, pulp removed and peel sliced into strips
2 cups assorted Greek olives, cracked
3 Tbs. fresh lemon juice

Nutritional Values (per serving)	
Calories	386
Carbohydrate	40.7g
Protein	23.4g
Fiber	2.6g
Sugar	38.2g
Fat Calories	204
Total Fat	22.7g
Saturated Fat	7.2g
Cholesterol	83.3g
Sodium	2070mg

Preparation

To "crack" olives, press each olive with flat side of knife until it "cracks". Set aside. Rinse chicken, pat dry and cut breasts in half to make 8 portions similar in size to thigh pieces. In a large glass bowl, combine chicken, onion, garlic, paprika, chile powder, tumeric, cumin, onion flakes, salt and pepper. Mix well, cover bowl with plastic wrap and refrigerate 2-3 hours, turning chicken pieces often to distribute seasonings evenly.

In a large stew pot, heat olive oil and butter over medium heat. Pour in marinated chicken, sauce and all. Add cilantro and parsley. Cook slowly, turning chicken in oil for 5 minutes or so to wake up the spices.

Recipe instructions continued on next page.

Preparation...continued

Pour in chicken broth and bring to boil. Reduce heat to a simmer and cover pot. Turn chicken (once or twice) while simmering. After 15 minutes, add potato cubes, preserved lemon peel, cracked olives and 2 tablespoons of lemon juice. Continue to cook uncovered until chicken is tender, potatoes are cooked and sauce has thickened, about 20-25 minutes. Add remaining tablespoon of lemon juice. Taste for seasoning and adjust if necessary.

PRESERVED LEMON PEEL

These lemons take three weeks to cure in the brine. This may seem like an inconvenience, but the unique, pungent lemon flavor this ingredient adds to the recipe is so delicious that it makes up for the wait!

Ingredients

6 ripe, thin skinned lemons
6 tsp. coarse salt
1 Tbs. coarse salt

¼ cup fresh lemon juice
3 cups boiling water, approximate
Sterilized jar and lid

Preparation

Rinse lemons. With the point of a knife, make 6 lengthwise cuts in each lemon, leaving ends still attached. Squeeze cut lemons open to spread out sections and insert 1 teaspoon salt in center of each. Pack all salted lemons into sterilized jar and add 1 tablespoon salt, lemon juice and enough boiling water to cover lemons. Place lid on jar, tighten and leave lemons to cure in this mixture for 2 to 3 weeks.

These lemons will keep indefinitely if stored in a cool, dry place or refrigerator. You can also use the pickling liquid as a substitute for vinegar in salads.

Nutritional Values (per Lemon)	
Calories	8
Carbohydrate	3.7g
Protein	0.4g
Fiber	0g
Sugar	3.7g
Fat Calories	1
Total Fat	0.1g
Saturated Fat	0g
Cholesterol	0g
Sodium	2759.8mg

PALMER'S RESTAURANT AND PUB

If a secluded booth for a quiet drink, or a table with a view through lace-curtained casement windows is your hearts' desire, Palmer's restaurant is your destination with its country elegance and the romantic flavors of its progressive cuisine. With a focus on Northwest and European preparation and a wine list selected to complement every entrée, your palate will be sated at Palmer's.

Skagit Valley's most diverse selection of cognacs, single malt scotches and liqueurs can be poured in the turn-of-the-century reproduction pub on the entry level of the restaurant. The best Northwest micro-brews on tap are also available for self-proclaimed pub-o-philes!

A charming, secluded deck with a view across the Swinomish Channel is the best place to be seated on the warm "dog days" of summer.

205 EAST WASHINGTON STREET   360-466-4261

ROLLED STEAK

A great way to make steak go a little farther for a large family. The stuffing could easily take the place of a rice or potato dish and a simple vegetable completes the meal.

Recipe contributed by: Bill Matheson, Matheson Metal Sculpture

Preparation time: 15 minutes   Roasting time: 45 minutes   Serves: 6-8

Ingredients

2 pounds beef round steak
1 tsp. salt
¼ tsp. pepper
1 egg, well beaten
2 cups bread crumbs

2 Tbs. onion, grated
1 tsp. poultry seasoning
⅓ cup milk
3 Tbs. butter
4 Tbs. Italian dressing

Preparation

Preheat oven to 350°. Season steak with salt and pepper. In a bowl, combine remaining ingredients. Spread mixture evenly over steak. Roll up steak like a jelly roll and tie at intervals with string. Place open face down in roasting pan. Roast, uncovered, in preheated oven, basting periodically with Italian dressing until tender, approximately 45 minutes.

Nutritional Values (per serving)	
Calories	681
Carbohydrate	57.3g
Protein	58.5g
Fiber	3.4g
Sugar	53.9g
Fat Calories	201
Total Fat	22.3g
Saturated Fat	8.8g
Cholesterol	135.8g
Sodium	1255.4mg

CRAB AND RICE CASSEROLE

Another great recipe from the kitchen of Sally Cram. Actually, Sally confessed that she "swiped" it from one of her friends who is unaware of the dastardly deed.

Recipe contributed by: Sally Cram, O'Leary's Books and Other Comforts

Preparation time: 40 minutes **Bake time: 30 minutes** **Serves: 4-6**

Ingredients

¾ cup uncooked rice
1 can cheddar cheese soup
3 Tbs. margarine
1 cup evaporated milk
8 ounces cheddar cheese, grated
1 cup Dungeness crab, cooked
  and shelled

3 Tbs. green peppers, chopped
3 Tbs. pimientos, chopped
1 small onion, chopped
pepper to taste
¼ cup cheddar cheese, grated

Preparation

Preheat oven to 375°. Cook rice according to package instructions. In a saucepan, combine and heat cheddar cheese soup, margarine and evaporated milk. When hot, remove from heat and incorporate 8 ounces of cheddar cheese. Add crabmeat, green pepper, pimiento, onion, pepper and mix well. Transfer mixture to a 8x8x2" greased casserole dish and sprinkle with remaining cheddar cheese. Bake in preheated oven for 30 minutes.

Nutritional Values (per serving)	
Calories	649
Carbohydrate	26.7g
Protein	37.8g
Fiber	1.2g
Sugar	25.5g
Fat Calories	392
Total Fat	43.5g
Saturated Fat	24g
Cholesterol	159.6g
Sodium	1237.1mg

ABALONE CORDON BLEU WITH CHAMPAGNE SAUCE

Linda Banaszak, co-owner of The Padilla Bay Store, says that if you are unable to procure Puget Sound abalone (which, of course are the best) prepare this mouth-watering entrée substituting chicken breasts.

Recipe contributed by: Linda Banaszak, The Padilla Bay Store

Preparation time: 45 minutes   Cook time: 20 minutes   Serves: 4

Ingredients

4 large Puget Sound abalone, shelled and cleaned
8 ounces cooked ham, thinly sliced
8 ounces Swiss cheese, thinly sliced
8 ounces Provolone cheese, thinly sliced
4 eggs, well beaten

3 cups cracker crumbs
½ cup vegetable oil
8 ounces canned pineapple rings, reserve juice
2 cups champagne

Preparation

Preheat oven to 350°. Slice each abalone lengthwise into four steaks. Pound each steak with flat side of wooden mallet until tender.* Divide ham and cheeses into 8 equal portions. Using an abalone steak as a base, alternately layer with 1 portion of ham and cheeses. Top with second steak and secure with toothpicks. Dip into egg batter then gently roll in cracker crumbs. Repeat procedure for rest of steaks. Heat oil in skillet. Fry each assembled steak until golden brown, approximately 2-3 minutes. Drain steaks on paper towels and place in shallow glass baking dish. Bake in preheated oven until hot and cheeses have melted, approximately 15 minutes. While steaks are baking, prepare the champagne sauce. In a saucepan, combine reserved pineapple juice and champagne and bring to boil. Reduce heat and keep warm until ready to serve. When steaks have finished baking, remove from oven and arrange on serving dish placing a pineapple ring on each steak. Spoon champagne sauce over each and serve.

*Place individual steaks in freezer bags to pound - less mess and easy to clean up!

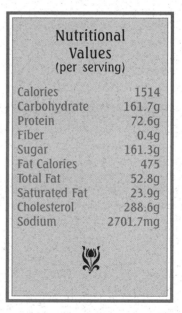

Nutritional Values (per serving)	
Calories	1514
Carbohydrate	161.7g
Protein	72.6g
Fiber	0.4g
Sugar	161.3g
Fat Calories	475
Total Fat	52.8g
Saturated Fat	23.9g
Cholesterol	288.6g
Sodium	2701.7mg

Rainbow Bridge Shirtworks

T-shirts! T-shirts! T-shirts! Need a T-shirt to tell you where you've been? (LaConner!) Shirtworks can fix you right up! You can even buy a T-shirt with, (no kidding), T-U-L-I-P-S on it. The official Skagit Valley Tulip Festival shirts line the shelves along with other beautiful floral T's and sweatshirts.

For a man, you say? Ray Troll© fishing T's were designed with him in mind. The answer to some of life's most pressing questions can be found in his philosophies!

From the hysterical Far Side Collection to elegant embroidered T's and sweatshirts; from bright, graphic animal and sea-life designs to subdued, simple logos for the understated, Shirtworks can be counted on to have the perfect T-shirt or sweatshirt.

Don't forget the kids! Shirtworks has a great selection of T's and sweats for the kids you left at home with grandma while you came to LaConner for a weekend away! Let them know you care with that special gift of a...T-shirt!

128 South First Street   360-466-4300

HALIBUT AMONTILLADO

Halibut, being a more expensive fish, should be treated well! The crunchy texture of the hazelnuts is a perfect counterpoint to the smoothness of the mildly flavored cream sauce. Be sure to seek out "Amontillado" sherry as it retains its distinctive flavor even in the cooking.

Recipe contributed by: Thomas and Danielle Palmer, Palmer's

Preparation time: 20 minutes   Bake time: 20 minutes   Serves: 2

Ingredients

2 7 ounce fresh halibut fillets
½ cup flour
½ cup hazelnuts, roasted and finely chopped
salt and pepper to taste
¼ cup olive oil

2 Tbs. shallots, diced
½ cup Amontillado sherry
3 Tbs. heavy cream
¼ pound unsalted butter, cubed

Preparation

Preheat oven to 375°. In a bowl, combine flour, hazelnuts, salt and pepper. Lightly moisten halibut fillets with cold water and press both sides of each fillet into flour hazelnut mixture. Heat olive oil in skillet and brown fillets. After browning, transfer fillets to baking dish and bake in preheated oven for 10 minutes. While fillets are baking, prepare butter sauce. In a small saucepan, combine shallots, sherry and cream. Cook sauce, stirring constantly, and reduce by half. Remove from heat and whisk in cold butter. Remove fillets from oven, plate up and spoon sauce over halibut and serve. Bon appetit!

Nutritional Values (per serving)	
Calories	763
Carbohydrate	32.2g
Protein	18.1g
Fiber	0.8g
Sugar	31.4g
Fat Calories	548
Total Fat	60.9g
Saturated Fat	20.4g
Cholesterol	91.9g
Sodium	3523.5mg

SPAGHETTI WITH GARLIC, WALNUTS AND TOMATOES

Jolene shared several recipes that she and her husband have acquired when they have stayed with friends in Italy. This is one of the most "authentic" Italian recipes and so delicious you may never buy ready-made spaghetti sauce again.

Recipe Contributed by: Jolene Berry, The Padilla Bay Store

Preparation time: 20 minutes   Cook time: 10 minutes   Serves: 4

Ingredients

1 pound spaghetti, uncooked
2 Tbs. salt
¼ cup olive oil
3 large garlic cloves, peeled
¾ cup fresh parsley, chopped

4 whole canned tomatoes, drained
2 Tbs. bread crumbs
2 Tbs. walnuts, finely chopped
2 pinches red pepper flakes
⅓ cup Pecorino cheese, grated

Preparation

Drain tomatoes and seed. Cut into ⅛" slices. Set aside. Bring large pot of water to boil. Add 1 tablespoon olive oil, salt and spaghetti and cook until al denté. While pasta is cooking prepare sauce. In a large deep skillet, heat 3 tablespoons olive oil over medium low heat. Add garlic and cook, turning until browned, about 6-8 minutes. Add cooked pasta and all remaining ingredients. Salt and pepper to taste. Toss and continue to cook 1-2 minutes. Divide pasta between 4 plates and serve immediately.

Nutritional Values (per serving)	
Calories	473
Carbohydrate	96.1g
Protein	18.7g
Fiber	3g
Sugar	93.1g
Fat Calories	186
Total Fat	20.7g
Saturated Fat	5.5g
Cholesterol	14.9g
Sodium	1823.1mg

LINGUINE WITH SCALLOPS

Who says that low-fat has to be boring? This seafood pasta dish combines flavor with low counts in everything we all need to keep a watchful eye on.

Recipe contributed by: Sharon Scott, The Scott Collection

Preparation time: 15 minutes   Cook time: 15 minutes   Serves: 6

Ingredients

1 pound fresh or frozen scallops
12 ounces linguine pasta, uncooked
1 tsp. margarine
1 tsp. olive oil
1½ cups chicken broth
¾ cup dry white wine

3 Tbs. fresh lemon juice
2 Tbs. capers, drained (optional)
¾ cup green onions, sliced
¾ cup parsley, snipped
1 tsp. dill, dried
¼ tsp. pepper

Preparation

Thaw scallops, if frozen and halve any large scallops. Set aside. Cook linguine according to package instructions, being careful not to overcook. Meanwhile, in a large skillet, heat margarine and oil over medium high heat. Add scallops, cook and stir about 2 minutes or until scallops appear opaque. Remove scallops from skillet with slotted spoon, leaving juices in skillet. Add chicken broth, white wine and lemon juice to juices in skillet. Bring to boil and boil about 10-12 minutes or until liquid is reduced to about 1 cup. Stir in capers, green onions, parsley, dill and pepper. Reduce heat and simmer uncovered for about 1 minute. Add scallops, stirring until just heated through. Pour scallop mixture over warm linguine, toss gently, garnish with sprig of parsley and serve.

Nutritional Values (per serving)	
Calories	326
Carbohydrate	67.6g
Protein	20.8g
Fiber	0.8g
Sugar	66.8g
Fat Calories	24
Total Fat	2.6g
Saturated Fat	0.8g
Cholesterol	25.5g
Sodium	454.5mg

RAINBOW INN BED AND BREAKFAST

If the tulips are blooming, it must be April. Extravagant rows of vibrant blooms color the floor of the Skagit Valley. If you stayed at the Rainbow Inn Bed and Breakfast overnight, you could wake up surrounded by this little piece of heaven. Situated in the farmlands just outside LaConner, it's close to lots of activities.

The Squires family serves up a full breakfast to get you underway for shopping or "tip-toeing through the tulips" with camera in hand. Maybe you'd rather kick back and enjoy some "downtime" in the hot tub or hammock, watching the sunset transform Mt. Baker. On a perfect day you might even see Mt. Rainier and the Olympics.

This Craftsman-style farmhouse offers it all and more to LaConner's overnight visitors. And the cookie jar is always full!

1075 CHILBERG ROAD   360-466-4578

Pork Tenderloin with Orange Mustard Sauce

Perfect for holiday entertaining or just a special dinner any time of the year. One taste of this succulent dish and it will be the most popular request from friends and family for all future gatherings.

Recipe contributed by: Charlotte VonMoos, Serendipity Gallery

Preparation time: 20 minutes   **Cook time: 25 minutes**   **Serves: 4**

Ingredients

1 cup low-salt chicken broth
1 cup Gewurztraminer wine
1-2 Tbs. orange marmalade
1 tsp. Dijon mustard
¼ tsp. cornstarch

2 ½ pound pork tenderloins
¼ tsp. salt
¼ tsp. white pepper
1 tsp. olive oil
vegetable cooking spray

Preparation

Preheat oven to 425°. In a large non-stick skillet, combine chicken broth and wine and cook 10 minutes over high heat or until liquid is reduced to ⅔ cup. In a bowl, mix together marmalade, Dijon mustard and cornstarch. Stir into wine broth. Bring to boil and cook 1 minute. Set aside, keeping mixture warm. Trim tenderloins of any excess fat and sprinkle with salt and pepper. Heat oil in oven-proof skillet coated with cooking spray. Add tenderloins and brown on all sides. Place skillet with tenderloins in preheated oven and cook for 20-25 minutes or until pork reads 160° on a meat thermometer. Remove pork from oven and transfer to warm serving plate. Add wine marmalade mixture to meat juices in skillet and heat. Cut pork into ⅜" thick slices and serve with sauce on the side or over the tenderloins.

Charlotte offers a variation for the wine marmalade sauce: Add, per two people, 3 tablespoons to ¼ cup whipping cream or just enough to give sauce good color and add a little more mustard to taste.

Nutritional Values (per serving)	
Calories	644
Carbohydrate	6g
Protein	85.2g
Fiber	0g
Sugar	6g
Fat Calories	220
Total Fat	24.4g
Saturated Fat	8.5g
Cholesterol	266.5g
Sodium	648.2mg

SKAGIT BAY RIBS

Some meat markets call them "Texas Style" or "Flat Ribs." Whatever the name, the ribs combined with this most flavorful marinade makes an afternoon barbeque deliciously enjoyable.

Recipe contributed by: Earlene Beckes and Kevin Haberly, Skagit Bay Hideaway

Preparation time: 15 minutes   **Marinate:** 2 days   **Cook time:** 30-40 minutes   **Serves:** 6

Ingredients

3 cloves garlic, peeled
2 Tbs. fresh ginger root, peeled
2 Tbs. onion, coarsely chopped
¼ cup fresh papaya, peeled or 1 Tbs.
    Adolph's meat tenderizer
18 ounces pineapple juice, unsweetened
1 Tbs. dry mustard
1½ cups brown sugar

1 Tbs. Worcestershire sauce
3 Tbs. molasses
¼ cup vegetable oil
¼ cup apple cider vinegar
2 cups soy sauce
18 beef short ribs, ½" thick, cut
    across the bone

Preparation

Place garlic, ginger root, onion, papaya or meat tenderizer and portion of pineapple juice in blender and purée. Mix puréed mixture in large bowl with dry mustard, brown sugar, soy sauce, Worcestershire sauce, molasses, vegetable oil, vinegar and remaining pineapple juice. Stir thoroughly. Divide ribs into thirds and place in gallon size plastic bags. Pour equal amounts of marinade into each bag. Squeeze out excess air and twist tie. Place bag in second bag to contain any leakage and twist tie also. Place ribs in refrigerator, turn occasionally and hold for about 2 days.

Preheat oven to 350°. Drain off marinade to prepare ribs for barbequing. Place ribs in shallow pan and cook 15-20 minutes in preheated oven to remove excess fat. Move ribs to grill and barbeque slowly over low flame for 15-20 minutes until done.

Note: Three ribs per adult is generally adequate, as they are rich. This marinade may also be used for pork ribs, chicken and seafood.

Nutritional Values (per serving)	
Calories	1171g
Carbohydrate	64.3g
Protein	91.3g
Fiber	0.8g
Sugar	63.5g
Fat Calories	529
Total Fat	58.8g
Saturated Fat	23g
Cholesterol	263.7g
Sodium	3488mg

ARROZ CON POLLO

Puerto Rico's national dish has as many variations as it does cooks. Having tried several, this is our personal favorite. Kay says this dish exemplifies the international flavor of her store, The Stall.

Recipe contributed by: Kay Trelstad, The Stall

Preparation time: 20 minutes   Cook time: 1 hour 30 minutes   Serves: 6

Ingredients

4-6 chicken breasts, boneless and skinless,
   rinsed and patted dry
1 tsp. garlic salt
¼ tsp. pepper
1 cup long grain rice, uncooked
15 ounces chicken broth
30 ounces canned black beans, drained
10 ounces frozen corn
1 cup medium-hot chunky salsa

8 ounces tomato sauce
½ cup green onions, sliced
½ cup bell pepper, diced
¼ tsp. cumin seed, crushed
2 cloves garlic, crushed
½ cup cheddar cheese, shredded
½ cup Monterey jack cheese, shredded
6 Tbs. sour cream
3 Tbs. fresh cilantro, chopped

Preparation

Preheat oven to 350°. Sprinkle both sides of chicken breasts with garlic salt and pepper. Pour enough chicken broth to cover bottom of 13x9x2" baking dish. Reserve remaining broth. Spread rice over broth, then spread beans and corn over rice. Arrange chicken breasts over top of corn. In a bowl, combine reserved chicken broth, salsa, tomato sauce, onion, bell pepper, cumin and garlic cloves. Pour mixture over chicken. Bake, covered, in preheated oven for 1 hour 20 minutes. Uncover, sprinkle on cheeses and bake 5-10 minutes longer or until cheeses are bubbly. To serve, spoon dollops of sour cream on top and sprinkle with cilantro.

Nutritional Values (per serving)	
Calories	651
Carbohydrate	64g
Protein	57.8g
Fiber	1g
Sugar	63g
Fat Calories	207
Total Fat	23g
Saturated Fat	13.5g
Cholesterol	124.1g
Sodium	1267.2mg

THE SCOTT COLLECTION

You've arrived! The minute you walked in the door of the Scott Collection you started smiling. The bright, cheerful scenes of everyday life in Alaska by Rie Muñoz' seem to affect people that way!

Alaskan artists are the focus of the Scott Collection, but many other outstanding artworks by Northwest artists are gathered together in this contemporary gallery for your pleasure.

Large and small pieces of jewel-like blown glass catch your eye instantly, while stone sculptures merit closer inspection. The graphic styling and design of the wearable art is so appealing you just have to try on a jacket or sweatshirt. Elegant 14k gold or sterling silver jewelry will start you thinking you really need some new earrings!

Maybe you just need a smile and some good conversation? You can get that too at the Scott Collection!

128 SOUTH FIRST STREET   360-466-3691

CRUSTED RACK OF LAMB WITH ROSEMARY AND GARLIC

Roasted vegetables make a great accompaniment for this dish along with Arberta's Mint Meringue Pears. Your favorite Merlot is the perfect balance for this wonderful savory entrée.

Recipe contributed by: Arberta Lammers, Tillinghast Seed Company

Preparation time: 15 minutes   Cook time: 20 minutes   Serves: 4

Ingredients

2 racks lamb
4-6 garlic cloves, peeled and slivered
½ cup Dijon mustard
½ ounce Romano cheese

¼ cup bread crumbs*
½ tsp. black pepper, cracked
½ tsp. rosemary, crushed

Preparation

Preheat oven to 450°. Trim fat from rib. Press garlic slivers between chops. Using a brush, lightly coat meat side with Dijon mustard. In a food processor, mix together Romano cheese, bread crumbs, pepper and rosemary. Gently press mixture onto mustard coating. Place racks on parchment lined roasting pan. Reduce heat to 400°. Roast for 20 minutes for medium rare or until done to your liking. Remove from oven and let rest 15 minutes. Carve into chops and place on individual heated plates.

*Use dry French bread to make crumbs.

Mint Meringue Pears recipe on page 107

Nutritional Values (per serving)	
Calories	717
Carbohydrate	15.6g
Protein	82g
Fiber	1g
Sugar	14.6g
Fat Calories	296
Total Fat	32.9g
Saturated Fat	11.9g
Cholesterol	269.9g
Sodium	336.8mg

LAURIE'S SUN-DRIED TOMATO PASTA

Laurie says, "Serve this pasta with a nice tossed green salad, fresh Italian bread, and while preparing this dish don't forget the glass of red wine for the cook. It makes all the difference!"

Recipe contributed by: Laurie Traini, Two Moon's

Preparation Time: 20 minutes   **Cook time:** 20 minutes   **Serves:** 8

Ingredients

3 hot Italian sausages, skins removed
3 mild Italian sausages, skins removed
1 red pepper, roasted and coarsely chopped
8-10 Roma tomatoes, coarsely chopped
½ cup Ursula Island Farm's Sun-dried Tomato Pesto*

2-4 cloves garlic, finely chopped
½ - ⅔ cup burgundy wine
16 ounces of your favorite pasta

Preparation

Prepare pasta according to package instructions. In large, non-stick skillet, break up sausages and brown over medium-high heat. Drain off almost all fat. Lower heat to medium, add garlic, and continue cooking until garlic is lightly cooked through. Do not allow garlic to brown or it will be bitter. Stir in roasted pepper, tomatoes, Ursula Farms Tomato Pesto and red wine. Simmer over low heat until sauce is reduced by almost half, about 20 minutes. Serve over pasta and enjoy!

*You may purchase Ursula Island Farm's Sun-Dried Tomato Pesto at Two Moon's.

Nutritional Values (per serving)	
Calories	328
Carbohydrate	24.9g
Protein	17g
Fiber	0.3g
Sugar	24.5g
Fat Calories	159
Total Fat	17.7g
Saturated Fat	5.9g
Cholesterol	48.6g
Sodium	1340.8mg

Two Moon's Skirt Steak Barbeque

Simple? Deceptively so! Your barbequed steak will never taste the same after you try this marinade. It's well worth the trip to LaConner to find Ursula Island Farm's products. They do make a difference in the resulting flavor, though other garlic pestos may be substituted.

Recipe contributed by: Dominique Darcy, Two Moon's

Preparation time: 5 minutes   **Marinate time:** 2 days   **Cook time:** 10 minutes   **Serves:** 4

Ingredients
1 pound skirt steaks or other favorite barbeque meat
2 Tbs. Ursula Island Farm's Garlic Pesto*
½ cup teriyaki sauce

Preparation
Coat one side of meat with generous tablespoon Ursula Island Farm's Garlic Pesto. Put garlic-pesto side of meat face down in glass dish large enough to allow 1" between meat and sides of dish. Coat top of meat with another generous tablespoon garlic-pesto. Pour teriyaki sauce around sides of meat being careful not to displace garlic-pesto on top of meat. Cover with plastic wrap, place in refrigerator and marinate for 2 days. Grill or barbeque to personal taste.

*You may purchase Ursula Island Farm's Garlic Pesto at Two Moon's.

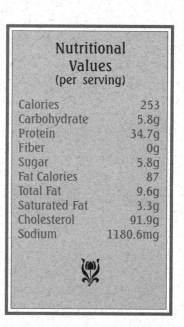

Nutritional Values (per serving)	
Calories	253
Carbohydrate	5.8g
Protein	34.7g
Fiber	0g
Sugar	5.8g
Fat Calories	87
Total Fat	9.6g
Saturated Fat	3.3g
Cholesterol	91.9g
Sodium	1180.6mg

SERENDIPITY GALLERY

Serendipity, the faculty of making happy and unexpected discoveries by accident. The perfect name for a gallery that delights you every time you walk in!

As you cross the threshold into this exciting gallery, it's hard to decide what to look at first. Intense and vibrant floral watercolors by Teresa Saia, hand blown glass by James Nowak, stone sculptures by Cathy Jenkins and *then* you peek around the corner and see bronze sculptures by acclaimed Oregon sculptor and artist Deacon Sharp!

Serendipity offers a broad spectrum of contemporary arts and crafts from regionally and nationally acclaimed artists. Select from a vast array of original paintings, glass, bronze, ceramics, fiber, handcrafted jewelry and sculpture in a variety of media.

Serendipity, defining style now and in the new millennium!

106 A-B SOUTH FIRST STREET   360-466-1620

BREAKFAST FRITTATA WILD IRIS

A superb, tender oven-baked omelette served for breakfast at the Wild Iris Inn. Though their guests favorite vegetable combination is featured here, other possibilities include artichoke hearts, spinach with feta cheese and Greek olives, or any other combination of complimentary vegetables. Because this serves a crowd, it also makes an excellent brunch dish for special occasions.

Recipe contributed by: Susan Sullivan, Innkeeper, The Wild Iris Inn

Preparation time: 20 minutes   Cook time: 40-45 minutes   Serves: 12-15

Ingredients

15 eggs, separated
½ cup flour
1 cup milk
1 tsp. salt
½ tsp. pepper, freshly ground
2 tsp. fresh marjoram, minced
1 large red pepper, diced

1 sweet onion, chopped
2 yellow crookneck squash, sliced
½ pound cream cheese
3 cups homemade croutons
1 cup Parmesan cheese, grated
¼ cup fresh parsley, minced

Preparation

Preheat oven to 425°. Separate eggs and whisk whites until stiff. In a separate bowl, beat egg yolks until creamy and light yellow in color. Add flour, milk, salt, pepper and marjoram. In a skillet, sauté red pepper, onion, and squash until just tender, being careful not to over cook. Gently incorporate yolk mixture into beaten egg whites. Pour mixture into heavy 9x13x2" greased casserole dish. Fold sautéed vegetables into top half of egg mixture. Dot with small pieces of cream cheese, pressing pieces slightly into egg mixture. Press in croutons. Sprinkle top with ¾ cup Parmesan and half of parsley. Bake in preheated oven 40-45 minutes or until knife inserted into center comes out clean. Garnish with remaining Parmesan and parsley.

Nutritional Values (per serving)	
Calories	369
Carbohydrate	47.1g
Protein	18.9g
Fiber	2.9g
Sugar	44.2g
Fat Calories	116
Total Fat	12.9g
Saturated Fat	6.9g
Cholesterol	29g
Sodium	867mg

TURKEY CHILI

Invite the gang over and serve this chili piping hot with an assortment of toppings for everyone to choose from. New Mexico Cornbread and Loyd's Southwest Sangria are excellent accompaniments to this hearty dish.

Recipe contributed by: Loyd Alt, The Wood Merchant

Preparation time: 20 minutes   Cook time: 20-30 minutes   Serves: 6

Ingredients

1¼ -1½ pounds ground turkey
1 onion, chopped
1 clove garlic, minced
16 ounces canned kidney beans, not drained
16 ounces, canned Mexican-style stewed tomatoes
6 ounces tomato paste

2 Tbs. chili powder
½ tsp. oregano
½ tsp. cumin
½ tsp. paprika
½ tsp. pepper
½ tsp. salt

Preparation

In a stockpot, brown turkey with onion and garlic. Add remaining ingredients plus 1½ - 2 cups water. Amount of water is dependent on desired thickness for chili. Stir thoroughly and cook over medium heat, 20-30 minutes. Serve with favorite toppings, such as, sour cream, shredded cheese, sliced green onions, salsa or sliced black olives.

Loyd's Southwest Sangria recipe on page 29
New Mexico Cornbread recipe on page 95

Nutritional Values (per serving)	
Calories	139
Carbohydrate	26.1g
Protein	7.7g
Fiber	4.1g
Sugar	22g
Fat Calories	20
Total Fat	2.2g
Saturated Fat	0.3g
Cholesterol	3.7g
Sodium	701.3mg

RICH REWARDS

SKAGIT BAY HIDEAWAY

Escape to solitude. More than a bed and breakfast, Skagit Bay Hideaway is your own private retreat, a separate guesthouse nestled amongst fir trees on beautiful waterfront property. Cross LaConner's Rainbow Bridge to this very special get-away.

Watch the sun set over Skagit Bay while relaxing in front of a crackling fire or step through French doors to your own treetop deck and enjoy that sunset from your own private spa. Later, drift off to sleep under a plump goose down comforter as the stars twinkle at you through the skylight.

Begin the day with a quiet walk on the beach exploring the shoreline. Spend the afternoon in the quaint, historic town of LaConner, tour the surrounding countryside on your bicycle or just curl up with a good book. At Skagit Bay Hideaway you can reconnect your soul to the simple pleasures of life.

LOCATED ON GOLDENVIEW AVENUE   888-466-2262

SOUR CREAM LEMON PIE

A dessert so rich and filling, one serving will satisfy even the hard core sweet-tooth! The Calico's recipe is pure decadence with the perfect balance of "smooth and creamy" with a tangy lemon flavor.

Recipe contributed by: Tonia Hoefner, Calico Cupboard Cafe and Bakery

Preparation time: 25 minutes   **Chill time:** 2-4 hours   **Serves:** 8

Ingredients

1 9" baked pie shell
1½ cups sugar
¼ cup + 2 Tbs. cornstarch
3 eggs, well beaten
1½ cups milk

½ cup fresh lemon juice
1 Tbs. lemon zest, grated
2 Tbs. butter
1½ cups sour cream
1 cup whipping cream
lemon slices for garnish

Preparation

Bake a 9" pie shell using your favorite pie crust recipe. In a large saucepan, combine sugar and cornstarch. Add eggs and milk and stir well. Add lemon juice. Place saucepan over medium heat. Cook and stir until thick, about 10 minutes. Remove from heat and fold in butter. Transfer pudding to stainless steel or glass bowl and cool to room temperature, stirring occasionally, so pudding doesn't form a skin. Add sour cream and blend. Pour mixture into pie shell and chill until firm, about 2-4 hours. Whip cream and sweeten to taste. Using a pastry bag with star tip, garnish top of pie with whipped cream rosettes. Add lemon slices as a finishing touch.

Nutritional Values (per serving)	
Calories	394
Carbohydrate	59.5g
Protein	5.2g
Fiber	0.4g
Sugar	59.2g
Fat Calories	145
Total Fat	16.1g
Saturated Fat	9.2g
Cholesterol	102.2g
Sodium	94.5mg

Greek Rice Pudding with Lemon

It's a Greek themed dinner and everyone has gone all out to make it authentic. A perfect ending to the meal is this satisfying rice pudding that has the subtle flavor of lemon with the spice of cinnamon.

Recipe contributed by: Caravan Gallery

Preparation Time: 10 minutes   Cook Time: 20 minutes   Serves: 4

Ingredients

1²⁄₃ cups water
1 cup white rice, uncooked
1 Tbs. butter
2 eggs, well beaten
¹⁄₃ cup brown sugar

¾ tsp. lemon zest, grated
2 Tbs. fresh lemon juice
¼ tsp. vanilla extract
1 ts. cinnamon

Preparation

In medium saucepan, combine water, rice and butter. Bring to boil then lower heat to simmer. Cover and cook until rice is tender about 20 minutes. Remove saucepan from stove, add eggs and beat well for 1-2 minutes. Stir in brown sugar, lemon zest, lemon juice and vanilla extract. Transfer to serving bowl and sprinkle top of rice generously with cinnamon, then cool to room temperature. Cover tightly and refrigerate until cold.

Nutritional Values (per serving)	
Calories	221
Carbohydrate	34g
Protein	14.1g
Fiber	1.4g
Sugar	32.7g
Fat Calories	27
Total Fat	3g
Saturated Fat	1.8g
Cholesterol	7.8g
Sodium	242.2mg

The Stall

At the turn-of-the-century you could buy almost anything you needed for the smooth running of your household at the wonderful emporium known as Kastner's Department Store (Est. 1905). Today it's a global emporium of hand-crafted folk-art, jewelry, clothing, furniture and a myriad of other whimsys from other villages around the world.

Some of the items have been developed to recycle products into useful and unusual goods. Have you ever seen a chair made out of recycled tires? Some of the crafts are developed as cottage industries, providing income for people in remote areas of the world.

Whichever role they fulfill, all the crafts and folk-art (new and old), reflect the lifestyles and morés of the villages in which they are produced. They are at once colorful, whimsical and engaging.

Bring the global village into your own home with a decorative touch from The Stall.

712 South First Street   **360-466-3162**

RHUBARB CUSTARD PIE

Pick your most tender rhubarb stalks for this recipe, add the custard filling and you will have a new variation on a classic pie. This is the rhubarb pie that would have made your grandmother envious!

Recipe contributed by: Sharon Aamot, The Country Lady

Preparation time: 15 minutes   Bake time: 1 hour   Serves: 8

Ingredients
2 extra large eggs
1½ cups sugar
2 Tbs. flour
2 Tbs. vegetable oil
1½ tsp. vanilla extract
pastry for 10" double crust pie
4 cups rhubarb stalks, cut into ½" pieces

Preparation
Preheat oven to 410°. Whisk eggs until light and lemon colored. Beat in sugar, flour, oil and vanilla. Line 10" pie plate with half of prepared crust. Fill crust lined pie plate with rhubarb pieces. Pour custard filling over top of fruit. Cover rhubarb mixture with remaining half of pie crust, sealing and crimping the edges. Poke steam vents in top crust with knife. Bake in preheated oven for 10 minutes. Reduce oven temperature to 350° and continue baking until crust is golden brown, about 40-50 minutes. Check edges of pie midway through baking to make sure they are not burning. If they are getting too brown, cover loosely with strips of foil. Serve pie wam or cold. Refrigerate any leftovers.

Nutritional Values (per serving)	
Calories	304
Carbohydrate	51.9g
Protein	8.3g
Fiber	2.1g
Sugar	49.8g
Fat Calories	70
Total Fat	7.8g
Saturated Fat	1.5g
Cholesterol	3.8g
Sodium	172.1mg

ANNAPOLIS ANGEL FOOD DESSERT

Patty says this dessert takes patience to make but the result is worth the wait. It's also hard on dieting guests but no one will be able to resist it!

Recipe contributed by: Patty Person, The Ginger Grater

Preparation time: 30 minutes*   Bake time: 50 minutes   Serves: 12

Ingredients
1 angel food cake, 9 ½ "
24 ounces chocolate chips
6 tsp. warm water
3 eggs, separated
3 Tbs. powdered sugar
½ cup walnuts, chopped
1 ½ cups whipping cream

Preparation
In a double boiler, melt chocolate bits. Add warm water to melted chocolate and stir to mix. Remove from heat. In a small bowl beat egg yolks with powdered sugar. Add slowly to chocolate mixture. Incorporate nuts. Don't give up. This is usually hard to mix! In a separate bowl, beat egg whites until stiff. Fold gently into chocolate mixture. In medium bowl, whip cream until stiff peaks form. Fold into chocolate mixture. Cover frosting with plastic wrap and refrigerate 12 hours.

Prepare angel food cake from scratch or from package mix. Cool, then slice horizontally into three layers. Place bottom layer on cake plate and frost top with chocolate frosting. Repeat with second layer, then third, frosting sides as well. Place cake in refrigerator for 12 hours.

*Make this cake the day before serving.

Nutritional Values (per serving)	
Calories	91
Carbohydrate	6.9g
Protein	7.8g
Fiber	0.3g
Sugar	6.6g
Fat Calories	34
Total Fat	3.7g
Saturated Fat	0.6g
Cholesterol	1.7g
Sodium	118mg

BUTTERSCOTCH HEAVENLY DELIGHT

This cake is as good as it sounds! A rich and satisifying cake with a surprising toffee crunch is a great way to end a meal or as a party cake for a special celebration.

Recipe contributed by: Patty Person, The Ginger Grater

Preparation time: 30 minutes   Bake time: 50 minutes   Chill time: 6 hours   Serves: 12

Ingredients
1 angel food cake, 9½ "
¾ pound English toffee
1½ cups whipping cream
5½ ounces butterscotch topping
½ tsp. vanilla extract

Preparation
Prepare angel food cake from scratch or package mix. Let cake cool. Slice horizontally into three layers. In food processor, with the largest blade, crush toffee using pulse setting. Set aside. Using electric mixer, whip cream until it starts to thicken. Slowly add butterscotch topping and vanilla and continue beating until thick. Reserving ¼ cup crushed toffee, fold rest into whipped cream mixture.

Place bottom layer of angel food cake on cake plate and spread butterscotch mixture over top. Repeat with second layer, then third, frosting sides as well. Sprinkle reserved crushed toffee over top of cake. Refrigerate cake for a minimum of 6 hours.

Nutritional Values (per serving)	
Calories	244
Carbohydrate	40.5g
Protein	0.9g
Fiber	0g
Sugar	40.5g
Fat Calories	87
Total Fat	9.7g
Saturated Fat	6.1g
Cholesterol	31.8g
Sodium	181.8mg

TILLINGHAST SEED COMPANY

Tillinghast Seed Company is the oldest seed company in the Northwest. Established in 1885 by Gus and Emma Tillinghast, seeds still remain the heart of the business today. Lining the walls are upwards of 750 wooden bins filled with packets of seed...more than 1000 varieties of vegetables, herbs, and flowers! On any spring morning, you'll find the store full of gardeners selecting their crops and trading ideas.

Additionally, Tillinghast is a unique general store. It includes a flower shop, kitchen shop, garden shop and a year-round Christmas attic! They even have a greenhouse with an acre of nursery!

At Tillinghast, there is always conversation and laughter, hot coffee and a sense of being comfortable in the home of a friend. Gus and Emma would be proud to see their store so different, yet so very much the same.

623 MORRIS STREET   360-466-3329

PINA COLADA MOUSSE

You feel like indulging in something a little exotic. Enjoying this tropical mousse, you can just imagine yourself under balmy skies with palm trees swaying in the warm breeze. For a special effect place an orchid blossom on each glass before serving.

Recipe contributed by: Jean Tjersland, Just Imagine

Preparation time: 30 minutes*   Cook time: 5 minutes   Serves: 6

Ingredients
1 cup cream of coconut, canned
1 cup unsweetened crushed pineapple, drained
1 cup whipping cream
¼ cup dark rum
2 Tbs. water
2 tsp. unflavored gelatin
grated nutmeg

Preparation
In a blender, purée cream of coconut, pineapple, whipping cream and rum. Transfer mixture to medium size bowl and set aside. Pour 2 tablespoons water in small saucepan and sprinkle gelatin over top. Let stand 10 minutes. Stir over low heat until gelatin dissolves. Add gelatin mixture to coconut purée. Stir well. Divide evenly into 6 wine glasses or dessert dishes. Cover and chill overnight. Serve with a sprinkle of nutmeg.

*Make this mousse the day before serving.

Nutritional Values (per serving)	
Calories	242
Carbohydrates	7g
Protein	1.9g
Fiber	1g
Sugar	6g
Fat Calories	68
Total Fat	7.6g
Saturated Fat	6.5g
Cholesterol	54.3g
Sodium	36.3mg

Two Moon's

If you're looking for style, if you're looking for class, definitely if you're looking for whimsy, go to Two Moon's! Alan and Dominique will tell you they're not really a gift shop, thus the name Two Moon's, but they definitely cater to the person who is looking for the unusual and the hard-to-find in fine arts and crafts from the Northwest. Some of their most significant artists live and work right in the surrounding area of Skagit Valley.

The marvelous selection of paintings, ceramics, sculpture, furniture and gift items are all show-cased in a setting reminiscent of the Arts and Crafts period - right down to the "old" new waterfront building. Take time to browse the extraordinary jewelry collection. You'll be tempted. Turn the pages of a beautiful book on barns. Whatever you do, have fun while you're there and smile. It's impossible not to when there's a dog smiling back at you!

If you can tear yourself away from all the beautiful merchandise inside, go outside to the back deck of Two Moon's. The best view of the Rainbow Bridge begs to be photographed.

620 South First Street   360-466-1920

STRAWBERRIES WITH CASSIS

Strawberries are in season. You're not really sure you can stand to make one more jar of jam! This dessert will revive your interest in the fresh taste of such a bountiful, beautiful fruit!

Recipe contributed by: Jean Tjersland, Just Imagine

Preparation time: 1 hour 5 minutes   Serves: 15

Ingredients
6 pints Skagit Valley strawberries, rinsed and stems removed
1 ¼ cups creme de cassis liqueur
⅓ cup sugar
2 Tbs. fresh lemon juice
3 cups whipped cream, chilled
3 Tbs. powdered sugar

Preparation
In a large bowl, combine berries, creme de cassis, sugar and lemon juice. Let stand at room temperature for 1 hour, stirring occasionally. Serve strawberries in dessert dishes sprinkled with powdered sugar and topped with whipped cream. You could also serve these strawberries on a slice of pound cake.

Nutritional Values (per serving)	
Calories	258
Carbohydrate	23g
Protein	2.1g
Fiber	4.2g
Sugar	18.8g
Fat Calories	16
Total Fat	1.8g
Saturated Fat	0.7g
Cholesterol	65.1g
Sodium	19.8mg

BANANA LAYER CAKE

Margie says this layer cake is, "Oh, so easy to make!" This deliciously moist "scratch cake" will have you wondering why you ever made anything from a mix.

Recipe contributed by: Marjorie Hart, LaConner Flats, a garden-The Granary

Preparation time: 20 minutes   Bake time: 30 minutes   Serves: 10

Ingredients
2 cups flour
1 ½ cups sugar
1 ½ tsp. baking powder
¾ tsp. baking soda
½ tsp. salt
1 cup ripe bananas, mashed
½ cup buttermilk
½ cup shortening
2 eggs
1 tsp. vanilla extract

Preparation
Preheat oven to 350°. Grease and flour two 9" round cake pans. With electric mixer, combine flour, sugar, baking powder and soda and salt. Add bananas, buttermilk, shortening, eggs and vanilla. Beat on low speed until all ingredients are incorporated. Beat on medium speed for 3 minutes. Pour batter in equal proportions into prepared pans. Bake in preheated oven for 30 minutes. Remove from oven and cool. Place first layer on serving plate and frost top with your favorite frosting or whipped cream. Place second layer on top of first and frost top.

Nutritional Values (per serving)	
Calories	448
Carbohydrate	75.3g
Protein	10.4g
Fiber	1.8g
Sugar	73.5g
Fat Calories	108
Total Fat	12g
Saturated Fat	3.6g
Cholesterol	0.5g
Sodium	283.2mg

APRICOT BAKLAVA

Don't let this recipe intimidate you. It does require more work than some, but the results will gain you the title of "Dessert Queen." This is an exceptional dessert that will have everyone begging for just one more piece.

Recipe contributed by: LaConner Seafood and Prime Rib House

Preparation time: 1 hour   Cook time: 45 minutes   Serves: 24

Ingredients

1 package phyllo pastry
½ cup canola oil
1½ cup clarified butter
4-5 cups pecans
½ cup brown sugar

¼ tsp. cinnamon
1 jar apricot jam

Honey Syrup
1½ cups sugar
1-2 Tbs. lemon juice
¾ cup water
2 Tbs. honey

Preparation

Preheat oven to 350°. Generously butter 9x13x2" baking dish. Combine canola oil and clarified butter in small bowl. Set aside. In food processor, chop pecans to very fine consistency. Add brown sugar and cinnamon. Begin by laying one phyllo pastry sheet in prepared baking dish. Press flat, folding edges into center. Using pastry brush lightly coat surface with butter mixture. Repeat process with second layer. On third layer sprinkle 2-3 tablespoons of nut mixture over butter. Repeat phyllo layering. This time on third layer spread 2-3 tablespoons apricot jam, first, then sprinkle nut mixture. Continue with phyllo, butter, jam and nut, layering until baking dish is almost filled. Brush last layer of phyllo with butter mixture only.

With a sharp knife, cut pastry in parallel lines 2" apart and ½" to ¾" deep. Cut diagonally 2" apart to form diamond shapes. Bake in preheated oven for 30 minutes. Reduce heat to 250°-300° and continue baking 15-20 minutes or until crisp and golden. While pastry is baking, prepare honey syrup. In saucepan, combine sugar, lemon juice and water and bring to boil, stirring constantly, until sugar dissolves. Continue cooking at a boil, uncovered, 5 minutes until candy thermometer reaches 220°. Remove from heat and stir in honey. Set aside. When baklava is done, remove from oven and gently spoon on honey syrup. Cool to room temperature to serve.

Nutritional Values (per serving)	
Calories	492
Carbohydrate	29.5g
Protein	3.9g
Fiber	3.6g
Sugar	25.8g
Fat Calories	385
Total Fat	42.8g
Saturated Fat	7.6g
Cholesterol	20.7g
Sodium	86.8mg

WEST SHORE ACRES

The John Gardner family invites you to enjoy the beauty of spring in their unique West Shore Acres garden. Thousands of flowering bulbs are planted among established trees and shrubs. A leisurely stroll along the pathways affords a perfect opportunity to see how the springtime bulbs will look in your own garden. Dominating the landscape of their 1½ acre garden is a beautiful Copper Beech tree, complemented by daffodils, tulips, crocuses and hyacinths creating a perfect setting for the 1886 Victorian home.

Browse around the "Flower Shop," enjoy a cup of coffee and select a bouquet of daffodils or tulips to take home or send to someone who couldn't be here to share the season's color. Ship fresh cut daffodils and tulips anywhere in the continental United States!

Ride around the tulip field on the horse drawn "Tulip Trolley" during the annual Tulip Festival. Who can help but be inspired to make plans for their own gardens after spending just a little time in this beautiful setting! Open March through April and September through October.

956 DOWNEY ROAD   360-446-3158

CHOCOLATE OAT SQUARES

The kids are home from school and want a snack. Give them the recipe, ingredients and the supervision and let them make these easy to prepare oat squares.

Recipe contributed by: Marlo Frank, Nasty Jack's Antiques

Preparation time: 30 minutes   Cook time: 5 minutes   Serves: 8

Ingredients
¼ cup butter
2 cups sugar
½ cup cocoa
½ cup milk
1 tsp. vanilla extract
2 cups rolled oats
¼ cup hazelnut chocolate spread

Preparation
Butter 8x8x2" baking pan. Set aside. In a saucepan, combine butter, sugar, cocoa, milk and vanilla extract. Heat until sugar has melted, then boil 1 minute. Remove from heat and mix in rolled oats and hazelnut chocolate spread. Pour mixture into prepared pan, distribute evenly and refrigerate 20 minutes before cutting into squares.

Nutritional Values (per serving)	
Calories	533
Carbohydrate	97.3g
Protein	19.3g
Fiber	1.5g
Sugar	95.8g
Fat Calories	105
Total Fat	11.7g
Saturated Fat	21g
Cholesterol	17.5g
Sodium	64.4mg

SAUTÉED BANANAS

Personal note: The authors made this dessert in Hawaii where banana liqueur was not available so Macadamia Nut liqueur was substituted. The combination was a winner and we didn't even burn down the condo!

Recipe contributed by: Vernee Neff, The Olive Shoppe and More

Preparation time: 10 minutes   Cook time: 12 minutes   Serves: 4

Ingredients
6 Tbs. butter
1½ cups dark brown sugar, firmly packed
¾ tsp. cinnamon
⅓ cup banana liqueur
6 bananas, peeled, split and halved
⅓ cup gold rum

Preparation
In a skillet melt butter. Add brown sugar, cinnamon and banana liqueur. Stir to mix and heat for 2-3 minutes. Add bananas and sauté until slightly browned. Pour rum over top of bananas. Do not stir. Let sauce heat but not simmer, then ignite carefully. Allow sauce to flame until it dies out, tipping pan with a circular motion to prolong flaming. Spoon hot sauce and bananas over ice cream and serve.

Nutritional Values (per serving)	
Calories	853
Carbohydrate	162.5g
Protein	3.6g
Fiber	8.6g
Sugar	153.9g
Fat Calories	171
Total Fat	19g
Saturated Fat	11.4g
Cholesterol	46.6g
Sodium	212.8mg

Olive's Shortbread Cookies

Cookies that look deceptively plain, but are so rich and buttery it's guaranteed you won't be able to eat just one. They're perfect with that late afternoon cup of tea.

Recipe contributed by: Stephanie Banaszak, Organic Matters

Preparation time: 20 minutes   Bake time: 25 minutes   Serves: 24

Ingredients
1 pound butter, softened
1 cup sugar
4 cups flour
¾ cup rice flour

Preparation
Preheat oven to 300°. Cream butter and sugar until sugar is almost dissolved. Add flour and rice flour. Stir until dry ingredients are incorporated. Turn cookie dough out on lightly floured surface and divide in half. Roll each dough half out until ½" thick. Cut into desired shapes with cookie cutters. Place on cookie sheet and bake in preheated oven for 25 minutes.

Nutritional Values (per serving)	
Calories	334
Carbohydrate	43.6g
Protein	4.5g
Fiber	1.2g
Sugar	42.4g
Fat Calories	142
Total Fat	15.8g
Saturated Fat	9.6g
Cholesterol	41.4g
Sodium	157.1mg

The White Swan Guest House

This lovely Queen Anne farmhouse was built on Fir Island in 1898 and converted into a charming bed and breakfast in 1986. Surrounded by lush and colorful English-style gardens, the White Swan sits in the middle of the fertile Skagit farmland with spectacular views of Mt. Baker and the Olympics.

Three cozy guest rooms embrace you in the old farmhouse and the separate Garden Cottage behind the house is the perfect romantic retreat. Regionally acclaimed chocolate chip cookies and tail-wagging dogs will greet you.

For breakfast, healthy and delicious muffins or scones are Peter's specialty. Served along with these homemade delights is fresh seasonal fruit. Situated on a quiet back road and surrounded by farmland, the White Swan is in a perfect setting for long bicycle rides, exciting bird walks and pleasant strolls along the river.

The perfect cure for the urban blues, The White Swan.

1388 Moore Road   360-445-6805

PADILLA BAY BANANA SPLIT CAKE

If you have teenagers around the house you won't have any of this cake leftover. This cake is also the perfect alternative to just another birthday cake with frosting. Be sure to keep it refrigerated until used.

Recipe contributed by: Linda Banaszak, The Padilla Bay Store

Preparation time: 40 minutes*   Bake time: 8 minutes   Serves: 12

Ingredients

½ cup butter, softened
½ cup butter, melted
½ cup margarine, softened
2½ cups graham cracker crumbs
3 Tbs. sugar
2½ cups powdered sugar
2 eggs
1 Tbs. vanilla extract

5 bananas, sliced and sprinkled with lemon juice
3 Tbs. lemon juice
20 ounces crushed pineapple, drained well
8 ounces Cool Whip
4 ounces Hershey's Chocolate syrup
4 ounces maraschino cherries, drained
1 cup walnuts, chopped

Preparation

Preheat oven to 325°. Grease 9x13x2" baking dish and set aside. To prepare crust, mix melted butter in bowl with graham cracker crumbs and sugar. Press crumb mixture in bottom of prepared baking dish. Bake in preheated oven 8 minutes and cool.

Prepare filling by combining softened butter and margarine, powdered sugar, eggs and vanilla extract in electric mixer. Beat on low speed for 20 minutes. Mixture should look like marshmallow, smooth and shiny. Pour onto cooled crust. Layer bananas and pineapple over filling. Spread Cool Whip evenly over top. Drizzle with Hershey Chocolate syrup and sprinkle with nuts. Dot with maraschino cherries. Refrigerate overnight.

*Make this the day before serving.

Nutritional Values (per serving)	
Calories	778
Carbohydrate	129.2g
Protein	11.7g
Fiber	4.7g
Sugar	124.6g
Fat Calories	248
Total Fat	27.5g
Saturated Fat	11.8g
Cholesterol	41.4g
Sodium	538.3mg

TIRAMISU

Another recipe from Jolene Berry's collection of Italian classics. She says she refined this one until it's as close to the "real" tiramisu as you will find outside of Italy.

Recipe contributed by: Jolene Berry, The Padilla Bay Store

Preparation time: 45 minutes*   Serves: 8

Ingredients

4 eggs
½ cup Tia Maria liqueur
1 pound Mascarpone cheese
½ cup sugar

1 package ladyfingers cookies, stale
½ cup strong espresso
2 ounces semi-sweet chocolate, grated

Preparation

Separate eggs. Incorporate Tia Maria liqueur into yolks. Blend in Mascarpone cheese. Set aside. Whisk egg whites into soft peaks. Whisk in sugar, a little at a time, until stiff peaks form. Take half of egg white mixture and combine with cheese mixture. Fold in remaining egg whites. Set aside. Dip ladyfingers into espresso, being careful not to saturate. Arrange in single layer in shallow dish. Layer ½ of cheese mixture over ladyfingers, smooth, and top with ½ of grated chocolate. Layer remaining ladyfingers dipped in espresso, remaining cheese mixture, smooth, and top with remaining grated chocolate. Cover and refrigerate overnight.

*Make this the day before serving.

Nutritional Values (per serving)	
Calories	226
Carbohydrate	28.8g
Protein	13.6g
Fiber	0.4g
Sugar	28.4g
Fat Calories	37
Total Fat	4.1g
Saturated Fat	1.4g
Cholesterol	17.8g
Sodium	208.8mg

Mocha Soufflé

What do you crave most when trying to watch those nasty, little calories? Dessert, of course! Sharon's Mocha Soufflé will satify the sweet-tooth, keep the fat calories at bay and let you sleep at night guilt free!

Recipe contributed by: Sharon Scott, The Scott Collection

Preparation time: 20 minutes   Bake time: 20-25 minutes   Serves: 6

Ingredients

6 egg whites, room temperature
¼ cup sugar
2 Tbs. cornstarch
3 Tbs. unsweetened cocoa powder
2 tsp. instant coffee crystals

1 can evaporated skim milk
1 Tbs. coffee or orange flavored liqueur
1½ tsp. vanilla extact
½ tsp. cream of tartar

Preparation

Preheat oven to 375°. Combine sugar, cornstarch, cocoa powder and coffee crystals in saucepan. Pour in evaporated milk, while stirring. Continue to stir while cooking chocolate mixture over medium heat till bubbly. Cook and stir 2 additional minutes. Remove from heat. Stir in liqueur and vanilla. Pour into large bowl. Cover surface with plastic wrap and set aside.

In large bowl, beat egg whites and cream of tartar until stiff peaks form; tips stand straight. Fold about ½ of egg whites into chocolate mixture to lighten. Gently fold in remaining egg whites. Gently pour chocolate mixture into ungreased 2-2 ½ quart soufflé dish and bake in preheated oven 20-25 minutes or until knife inserted near center comes out clean. Serve immediately.

Nutritional Values (per serving)	
Calories	120
Carbohydrate	22.4g
Protein	6.7g
Fiber	2.4g
Sugar	20g
Fat Calories	9
Total Fat	1g
Saturated Fat	0.6g
Cholesterol	0.9g
Sodium	77.5mg

The Wild Iris Inn

Irresistibly romantic, the Wild Iris Inn is LaConner's luxury Victorian get-away. It is a charming destination within an easy walk to all the great shops, galleries and museums.

Well known for its romantic themes and comfortable style, it is also known for unique cuisine utilzing free range poultry, wild sea food and game. The Wild Iris pours the finest that Skagit Valley has to offer into both its complimentary full breakfast and its cozy dinner service.

With meticulous attention to detail, each suite is a unique experience, every room distinctively decorated. Private spa tubs provide opportunity to restore and relax before you re-enter the city!

Susan Sullivan, Innkeeper, has been with the Wild Iris since its inception and will make sure your stay is memorable.

121 Maple Avenue   800-477-1400

DILETTANTE CHOCOLATE MOUSSE

Beware! If you have any of these left over when the company's left and the dishes are done, you'll probably keep going back to the refrigerator to sneak just one more bite. We speak from personal experience!

Recipe contributed by: Arberta Lammers, Tillinghast Seed Company

Preparation time: 12 minutes   Cook time: 15 minutes   Chill time: 1 hour   Serves: 6

Ingredients
1 cup Dilettante Emphemere or Chocolate Truffle sauce
2 Tbs. Grand Marnier liqueur*
½ pint whipping cream
1 ounce semi-sweet chocolate square

Preparation
Combine Dilettante sauce and liqueur and beat until glossy. In separate bowl, whip cream to soft peaks. Gently fold chocolate mixture into whipped cream. Spoon into individual parfait glasses. Chill 1 hour. Garnish with extra dollop of whipped cream and shaved chocolate.

*May substitute espresso or milk.

Nutritional Values (per serving)	
Calories	174
Carbohydrate	27.5g
Protein	1.9g
Fiber	0.7g
Sugar	26.8g
Fat Calories	63
Total Fat	7g
Saturated Fat	3.3g
Cholesterol	6.8g
Sodium	50.7mg

The Wood Merchant

Walk into The Wood Merchant and find yourself capitivated by the profusion of woods that greet the eye. Walnut, birdseye maple, cherry, rosewood, bubinga, paduk, koa, purple heart and burled woods, too!

The Wood Merchant has the largest selection of handcrafted jewelry boxes in the Northwest. The perfect gift for that special individual on your gift list who deserves the best!

Peruse dining room tables and chairs, desks, end tables, coffee tables, lamps and occasional chairs. Sit in one of the Brendan Rocking Chairs by local woodworker Greg Aãnes. Feel how it seems to conform to the curve of your back. Want a special piece of furniture made? The Wood Merchant can help you achieve that dream. Nothing is nicer than a custom piece made to your specifications.

Need a Sunday afternoon board game? Choose from cribbage boards, solitaire, checkers and chess, backgammon or dominoes.

The Wood Merchant, one store that you don't want to miss on your next visit to LaConner.

709 South First Street   360-466-4741

WHITE SWAN CHOCOLATE CHIP COOKIES

Delectable, little bite-sized cookies for which Peter is famous. He keeps a cookie-jar full of these for his guests at the White Swan and assures us it doesn't stay full long.

Recipe contributed by: Peter Goldfarb, The White Swan Guest House

Preparation time: 15 minutes   Bake time: 7-9 minutes per batch   Serves: 20

Ingredients

2½ cups flour
1 tsp. salt
1 tsp. baking soda
1 cup butter flavored Crisco
¾ cup sugar

¾ cup brown sugar
1 Tbs. vanilla extract
2 eggs
2 cups chocolate chips

Preparation

Preheat oven to 375°. Sift together flour, salt and baking soda. With electric mixer combine Crisco, sugar, brown sugar and vanilla extract until light and creamy. Add eggs, one at a time, mixing after each egg. Add flour mixture, in small amounts, until wet and dry ingredients are thoroughly mixed. Stir in chocolate chips until evenly distributed through dough. Spoon by teaspoonfuls onto ungreased cookie sheet. Bake 7-9 minutes in preheated oven until light golden brown and still soft. De-e-elicious!!
Yield: About 60 cookies.

Nutritional Values (per serving)	
Calories	276
Carbohydrate	38.3g
Protein	3.5g
Fiber	1g
Sugar	37.3g
Fat Calories	108
Total Fat	12g
Saturated Fat	37g
Cholesterol	0g
Sodium	169.4mg

HAZELNUT BISCOTTI

If one could possibly find room for dessert after a meal at the Wild Iris Inn, Susan Sullivan, Innkeeper, suggests trying this biscotti. In the summer it is served with fresh seasonal berries and a lavender-infused creme anglaise. According to Susan, "Yummy!"

Reciped contributed by: Susan Sullivan, Innkeeper, The Wild Iris Inn

Preparation time: 15 minutes   Bake time: 1 hour 20 minutes   Serves: 12

Ingredients
2 cups flour
¾ cups sugar
2 tsp. baking powder
¼ tsp. salt
3 eggs

4 Tbs. Madeira or Brandy
1 tsp. vanilla extract
1 tsp. anise seed
1½ cups hazelnuts, toasted and
        coarsely chopped

Preparation
Preheat oven to 325°. Mix flour, sugar, baking powder, salt, anise seed and hazelnuts. Set aside. In separate bowl, beat eggs. Add Madeira and vanilla. Pour mixture over dry ingredients. Stir gently. Dust hands with flour and form dough into bar shape on greased cookie sheet. Bake in preheated oven 40 minutes. Remove from oven and cut bars, diagonally, ½" thick. Lay sliced bars on their sides and bake 20 minutes. Turn bars over and bake 20 more minutes, or until each side is golden brown.

Nutritional Values (per serving)	
Calories	419
Carbohydrate	49.7g
Protein	13.2g
Fiber	1.1g
Sugar	48.6g
Fat Calories	173
Total Fat	19.2g
Saturated Fat	1.4g
Cholesterol	0g
Sodium	140.5mg

BLACK BOTTOM CUPCAKES

The rumor is that any merchant meetings that take place in LaConner can not start until Laurie's plate of cupcakes has arrived. They are everybody's favorite indulgence and you'll surely agree after the first time you make them.

Recipe contributed by: Laurie Hutt, The Wood Merchant

Preparation time: 20 minutes   Bake time: 25-30 minutes   Serves: 12

Ingredients

8 ounces cream cheese, softened
1 egg
⅓ cup sugar
⅛ tsp. salt
6 ounces chocolate chips

Filling
1½ cups flour
1 cup sugar
1 tsp. baking soda
½ tsp. salt
¼ cup cocoa powder

1 cup water
⅓ cup vegetable oil
1 Tbs. apple cider vinegar
1 tsp. vanilla extract

Preparation

Preheat oven to 350°. Combine cream cheese, egg, sugar and salt. Beat well. Stir in chocolate chips and set aside. In a separate bowl combine all filling ingredients and beat together. Place paper cup liners in cupcake tins and fill ½ full with cake batter. Drop about 1 tablespoon, or a little more, of filling in center of batter. Bake in preheated oven for 25-30 minutes.

Nutritional Values (per serving)	
Calories	344
Carbohydrate	57.6g
Protein	7.4g
Fiber	2.3g
Sugar	55.3g
Fat Calories	125
Total Fat	13.9g
Saturated Fat	5.5g
Cholesterol	20.8g
Sodium	295.6mg

EQUIVALENTS

Here are some helpful measures that even the best of us can't remember all the time.

3 teaspoons = 1 tablespoon
2 tablespoons = 1 fluid ounce
4 tablespoons = ¼ cup
5 tablespoons + 1 teaspoon = ⅓ cup
1 cup = ½ pint
2 cups = 1 pint
4 cups = 1 quart
2 pints = 1 liquid quart
4 quarts = 1 liquid gallon

3 small eggs = 2 large eggs
1 square chocolate = 1 ounce
1 medium lemon = 3 tablespoons lemon juice
1 cup raw rice = about 3½ cups cooked
1 cup whipping cream = about 2 cups, whipped

SUBSTITUTIONS

Here is a list of substitutions for when you're in a pinch and don't have time to run to the grocery store.*

1½ tablespoons vinegar plus enough sweet cream to fill 1 cup; let stand a few minutes = 1 cup sour cream

1 teaspoon baking soda plus 2 teaspoons cream of tartar plus
1 teaspoon cornstarch = baking powder
(use 2 teaspoons per cup of flour)

1 cup vegetable shortening plus ½ teaspoon salt = 1 cup butter; for baking only

1 cup sifted all-purpose flour less 2 tablespoons = 1 cup cake flour

*All the above are for those situations when you thought you had the ingredient but you didn't. The finished recipe won't be quite as good as if you had used the proper ingredient, but it will be adequate.

GLOSSARY

AL DENTÉ An Italian term to describe pasta that is cooked until it offers a slight resistance to the bite.

BASTE A seasoned liquid brushed over food, at intervals, as it cooks to keep surface moist and add flavor.

BISQUE A thick, rich, cream soup usually made with seafood or puréed vegetables.

BROWN To cook meat or vegetables until surface is light brown in color.

CAPERS Young berries from the caper plant that have been harvested and pickled.

CARAMELIZE To stir sugar in a skillet over low heat until it melts, turning golden brown in color and developing a "caramel" flavor.

CHIFFONADE To cut ribbon-like strips from leafy herbs and vegetables. (See "Kitchen Tips", page 13)

CHOP To cut food into small pieces with a knife, blender or food processor.

CLARIFY In cooking, to remove fatty solids and water from butter. (See "Kitchen Tips", page 13)

CREAM To make soft, smooth and creamy by beating with a spoon or mixer. This term is usually applied to blending sugar and a fat.

CUBE To cut food into small cubes, approximately ½" square.

DEGLAZE To loosen drippings in the bottom of a roasting or frying pan by stirring in wine, stock or other liquid.

DICE To cut food into very small pieces, approximately ¼" square.

DRIZZLE To slowly pour liquid in a thin, ribbon-like stream.

FILLET A piece of meat, fish or poultry which is boneless or has had all bones removed.

GRATE To rub food on a grater to produce fine, medium or coarse particles.

INFUSED To impart the flavor of herbs, vegetables or fruit in liquids, such as, oils, vinegars or honeys.

JULIENNE To cut vegetables into match-stick size pieces.

MARINADE A seasoned liquid, usually containing an acidic ingredient, such as wine, vinegar or citrus juice in which food is immersed. Marinades are used to tenderize and enhance flavor.

MINCE To cut into tiny pieces using a knife, blender or food processor.

MOUSSE A cold dessert made with whipped cream or beaten egg whites.

POLENTA A very thick mush, usually made from cornmeal or farina.

Glossary...Continued

Pressed As with garlic, to crush into a pulp, by hand or with a garlic press.

Proofing To test yeast to ensure it's still active.

Purée To press food through a fine sieve or food mill, or to blend in a blender or food processor to a smooth, thick texture.

Reduce To reduce volume of liquid by rapidly boiling in an uncovered pan. This process concentrates its flavor.

Reserve To save out a portion of ingredient(s) for later use in a recipe.

Roux A cooked mixture of butter or other fat and flour used to thicken sauces and soups.

Sauté To quickly fry food in just enough oil or fat to prevent sticking.

Sear To brown meat directly above heat source, at a high temperature, for a brief time. This process seals in the meats juices.

Shred To cut food into slivers or slender pieces, using a knife or shredder.

Simmer To cook food over low heat in a liquid just below the boiling point.

SLICE To cut with a knife into equal portions.

SLIVER To cut into long, slender pieces.

SOUFFLÉ An entrée or dessert dish that includes stiffly whipped egg whites that, when the dish is baked, expand causing the soufflé to puff up.

SPRINGFORM A type of baking pan that has a tension clasp on its side. When the clasp is released, the sides of the pan loosen and the cake is easily removed.

WHISK To rapidly beat or fluff up.

ZEST The thin outermost layer of peel of citrus fruits. This layer of peel, the colored part only, contains the fragrant essential oils of the fruit.

Recipe Index

RECIPE INDEX...CONTINUED

NOTES

Merchant Mailing Address Index

A Class Act Gallery, page 15
P. O. Box 1379, LaConner, WA 98257
Phone: 800-50-Linda   360-466-2000
Linda Cole and Bob Cole, Proprietors

Andiamo Ristorante Italiano, page 18
P. O. Box 599, LaConner, WA 98257
Phone: 360-466-9111
Thomas and Danielle Palmer, Proprietors

Art's Place Bed and Breakfast, page 22
P. O. Box 557, LaConner, WA 98257
Phone: 360-466-3033
Art and Rity Hupy, Proprietors

Brassy's, page 26
P. O. Box 756, LaConner, WA 98257
Phone: 360-466-4313
Marlys Rodgers, Proprietor

Calico Cupboard Cafe and Bakery, page 30
P. O. Box 970, LaConner, WA 98257
Phone: 360-466-4451
Linda Freed, Proprietor

Caravan Gallery, page 34
P. O. Box 721, LaConner, WA 98257
Phone: 360-466-4808
Radha Speer, Proprietor

Champagne Cove, page 38
P. O. Box 204, LaConner, WA 98257
Phone: 360-466-2085
Joe and Diane Carter, Proprietors

Cottons, page 42
P. O. Box 354, LaConner, WA 98257
Phone: 800-995-5825   360-466-5825
Tia Kurtz, Proprietor

The Country Lady, page 46
P. O. Box 595, LaConner, WA 98257
Phone: 800-736-4831   360-466-4833
Jan Marie McGehee, Proprietor

Dandelion, page 51
P. O. Box 1368, LaConner, WA 98257
Phone: 360-466-2033
Linda Morris, Proprietor

Ginger Grater, The, page 54

P. O. Box 1091, LaConner, WA 98257
Phone: 360-466-4161
Patty Person and Patti Dynes, Proprietors

Go Outside, page 58

P. O. Box 216, LaConner, WA 98257
Phone: 360-466-4836
Mark and Heidi Epstein, Proprietors

Homespun Market, page 62

P. O. Box 592, LaConner, WA 98257
Phone: 360-466-4441
Jim and Judi Reeves, Proprietors

Hope Island Inn, page 66

P. O. Box K-2110, LaConner, WA 98257
Phone: 360-466-3221
Grant Lucas, Proprietor

Just Imagine, page 70

P. O. Box 193, LaConner, WA 98257
Phone: 360-466-3003
Colleen Scott, Manager

Katy's Inn Bed and Breakfast, page 74

P. O. Box 869, LaConner, WA 98257
Phone: 800-914-7767   360-466-3366
Bruce and Kathie Hubbard, Innkeepers

Kokomo Joe's, page 78

P. O. Box 204, LaConner, WA 98257
Phone: 360-466-2085
Joe and Diane Carter, Proprieters

LaConner Brewing Company, page 81

P. O. Box 328, LaConner, WA 98257
Phone: 360-466-1415
Scott and Cindy Abrahamson, Proprietors

LaConner Flats, a garden-The Granary, pg.84

1592 Best Road, Mt. Vernon, WA 98273
Phone: 360-466-3190
Bob and Marjorie Hart, Owners

LaConner Seafood & Prime Rib House, page 88

P. O. Box 577, LaConner, WA 98257
Phone: 360-466-4014
Jim and Mary Lou Caudill, Proprietors

MERCHANT MAILING ADDRESS INDEX...CONTINUED

LEGENDS, PAGE 92
936 Smoke House Road, LaConner, WA 98257
Phone: 360-466-5240
Nancy Wilbur Foster, Proprietor

LIGHTHOUSE INN, PAGE 96
P. O. Box 485, LaConner, WA 98257
Phone: 360-466-3147
Tore and Diana Dybfest, Proprietors

MARINA CAFE, PAGE 100
P. O. Box 1163, LaConner, WA 98257
Phone: 360-466-4242
Craig Reeves, Proprietor

MATHESON METAL SCULPTURE, PAGE 104
P. O. Box 1283, LaConner, WA 98257
Phone: 360-466-3341
Bill Matheson, Sculptor

NASTY JACK'S ANTIQUES, PAGE 109
P. O. Box 251, LaConner, WA 98257
Phone: 360-466-3209
Gary and Marlo Frank, Proprietors

O'LEARY'S BOOKS AND OTHER COMFORTS, PG. 112
P. O. Box 218, LaConner, WA 98257
Phone: 360-466-1305
Sally Cram, Proprietor

OLIVE SHOPPE AND MORE, THE, PAGE 116
P. O. Box 1233, LaConner, WA 98257
Phone: 360-466-4101
Mike and Vernee Neff, Proprietors

ORGANIC MATTERS, PAGE 120
P. O. Box 598, LaConner, WA 98257
Phone: 360-466-4012
Stephanie Banaszak, Proprietor

PADILLA BAY STORE, THE, PAGE 124
P. O. Box 679, LaConner, WA 98257
Phone: 360-466-3825
Linda Bañaszak and Jolene Berry, Proprietors

PALACE MARKET INTERIORS, PAGE 130
P. O. Box 473, LaConner, WA 98257
Phone: 360-466-3440
Phil and Sue Perry, Proprietors

Merchant Mailing Address Index...continued

White Swan Guest House, The, page 170

1388 Moore Road, Mt. Vernon, WA 98273
Phone: 360-445-6805
Peter Goldfarb, Proprietor

Wild Iris Inn, The, page 174

P. O. Box 696, LaConner, WA 98257
Phone: 800-477-1400 360-466-1400
Susan Sullivan, Innkeeper

Wood Merchant, The, page 176

P. O. Box 511, LaConner, WA 98257
Phone: 360-466-4741
Stuart and Laurie Hutt, Proprietors

ORDERING INFORMATION

Ship to:

Name: _____ Day time Phone: _____

Address: _____

City: _____ State and Zip Code: _____

Please send me LaConner Palates, Illustrated Cookbook(s)

_____ at $21.95 each   _____
Quantity

Shipping and Handling*   _____

Subtotal   _____

Sales Tax (Washington Residents add 7.9%)   _____

Total Enclosed   _____

Please enclose $5.00 per cookbook ($1.25 per additional cookbook) for shipping and handling.

Please make check or money order (U. S. funds only) payable to Bookends Publishing.

Please send payment with order information to:

Bookends Publishing
P. O. Box 2734
Oak Harbor, WA 98277-6734

Please allow 2-3 weeks for delivery

A
Radiographer's
Handbook

Gary Bown

DCR R, CI cert., FETC, BSc (Hons), MSc
Formerly Senior Lecturer
Centre for Radiography Education
The University of Portsmouth
Portsmouth, UK

W. B. SAUNDERS COMPANY LTD
LONDON PHILADELPHIA TORONTO SYDNEY TOKYO

W. B. Saunders Company Ltd   24–28 Oval Road
London NW1 7DX

The Curtis Center
Independence Square West
Philadelphia, PA 19106-3399, USA

Harcourt Brace & Company
55 Horner Avenue
Toronto, Ontario M8Z 4X6, Canada

Harcourt Brace & Company, Australia
30–52 Smidmore Street
Marrickville, NSW 2204, Australia

Harcourt Brace & Company, Japan
Ichibancho Central Building, 22-1 Ichibancho
Chiyoda-ku, Tokyo 102, Japan

A catalogue record for this book is available from the British Library

ISBN 0–7020–2166–0

Typeset by Florencetype Ltd, Stoodleigh, Devon
Printed in Great Britain by The University Press, Cambridge

Foreword

There has always been considerable debate amongst radiographers as to the 'correct' technique to adopt to obtain commonly requested radiographic projections. Not surprisingly students have been somewhat confused, as a result of varying advice, as to which approach they should use.

A Radiographer's Handbook tries to overcome the problem by encouraging students to consider the issues relating to each technique and to make up their own mind which method works best for them in specific circumstances.

The author has been involved in teaching radiographic technique to students in a variety of clinical placements for a number of years and is well aware of the problems which confront students when trying to apply theory to clinical practice. His text includes photographs and radiographic appearances of all of the major projections of the skeleton, and each one is accompanied by 'tips' on how to undertake the examination and the radiological assessment of the final radiograph.

This handbook will, I am sure, be a valuable aid to all students of radiography as well as those involved in the teaching of radiographic technique. The freedom it allows in developing the knowledge and understanding of problems encountered and how they may be overcome will begin to dispel many 'sacred cows' historically associated with radiographic technique.

Dr Alan Castle
Principal Lecturer
Centre for Radiography Education
University of Portsmouth
Portsmouth, UK

Preface

A Radiographer's Handbook is intended to be used by student radiographers, newly qualified radiographers and all those who are involved in clinical education. This book is essentially designed to be used as an *aide-mémoire* in a pocket-sized form.

It contains the basic skeletal and some soft tissue radiographic examinations as described in the popular radiographic positioning textbooks.

This book is not intended to be a comprehensive textbook on radiographic positioning.

In life there are many ways to achieve the same end. Often radiographers use different angles yet achieve the same or at least a similar result to another. Therefore, the essential aim of this book is for the user to customise the text and images to suit their own working environment and practices.

In this book I have included the following points to help the user gain as much as possible from the examination:

- **Patient position photographs – to support the text and to give greater emphasis to the patient's position.**
- **Appropriate radiographs to confirm that the required result of the examination has been achieved.**
- **Simple hints to aid positioning** ✓.
- **Some common errors to be avoided** ✗.
- **Indication of susceptible areas of trauma or pathology.**
- **Indication of some epiphysis calcification dates.**
- **Supplementary pages for the user to customise the text for their own individual working situation.**

In an effort to condense the information in this book to a pocket-sized format there are a number of necessary **exclusions**, for example:

- **Exposure factors** – Specific exposure charts should be displayed in the appropriate imaging rooms, therefore the author sees no need to give a generalised basic exposure for a given examination. Today, there are a huge variety of speeds of imaging systems in use in an imaging department. More recently we have seen the introduction of programmable and automatic exposure devices coupled with the diversity of generators in modern imaging departments.
- **Some basic skeletal examinations** – Some examinations are now **not** recommended in consideration of the 'as low as reasonably achievable' (ALARA) principle. Should the user require inclusion of such an examination the extra text pages can be used.
- **Some specialised examinations such as computerised tomography (CT), magnetic resonance imaging (MRI), radio nucleide imaging (RNI), ultrasound and even fluoroscopy** – This is due to the diversity of the protocols used. There are specific books written in these fields that can be used for reference.
- **Pads and sandbags** – These may be absent from some of the photographs purely to aid visualisation of the image.

Acknowledgements

Thanks must be given to Maria Khan of W. B. Saunders for her guidance and encouragement, Bradley Webb for his patience as a model, Jenny for her valuable advice and for proofreading, Peter Ford, St Richard's Hospital, Chichester for the use of images, Lynn Tilley, St Mary's Hospital, Portsmouth for use of the imaging department. Special thanks to Commander Buxton, Haslar Hospital for allowing me to digitise the radiographs. Lower figure on page xii is reproduced with permission from Philip W. Ballinger (1995) *Merrill's Atlas of Positions and Radiologic Procedures*, 8th edn., Mosby–Year Book, St. Louis MO. Upper figure on page xii, and figures on pages xiii–xv are reproduced from R.L. Eisenberg, C. Dennis and R.T.C. May (1989), *Radiographic Positioning*, Little, Brown & Company, Boston and New York. Skull baselines (page 154) are reproduced from P.M. Kimber (1983), *Radiography of the Head*, Churchill Livingstone, Edinburgh.

This book is dedicated to Jenny, C and D

Important Considerations

PURPOSE

This book is intended to be a quick reference guide and is essentially for use in the clinical environment.

STANDARD FACTORS TO BE CONSIDERED THROUGHOUT

- **Focus to film distance (FFD) will be 100 cm unless stated.**

- **Patient care must be maintained at all times.**

- **Radiation dose must be considered for all examinations in the form of accurate collimation, application of lead rubber aprons and shielding, good radiographic techniques and the choice of exposure factors to apply the ALARA principle.**

- **# – Fracture**

- **< – Less than**

- **> – Greater than**

HOW TO USE THIS BOOK

This book is designed to be *customised* by the user and its aim is therefore to give a general synopsis of radiographic techniques.

To establish routine projections – these are indicated on the main Contents page and in the list of projections indicated for each region.

Each projection has the following dialogue box to help you customise your text:

Example

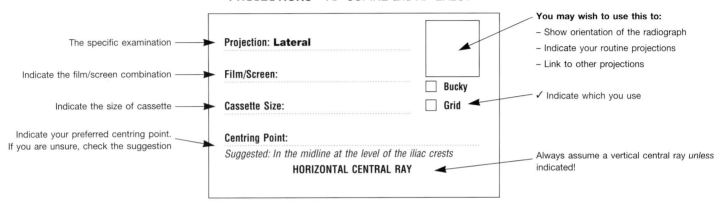

BODY REGION – ABDOMEN

PROJECTIONS – AP SUPINE and AP ERECT

The specific examination → Projection: **Lateral**

Indicate the film/screen combination → Film/Screen:

Indicate the size of cassette → Cassette Size:

Indicate your preferred centring point.
If you are unsure, check the suggestion → Centring Point:
Suggested: In the midline at the level of the iliac crests
HORIZONTAL CENTRAL RAY

☐ Bucky
☐ Grid

You may wish to use this to:
– Show orientation of the radiograph
– Indicate your routine projections
– Link to other projections

✓ Indicate which you use

Always assume a vertical central ray *unless* indicated!

Following each body region you will find a number of blank pages to include projections that *you* consider routine for your working environment and/or any supplementary projections you wish to include.

Also, at the back of the book, you will find a similar number of pages to accommodate skeletal surveys, mobiles, theatre radiography and contrast examinations.

CONCLUSION

In radiography today there is a need to extend the role of the radiographer, in particular by developing a more critical approach to imaging. But, to be able to take this approach:

- **There must be a good, established standard of radiographic techniques which the reader can then use as a foundation to critically evaluate each examination.**

Suggested centring points have therefore been included with gapped sections for the user to customise the examination text as required.

Radiographic Positioning Terminology

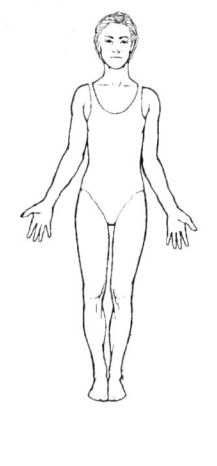

The Anatomical Position

- Subject facing forwards
- Body erect
- Arms and legs fully extended
- The palms of the hands are facing forwards and the feet are together

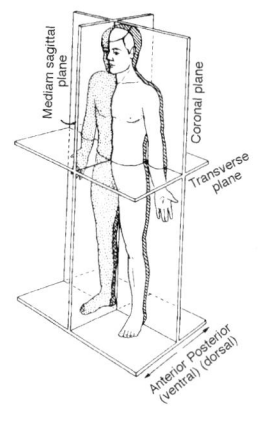

Median Sagittal Plane

- Passes vertically through the midline of the body dividing the body into a left and a right half in equal portions

Sagittal Plane

- Any plane passing through the body parallel to the median sagittal plane

Coronal Plane

- Passes vertically through the midline of the body dividing the body into an anterior and a posterior half in equal portions

Transverse Plane

- Any plane passing through the body at right angles to the median sagittal plane dividing the body into a superior and inferior portion

Radiographic Projections

Anteroposterior (AP)

- Patient can be supine on the x-ray table or erect with the back against the vertical stand. The central ray enters the front (anterior) and exits the back (posterior) surface of the body.

Posteroanterior (PA)

- Patient can be prone on the x-ray table or erect facing the vertical stand. The central ray enters the back (posterior) and exits the front (anterior) surface.

Lateral

- Patient can lie on either side on the x-ray table or erect with either side against the vertical stand. The projection is always named after the side of the body closest to the cassette.

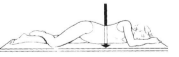

Left Anterior Oblique (LAO)

- Patient is erect or semi-prone. The *left* side of the body is closest to the cassette.

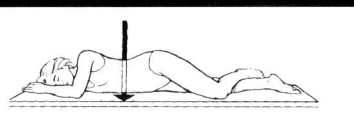

Right Anterior Oblique (RAO)

- Patient erect or semi-prone. The *right* side of the body is closest to the cassette.

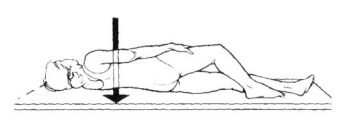

Left Posterior Oblique (LPO)

- Patient erect or semi-supine. The *left* side of the body is closest to the cassette.

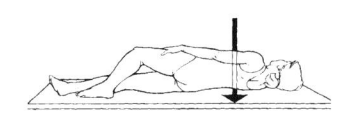

Right Posterior Oblique (RPO)

- Patient erect or semi-supine. The *right* side of the body is closest to the cassette.

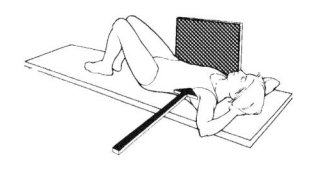

Dorsal Decubitus

- Patient is supine on the x-ray table or trolley. The central ray enters from one side of the patient and exits from the opposite side.

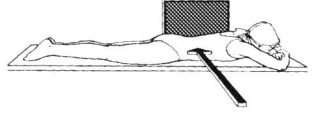

Ventral Decubitus

- Patient is prone on the x-ray table or trolley. The central ray enters from one side of the patient and exits from the opposite side.

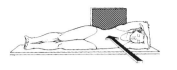

Lateral Decubitus

- Patient lying on either side.

Left Lateral Decubitus

- Patient lying on the left side with the right side uppermost.

Right Lateral Decubitus

- Patient lying on their right side with the left side uppermost.

Notes

Upper Extremity

Projection: PA (Dorsipalmar)

Film/Screen:

☐ Bucky

Cassette Size:

☐ Grid

Centring Point:

Suggested: To the head of the metacarpal

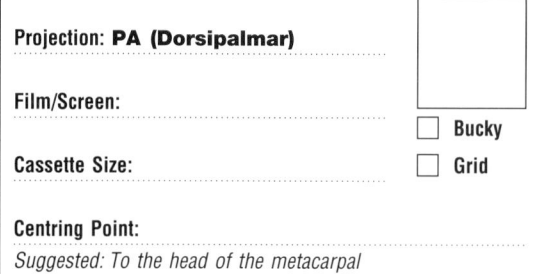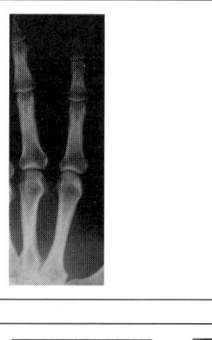

Projection: Lateral

Film/Screen:

☐ Bucky

Cassette Size:

☐ Grid

Centring Point:

Suggested: To the proximal interphalangeal joint

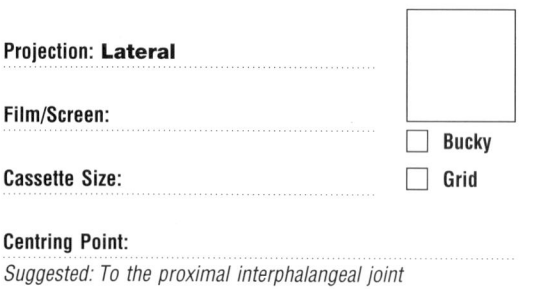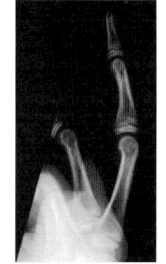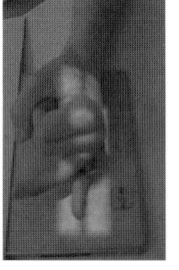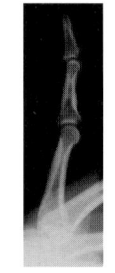

Second finger   Fifth finger

Points to Consider

Technique

✓ The metacarpophalangeal joint *must* be included
✓ Always include another finger to aid identification
✓ AP – the fingers *must* be placed flat upon the cassette
✓ Lateral – non-opaque pad can be used to help extend the finger
✗ Lateral – trauma – try not to let the finger flex too much

Radiological Assessment

✓ Avulsion #s are common – look for soft tissue swelling
✓ Mallet finger – direct blow plus avulsion of extensor tendon
✓ Dislocation – proximal interphalangeal joint – sporting injury
✓ Joint spaces should be uniform – approximately 1 mm in width
✓ Transverse # – result of hyperextension of the finger

PA (Dorsipalmar) – Affected Finger

- Patient seated, affected side towards the x-ray table
- Forearm placed on table
- Palmar aspect of fingers placed on the cassette
- Fingers extended and separated slightly

Collimation

To include: PROXIMALLY: Full length of metacarpal

                     DISTALLY: Terminal phalanx

                     LATERALLY: Soft tissue borders

Lateral – Index and Middle Fingers

- Hand rotated medially until the lateral aspect of the index finger is in contact with the cassette
- Index and middle fingers are extended and separated
- Remaining fingers are flexed
- The forearm is raised on pads and supported – middle finger may be supported with a non-opaque pad

Lateral – Little and Ring Fingers

- Hand rotated laterally so that the medial aspect of the little finger is in contact with the cassette
- Little and ring fingers are extended and separated
- Ring finger is supported on a non-opaque pad and parallel to the cassette
- Remaining fingers are flexed

Collimation

To include: PROXIMALLY: Proximal phalanx

                     DISTALLY: Terminal phalanx

                     LATERALLY: Soft tissue borders

Notes:

Projection: AP

Film/Screen:

☐ Bucky

Cassette Size:

☐ Grid

Centring Point:
Suggested: To the metacarpophalangeal joint

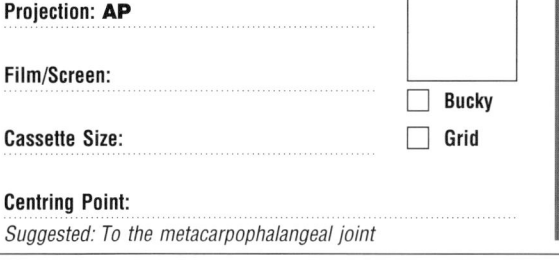
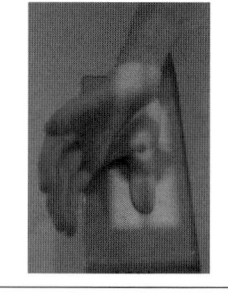

Projection: Lateral

Film/Screen:

☐ Bucky

Cassette Size:

☐ Grid

Centring Point:
Suggested: To the metacarpophalangeal joint

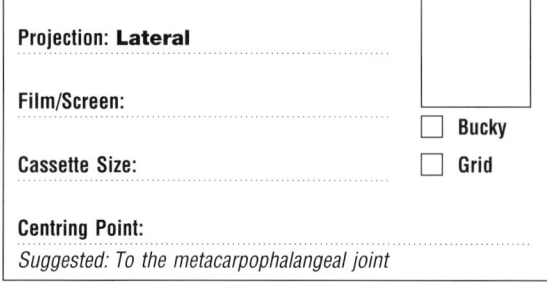
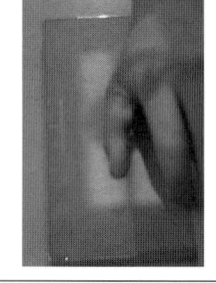
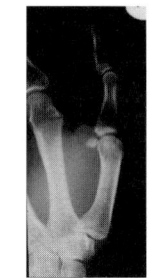

Points to Consider

Technique

✓ AP – condyles must be equidistant from the cassette
✓ Lateral – condyles must be superimposed
✓ ? Trauma – consider alternative AP (trauma) projection
✗ Underpenetration of proximal thumb due to thenal pad

Radiological Assessment

✓ Radiograph can appear normal – look for soft tissue swelling
✓ Avulsion #s may be present
✓ Bennett's # – # dislocation – result of forced abduction
✓ Skier's (gamekeeper's) thumb – acute sprain or rupture – ulnar
collateral ligament

AP

- Patient seated, affected side towards the x-ray table
- Thumb, elbow and shoulder at the same height
- The hand and forearm are extended
- Hand rotated medially so that the posterior aspect of the thumb is in contact with the cassette

Collimation

To include: PROXIMALLY: Proximal metacarpal
DISTALLY: Terminal phalanx
LATERALLY: Soft tissue borders
MEDIALLY: Soft tissue borders

Lateral

- Patient seated
- Hand prone, the palm is then rotated medially and supported on a non-opaque pad until the thumb is lateral
- The lateral aspect of the thumb is in contact with the cassette and is then slightly flexed

Collimation

To include: PROXIMALLY: Carpo-metacarpal joint
DISTALLY: Terminal phalanx
LATERALLY: Soft tissue borders
MEDIALLY: Soft tissue borders

Notes:

Projection: **AP (Trauma)**

Film/Screen:

☐ **Bucky**

Cassette Size:

☐ **Grid**

Centring Point:

Suggested: To the metacarpophalangeal joint

Points to Consider

Technique

✓ Use if injury to base of first metacarpal is suspected
✓ Support the thumb on a non-opaque pad
✓ *Must* include the carpo-metacarpal joint
✓ Increase FFD to reduce the magnification
✓ The thumb *must* be parallel to the cassette

Radiological Assessment

✓ Check the first carpo-metacarpal joint is included
✗ A magnified image unless an increased FFD is used
✗ Bennett's # – unlikely thumb will be parallel to the cassette

AP Alternative Position (Trauma)

- Medial border of the hand, placed in contact with the cassette
- Palmar aspect 90°
- Thumb is extended and placed on a non-opaque pad

Collimation

To include:　　PROXIMALLY: Proximal metacarpal
　　　　　　　　DISTALLY: Terminal phalanx
　　　　　　　　LATERALLY: Soft tissue borders
　　　　　　　　MEDIALLY: Soft tissue borders

Notes:

Projection: PA (Dorsipalmar)

Film/Screen:

☐ **Bucky**

Cassette Size:

☐ **Grid**

Centring Point:

Suggested: To the head of the third metacarpal

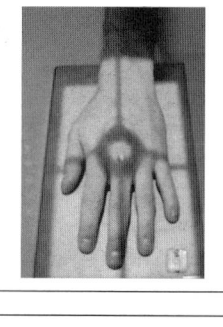
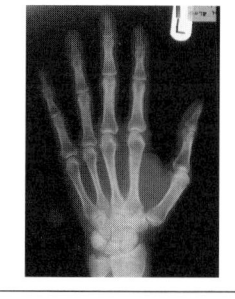

Projection: PA Oblique

Film/Screen:

☐ **Bucky**

Cassette Size:

☐ **Grid**

Centring Point:

Suggested: To the head of the third metacarpal

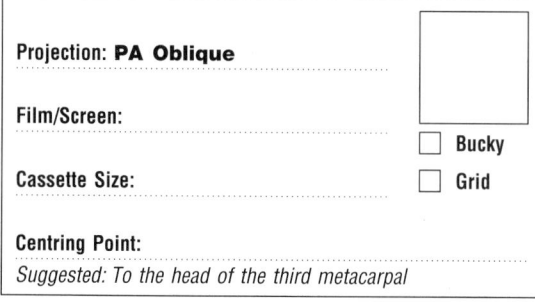
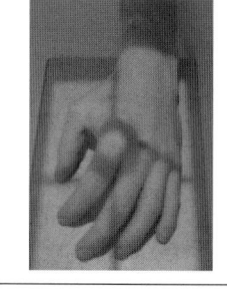
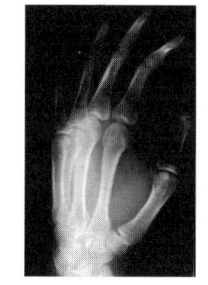

Points to Consider

Technique

✓ Include the whole of the hand including base of metacarpals
✓ ? Injury confined to distal digit – limit image to that digit
✓ If you identify an injury – proceed to a lateral
✓ PA oblique – better general assessment if fingers parallel
✗ PA oblique – avoid over-rotation – obscure metacarpals

Radiological Assessment

✓ #s metacarpal neck – usually the result of a direct blow
✓ Common site for #s – head of the fifth metacarpal
✓ Look for vertical # through the base with dislocation of joint
✓ Secondary ossification centres appear at the age 2–3 years
✗ PA poor at showing #s of the articular surface of the metacarpal heads

PA (Dorsipalmar)

- Patient seated, affected side towards the x-ray table
- Palmar aspect placed on the cassette
- Fingers are extended and slightly separated

Collimation

To include: PROXIMALLY: Distal radius and ulna
DISTALLY: Terminal phalanx
LATERALLY: Soft tissue borders
MEDIALLY: Soft tissue borders

PA Oblique

- From the PA position the hand is rotated onto the lateral side to form an angle of 45° and supported on a non-opaque pad
- Fingers slightly flexed and separated
- Fingertips in contact with the cassette

Collimation

To include: PROXIMALLY: Distal radius and ulna
DISTALLY: Terminal phalanx
LATERALLY: Soft tissue borders
MEDIALLY: Soft tissue borders

Notes:

Projection: Lateral

Film/Screen:

☐ Bucky

Cassette Size:

☐ Grid

Centring Point:
Suggested: To the head of the second metacarpal

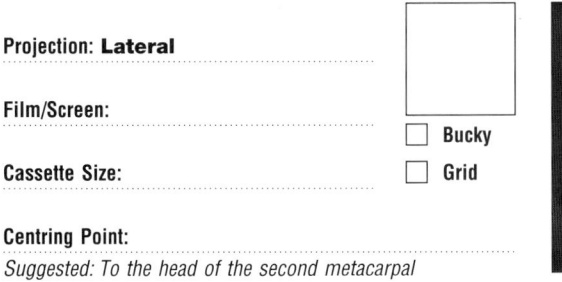
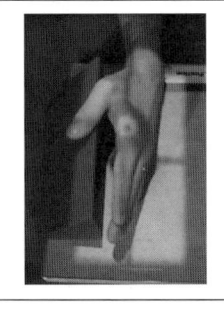

Projection: AP Oblique (Ball Catcher's)

Film/Screen:

☐ Bucky

Cassette Size:

☐ Grid

Centring Point:
Suggested: Midway between both hands at the level of the head of the fifth metacarpal

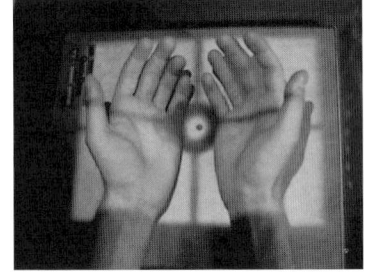
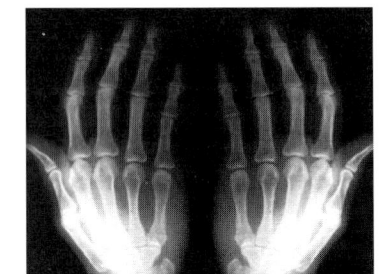

Points to Consider

Technique

✓ Lateral – support the thumb on a non-opaque pad
✗ If not a true lateral – may result in missing a dislocation
✓ An increase in exposure of up to 5 kV may be necessary
✓ Catcher's – obliquity – metacarpal heads *must* be free from superimposition

Radiological Assessment

✓ Look for bone alignment – displacement and dislocation
✓ Look for # through the articular surface at the base of phalanx
✓ Check the base of the fourth and fifth metacarpals – dislocation is common
✓ Ball Catcher's – look for early rheumatoid arthritis with loss of bony outline and associated demineralisation

Lateral

- From the oblique position the hand is rotated laterally so that the palmar aspect forms an angle of 90° to the cassette
- Fingers are extended and superimposed
- The thumb is extended away from the metacarpals upon a non-opaque pad

Collimation

To include: PROXIMALLY: Distal radius and ulna

                    DISTALLY: Terminal phalanx

                    LATERALLY: Soft tissue borders

AP Oblique (Ball Catcher's)

- Patient seated facing the x-ray table
- Both forearms and hands are supinated
- The dorsa of both hands are in contact with the cassette and fifth metacarpals and phalanges are touching
- Hands are then internally rotated 45° as if to catch a ball
- Hands are supported in position with non-opaque pads

Collimation

To include both hands

Notes:

Projection: PA

Film/Screen:

☐ Bucky

Cassette Size:

☐ Grid

Centring Point:

Suggested: Midway between the styloid processes

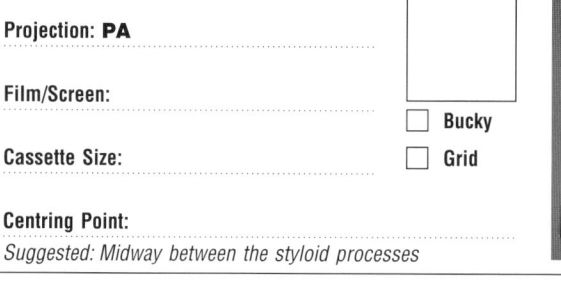
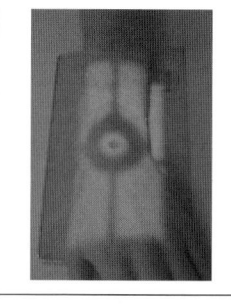

Projection: PA Oblique

Film/Screen:

☐ Bucky

Cassette Size:

☐ Grid

Centring Point:

Suggested: Midway between the styloid processes

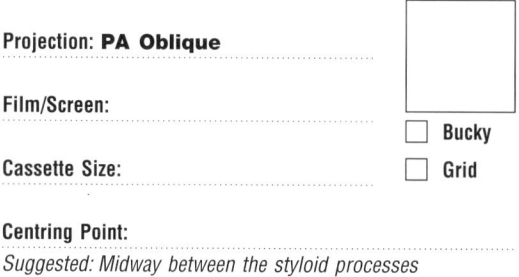
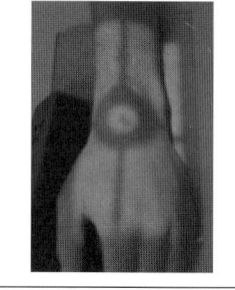
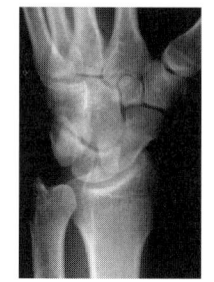

Points to Consider

Technique

- ✓ AP – shoulder, elbow and wrist at the same level
- ✓ Is there ulnar deviation if a scaphoid # is suspected?
- ✓ Slightly curl fingers so that carpals are in contact with cassette
- ✓ Wet plaster requires +5 kVp more than dry
- ✗ Be careful of abnormally thick plaster casts

Radiological Assessment

- ✓ Colles' # – posterior displacement – most common in the elderly – displacement described as 'dinner fork' deformity
- ✓ Smith's # – anterior displacement – uncommon
- ✓ Epiphyses – radial appears in the second year and fuses in the twentieth year – ulnar appears in the eighth year and fuses in the twentieth year

PA

- Patient seated, affected side towards the x-ray table
- Elbow is flexed, wrist and forearm placed onto the cassette
- Fingers are slightly flexed to raise the hand and keep the wrist in contact with the cassette
- Styloid processes are equidistant from the cassette

PA Oblique

- From the PA position the wrist is rotated laterally until the palmar aspect is approximately 45° to the cassette
- A non-opaque pad is placed under the radial side of the wrist

Collimation

To include: PROXIMALLY: Lower third of radius and ulna
DISTALLY: Head of the metacarpals
LATERALLY: Soft tissue borders
MEDIALLY: Soft tissue borders

Notes:

Projection: Lateral

Film/Screen:

☐ Bucky

Cassette Size:

☐ Grid

Centring Point:
Suggested: To the radial styloid process

Points to Consider

Technique

✓ Styloid processes *must* be superimposed – rotate further 5°
✓ To achieve superimposition try extending the elbow
✓ Wrist, elbow and shoulder should be at the same level
✓ Remember wet plaster requires more kVp than dry
✓ Acute injury – horizontal beam will be necessary

Radiological Assessment

✓ In children look for a slipped epiphysis
✓ Look for soft tissue swelling due to haemorrhage
✓ Commonest carpal dislocation – lunate dislocation due to forced dorsiflexion
✓ The triquetrum is the second commonest carpal bone to #
✓ In children – commonest # is the greenstick

Lateral

- The hand is rotated so that the palmar aspect is at 90° to the cassette
- Elbow is flexed
- The wrist may be rotated a further 5° to superimpose the styloid processes
- The thumb is supported on a non-opaque pad

Collimation

To include: PROXIMALLY: Lower third of radius and ulna

                DISTALLY: Head of the metacarpals

                LATERALLY: Soft tissue borders

                MEDIALLY: Soft tissue borders

Notes:

Projection: PA

Film/Screen:

☐ Bucky

Cassette Size:

☐ Grid

Centring Point:

Suggested: Midway between the styloid processes

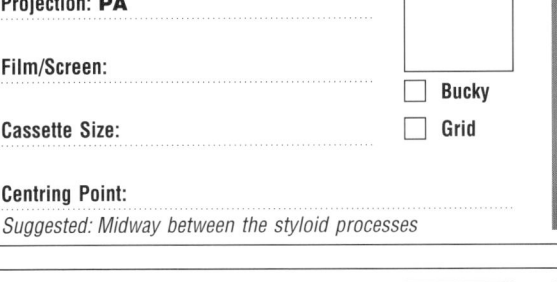
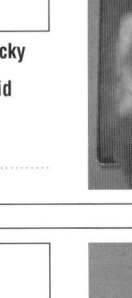

Projection: PA Oblique

Film/Screen:

☐ Bucky

Cassette Size:

☐ Grid

Centring Point:

Suggested: Midway between the styloid processes

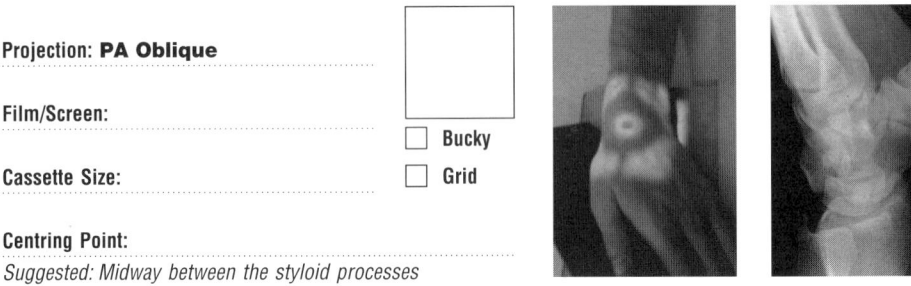

Points to Consider

Technique

✓ PA – ulnar deviation essential where injury will allow
✓ Fine focus is essential
✓ Long axis of the scaphoid should be parallel to the cassette
✓ Increase mAs slightly due to precise collimation
✗ *Do not* x-ray through plaster due to poor definition

Radiological Assessment

✓ PA – the scaphoid and joint spaces should be demonstrated
✓ 80% of #s occur at the waist of the scaphoid and jeopardise blood supply to the proximal part
✓ Scaphoid # may not be evident for 5–10 days after injury – *must* have a follow-up examination
✓ # of the proximal pole of scaphoid – increased chance of necrosis
✓ Look for reabsorption of bone on follow-up radiographs

PA

- Patient seated, affected side towards the x-ray table
- Elbow is flexed, wrist and forearm placed onto the cassette
- Fingers are slightly flexed to raise the hand and keep the wrist in contact with the cassette
- Styloid processes are equidistant from the cassette
- Ulnar deviation of the hand

PA Oblique

- From the PA position the wrist is rotated laterally until the palmar aspect is approximately 45° to the cassette
- A non-opaque pad is placed under the radial side of the wrist

Collimation

- For maximum image resolution – collimate precisely to include the carpal bones

Notes:

Projection: Lateral

Film/Screen:

Cassette Size:

☐ Bucky
☐ Grid

Centring Point:
Suggested: To the radial styloid process

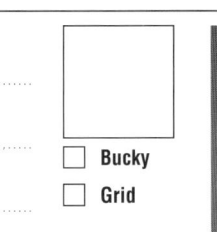
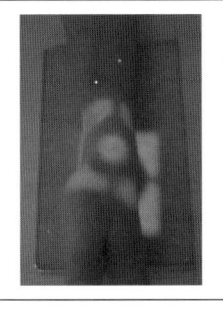
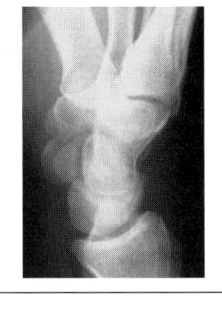

Projection: AP Oblique

Film/Screen:

Cassette Size:

☐ Bucky
☐ Grid

Centring Point:
Suggested: Midway between the styloid processes

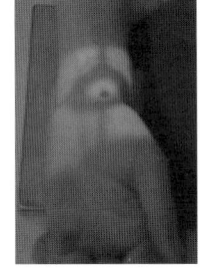
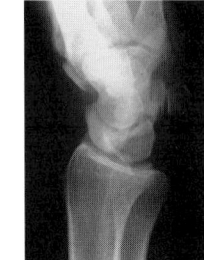

Points to Consider

Technique

✓ A slight over-rotation of the wrist will superimpose the styloid processes
✓ Minimise movement of the wrist as much as possible – move the wrist from the elbow and shoulder
✓ A kV increase will be required for the lateral projection
✓ Oblique – hand *must* be supported by non-opaque pads

Radiological Assessment

✓ If intercarpal joints measure more than 2 mm (adult) then suspect ligamentous injury
✓ 90% of carpal #s involve the scaphoid
✓ Lateral – most dislocations involve the lunate bone
✓ Oblique – pisiform and posterior triquetral should be visible

Lateral

- The hand is rotated so that the palmar aspect is at 90° to the cassette
- Elbow is flexed
- The styloid processes are superimposed and thumb is supported on a non-opaque pad

AP Oblique

- From the lateral position the wrist is rotated a further 45° so that the palmar aspect of the hand is uppermost
- A non-opaque pad is placed under the radial side of the wrist

Collimation

- For maximum image resolution – collimate precisely to include the carpal bones

Notes:

Projection: **Possible Scaphoid #**

Film/Screen:

☐ Bucky

Cassette Size:

☐ Grid

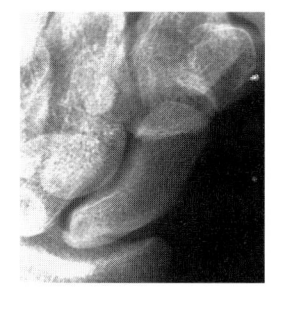

Centring Point:

Suggested: To the scaphoid – just distal to the anatomical snuff box

CENTRAL RAY 45° TOWARDS THE ELBOW

Points to Consider

Technique

✓ Ulnar deviation essential
✓ Slightly raised fingers are due to carpals in contact with cassette
✓ Angle the central ray 45° – check FFD is still 100 cm
✗ Too much angle of central ray will distort the scaphoid
✗ Take care not to project the image off the cassette

Radiological Assessment

✓ Frees the scaphoid from the carpal bones
✓ Exaggerates a # if present
✓ May require RNI if pain persists and x-rays show no abnormality
✗ Elongated projection – use as a supplementary projection only

Possible Scaphoid Fracture (Alternative 'Banana Projection')

- Patient seated, affected side towards the table
- Elbow is flexed to 90°
- Ulnar deviation of the wrist
- Central ray 45° towards the elbow along the axis of the radius and ulna

Collimation

- For maximum image resolution – collimate precisely to include the carpal bones

Notes:

Projection: AP

Film/Screen:

☐ Bucky

Cassette Size:

☐ Grid

Centring Point:

Suggested: To the middle of the forearm

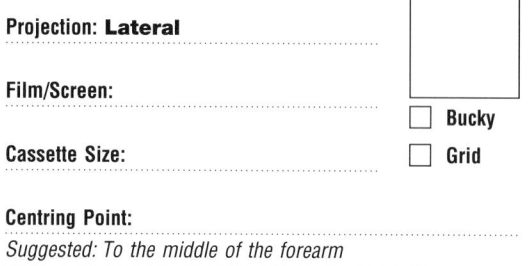

Projection: Lateral

Film/Screen:

☐ Bucky

Cassette Size:

☐ Grid

Centring Point:

Suggested: To the middle of the forearm

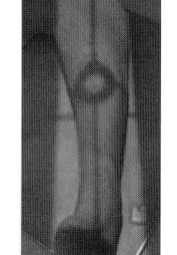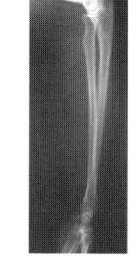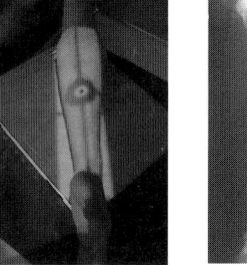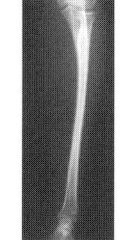

Points to Consider

Technique

✓ *Always* include both joints on the radiograph
✓ Lateral – full extension of the forearm and elbow

✓ Flexed elbow
✓ Acute injury – horizontal beam *will* be necessary

Radiological Assessment

✓ AP – slight superimposition of radial head over proximal ulna
✓ *Good* for bone alignment – radius and ulna superimposed,
✗ *But* poor projection of the elbow – oblique elbow
✓ *Good* projection of the elbow and wrist joints
✗ Radius and ulna superimposed at the wrist, but separated at elbow

AP

- Patient seated, affected side towards the x-ray table
- The wrist, elbow and shoulder should be at the same level
- The forearm is fully supinated and rotated from the shoulder joint so that the hand and elbow are in a true AP position

Collimation

To include: PROXIMALLY: The elbow joint

DISTALLY: The wrist joint

LATERALLY: Soft tissue borders

MEDIALLY: Soft tissue borders

Lateral

- The elbow is flexed to 90°
- Wrist, elbow and shoulder should be at the same level
- The hand is rotated so that the styloid processes are superimposed

Collimation

To include: PROXIMALLY: The elbow joint

DISTALLY: The wrist joint

LATERALLY: Soft tissue borders

MEDIALLY: Soft tissue borders

Notes:

Projection: AP

Film/Screen:

☐ Bucky

Cassette Size:

☐ Grid

Centring Point:
Suggested: 2.5 cm distal to a line joining the epicondyles

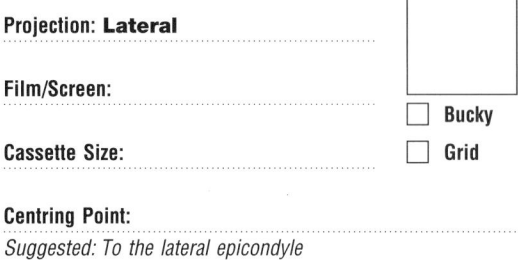

Projection: Lateral

Film/Screen:

☐ Bucky

Cassette Size:

☐ Grid

Centring Point:
Suggested: To the lateral epicondyle

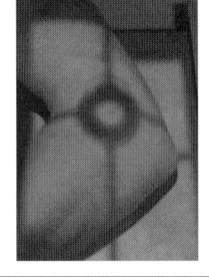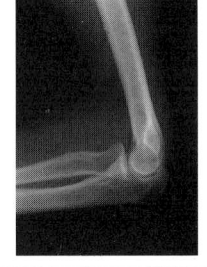

Points to Consider

Technique

✓ AP – epicondyles equidistant from the cassette
✓ AP – hand should be fully supinated
✓ Lateral – raise and immobilise the wrist on non-opaque pad
✓ Children – both elbows may be required for ossification centres
✗ Shoulder higher than the elbow is poor technique
✗ Possible supracondylar # – *never* forcibly extend the elbow

Radiological Assessment

✓ Look for displaced fat pads – indication of trauma
✓ Common site of injury is the radial head
✓ Normally only the anterior distal fat pad is visible
✓ Check the elbow for avulsion #s – usually the result of a fall onto an outstretched hand
✓ Check soft tissue for swelling – a positive sign of trauma
✓ Supracondylar #s account for 60% of childhood #s

AP

- Patient seated, affected side towards the x-ray table
- Arm is fully supinated so that the epicondyles are equidistant from the cassette
- Wrist, elbow and shoulder should be at the same level

Collimation

To include: PROXIMALLY: The distal humerus
DISTALLY: The proximal radius and ulnar
LATERALLY: Soft tissue borders
MEDIALLY: Soft tissue borders

Lateral

- The elbow is flexed 90°
- Wrist, elbow and shoulder should be at the same level
- The hand is rotated so that the radial and ulnar styloid processes are superimposed

Collimation

To include: PROXIMALLY: The distal humerus
DISTALLY: The proximal radius and ulnar
LATERALLY: Soft tissue borders
MEDIALLY: Soft tissue borders

Notes:

Projection: **1. Possible injury to radial head**

Film/Screen:

☐ Bucky

Cassette Size:

☐ Grid

Centring Point:

Suggested: To the middle at the crease of the elbow

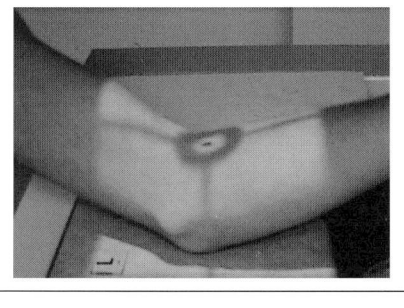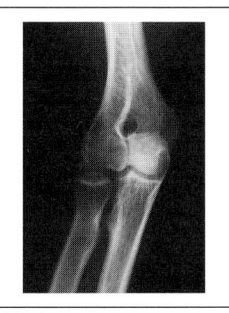

Projection: **2. Full flexion of the elbow**

Film/Screen:

☐ Bucky

Cassette Size:

☐ Grid

Centring Point:

Suggested: 5 cm above the olecranon process

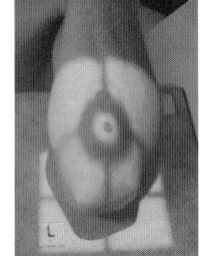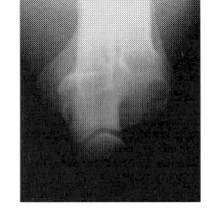

Points to Consider

Technique

✓ 1. Use as a general projection in the case of severe trauma
✗ Difficult position to maintain – immobilisation essential

✓ 2. Ensure epicondyles are equidistant from the cassette
✓ Adjust the table to just below the shoulder level

Radiological Assessment

✓ A visible fat pad is abnormal – probable #
✗ Radial head will be slightly superimposed on distal humerus

✓ Forearm and humerus should be superimposed
✓ Olecranon and distal humerus should be clearly seen

1. Possible Injury to the Radial Head – General Projection of the Elbow Joint

- Elbow flexed to 90°
- The olecranon of the elbow is placed directly onto the cassette
- The forearm and humerus form an angle of 45°
- Sandbags are placed to support the limbs

Collimation

To include: PROXIMALLY: Distal humerus
DISTALLY: Proximal radius and ulna
LATERALLY: Soft tissue borders
MEDIALLY: Soft tissue borders

2. Full Flexion of the Elbow

- The posterior aspect of the humerus in contact with the cassette
- Hand placed onto the shoulder
- Epicondyles equidistant to the cassette

Collimation

To include: PROXIMALLY: Distal humerus and radius/ulna
DISTALLY: Olecranon process
LATERALLY: Soft tissue borders
MEDIALLY: Soft tissue borders

Notes:

Projection: **Alternative Projection**

Film/Screen:

☐ **Bucky**

Cassette Size:

☐ **Grid**

Centring Point:

Suggested: To the radial head

CENTRAL RAY 45° TO THE HUMERUS

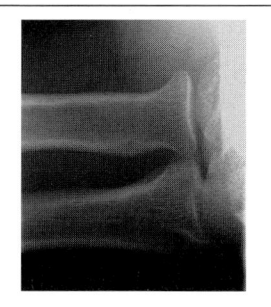

Points to Consider

Technique

✓ Ideally, hand is rotated with the thumb pointing upwards
✓ Painful joint – pronate the hand
✓ Take projection after the lateral – minimises movement
✓ Lead protection *must* be given – consider central ray
✗ Do not forcibly supinate hand

Radiological Assessment

✓ Common injury due to a fall on an outstretched hand
✓ Radial head should be projected clear of the ulna
✓ Impacted head – slight angulation of the cortex of the neck
✓ Is there a positive fat pad sign?
✗ The image will be magnified and elongated

Alternative Projection

- Patient seated with the affected arm placed upon the cassette
- The elbow is positioned as for the routine lateral projection
- The elbow is flexed to 90°
- Wrist and shoulder at the same level
- Wrist in true lateral position
- Central ray is angled *caudally* 45° to the forearm along the humeral axis

Collimation

To include: PROXIMALLY: Lower humerus and soft tissues
                DISTALLY: Posterior elbow joint
                LATERALLY: Soft tissue borders

Notes:

Projection: AP

Film/Screen:

☐ Bucky

Cassette Size:

☐ Grid

Centring Point:
Suggested: To the middle of the humerus

Projection: Lateral

Film/Screen:

☐ Bucky

Cassette Size:

☐ Grid

Centring Point:
Suggested: To the middle of the humerus

Points to Consider

Technique

✓ Humerus should be abducted away from the trunk
✓ AP – elbow epicondyles equidistant from the cassette
✓ Lateral – hand, where possible, should be placed on abdomen
✓ *Must* include shoulder and elbow joints on the radiograph
✗ Acute injury – *do not* remove the arm from the sling
✗ Beware – breast shadows may obscure the humeral shaft

Radiological Assessment

✓ #s occur at all levels – direct or indirect violence
✓ AP – head and greater tuberosity of humerus seen in profile
✓ Lateral – are the epicondyles superimposed?
✓ Common site in children – solitary bone cyst
✓ Adults – metastatic deposits – breast or bronchus
✗ Lateral – head of humerus *not* seen well – shoulder projection may be required

AP

- The patient may be supine or erect
- The body is rotated slightly onto the affected side so that the arm is in contact with the cassette
- The arm is fully supinated and slightly abducted where safe to do so
- Elbow epicondyles should be equidistant from the cassette

Lateral

- Patient may be prone or erect
- The body is rotated slightly onto the affected side so that the arm is in contact with the cassette
- The affected arm is carefully flexed and the hand is placed upon the upper abdomen
- The opposite arm is placed down by the side

Collimation

To include: PROXIMALLY: The shoulder joint
DISTALLY: The elbow joint
LATERALLY: Soft tissue borders
MEDIALLY: Soft tissue borders

Notes:

Projection:

Film/Screen:

Cassette Size:

Centring Point:

☐ Bucky

☐ Grid

Notes:

Projection:

Film/Screen:

Cassette Size:

Centring Point:

☐ Bucky

☐ Grid

Notes:

Projection:

Film/Screen:

☐ Bucky

Cassette Size:

☐ Grid

Centring Point:

Notes:

Projection:

Film/Screen:

☐ Bucky

Cassette Size:

☐ Grid

Centring Point:

Notes:

Projection: ....

Film/Screen: ....

☐ Bucky

Cassette Size: ....

☐ Grid

Centring Point: ....

Notes:

....
....
....
....
....
....
....
....

Projection: ....

Film/Screen: ....

☐ Bucky

Cassette Size: ....

☐ Grid

Centring Point: ....

Notes:

....
....
....
....
....
....
....
....

Projection: ....

Film/Screen: ....

☐ Bucky

Cassette Size: ....

☐ Grid

Centring Point: ....

Notes:

....
....
....
....
....
....
....
....

Projection: ....

Film/Screen: ....

☐ Bucky

Cassette Size: ....

☐ Grid

Centring Point: ....

Notes:

....
....
....
....
....
....
....
....

Projection: ....

Film/Screen: ....

☐ **Bucky**

Cassette Size: ....

☐ **Grid**

Centring Point: ....

Notes:

....

....

....

....

....

....

....

....

Projection: ....

Film/Screen: ....

☐ **Bucky**

Cassette Size: ....

☐ **Grid**

Centring Point: ....

Notes:

....

....

....

....

....

....

....

....

Shoulder Girdle

Projection: AP

Film/Screen:

☐ Bucky

Cassette Size:

☐ Grid

Centring Point:
Suggested: 10 cm below the coracoid process

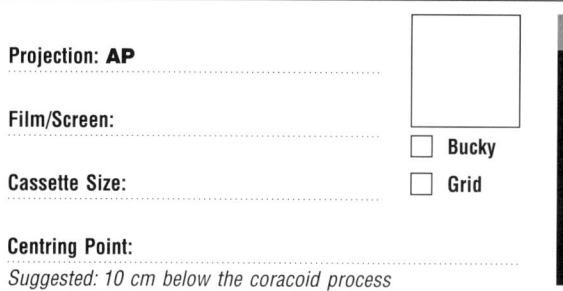
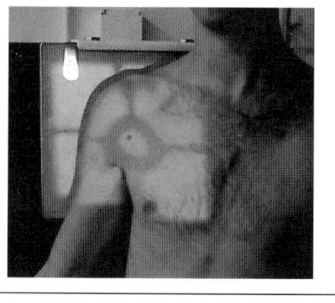
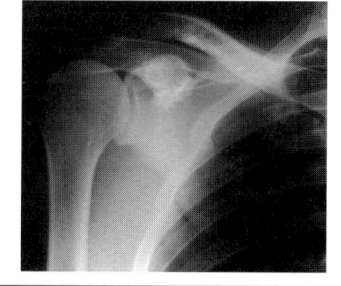

Projection: AP Oblique

Film/Screen:

☐ Bucky

Cassette Size:

☐ Grid

Centring Point:
Suggested: To the head of the humerus

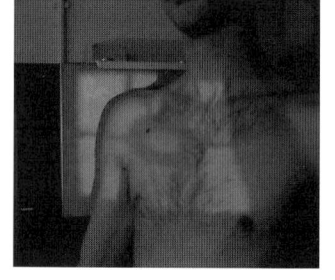
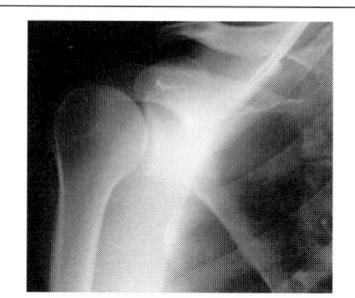

Points to Consider

Technique

✓ An axial projection of the shoulder may be required
✓ Exposure on *arrested* respiration
✗ *Never* forcibly abduct the humerus
✗ #ed clavicle – *do not* rotate patient – foreshortens the clavicle
✗ Lateral transthoracic – *do not* attempt because it increases radiation dose

Radiological Assessment

✓ Anterior dislocation – humeral head below coracoid process
✓ Posterior dislocation – rare (about 5% of cases) – seen in epileptics
✓ Common site of # – surgical neck of humerus
✓ Check for impaction – # may be overlooked
✓ Acute inflammation – look for calcification – rotator cuff muscles

AP

This projection gives a general assessment of the shoulder
- Patient may be supine or erect facing the x-ray tube
- The body is very slightly rotated onto the affected side
- Arm is abducted from the body and supinated

Collimation

To include: SUPERIORLY: Clavicle

INFERIORLY: Inferior angle of the scapula

LATERALLY: Soft tissues

MEDIALLY: Sternoclavicular joint

AP Oblique

- Patient may be supine or erect facing the x-ray table
- Body rotated approximately 40° to the affected side so that the scapula is parallel to the cassette
- Elbow flexed and forearm placed across the abdomen

Collimation

To include: SUPERIORLY: Clavicle

INFERIORLY: Inferior angle of the scapula

LATERALLY: Soft tissues

MEDIALLY: Sternoclavicular joint

Notes:

Projection: Axial Inferosuperior

Film/Screen:

☐ Bucky

Cassette Size:

☐ Grid

Centring Point:
Suggested: To the axilla – small angulation to the joint

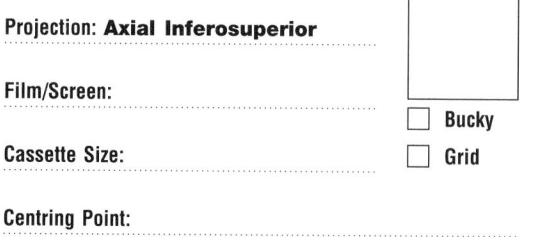
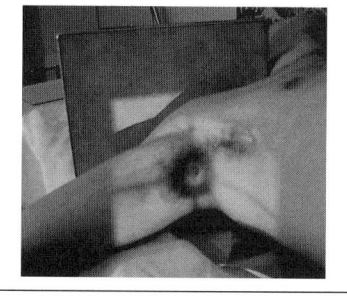
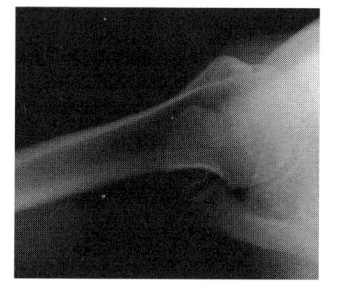

Projection: Axial Superoinferior

Film/Screen:

☐ Bucky

Cassette Size:

☐ Grid

Centring Point:
Suggested: To the acromion process

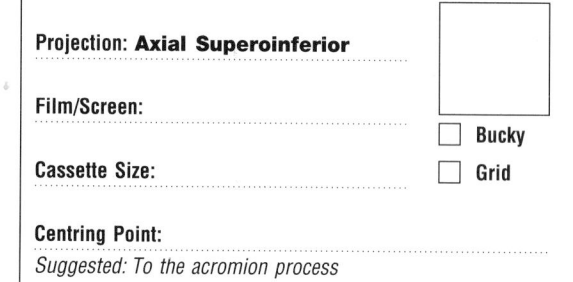
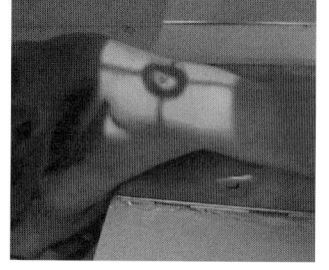
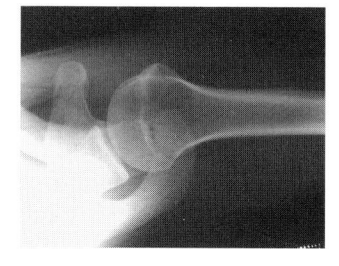

Points to Consider

Technique

✓ Superoinferior – only use when full abduction is possible
✓ *Must* include the glenohumeral joint on the radiograph
✓ Inferosuperior – when only limited abduction possible
✓ Axial projection should be taken in all cases of trauma
✗ Acute injury – *never* forcibly abduct the arm
✓ Consider the alternative 'Y' projection

Radiological Assessment

✓ Glenoid seen between coracoid, glenoid and acromion processes
✓ #s of coracoid and infraspinous processes can be clearly seen
✓ Children – epiphyseal lines vary – not to be confused with #s
✓ Check soft tissues for calcification of rotator cuff muscles
✗ The bicipital groove should not be confused with a #

Axial Inferosuperior

- Patient supine on the x-ray table
- Ideally the affected arm is abducted to 90°
- Hand turned with palm facing upwards
- Cassette supported vertically against the shoulder and gently pressed into the neck

Collimation

To include: ANTERIORLY: Anterior soft tissues
POSTERIORLY: Posterior soft tissues
DISTALLY: Upper humerus
PROXIMALLY: Glenohumeral joint

Axial Superoinferior

- Patient seated at the side of the x-ray table
- The body is inclined towards the table
- The affected arm is abducted as much as possible over a cassette
- The elbow rests upon the table top
- Palm of the hand is facing downwards

Collimation

To include: ANTERIORLY: Anterior soft tissues
POSTERIORLY: Posterior soft tissues
DISTALLY: Upper humerus
PROXIMALLY: Glenohumeral joint

Notes:

Projection: Supplementary 'Y' Projection

Film/Screen:

☐ Bucky

Cassette Size:

☐ Grid

Centring Point:

Suggested: To the glenohumeral joint

HORIZONTAL CENTRAL RAY

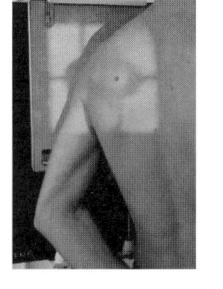

Points to Consider

Technique

✓ Projection useful in the evaluation of possible shoulder dislocation
✓ Visualise upper humeral head and lateral scapula
✓ The position of the arm is not critical, but should be placed for comfort
✓ Exposure on arrested respiration

Radiological Assessment

✓ Y is formed by acromion, coracoid and lateral border of scapula
✓ Normally head of humerus should sit at junction of the Y
✓ Anterior dislocation – humeral head beneath coracoid process
✓ Posterior dislocation – humeral head beneath acromion process
✗ Scapula should not be superimposed over the rib cage

Supplementary 'Y' Projection – Dislocated Shoulder

- Patient is in the erect position and facing the cassette in the upright stand
- Arm nearest the Bucky is relaxed and the back of the hand placed on the hip
- The opposite arm holds onto the erect Bucky for support
- The trunk is rotated approximately 60° away from the side under examination
- Anterior surface of the shoulder under examination is in contact with the cassette

Collimation

To include: SUPERIORLY: Clavicle

               INFERIORLY: Scapulae and proximal humerus

               LATERALLY: Humerus

               MEDIALLY: Scapulae and rib cage

Notes:

Projection: AP

Film/Screen:

☐ Bucky

Cassette Size:

☐ Grid

Centring Point:
Suggested: 8 cm below the midpoint of the clavicle

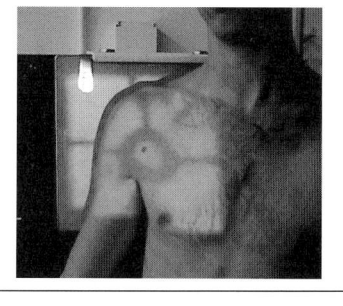
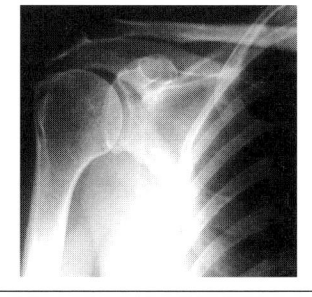

Projection: Lateral

Film/Screen:

☐ Bucky

Cassette Size:

☐ Grid

Centring Point:
Suggested: Just medial to the midpoint of the palpable scapula
HORIZONTAL CENTRAL RAY

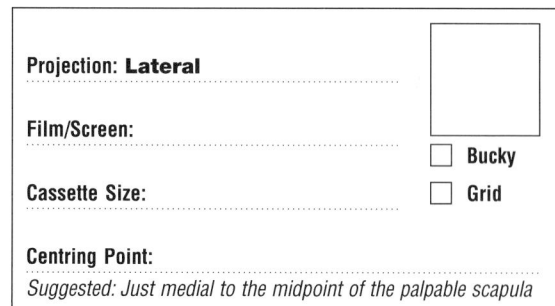
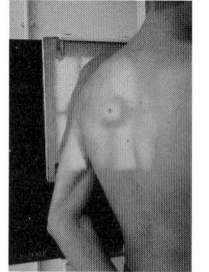
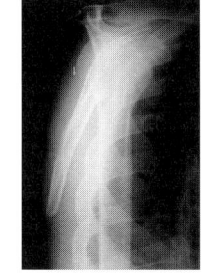

Points to Consider

Technique

✓ AP – better images are obtained if you use a Bucky
✓ Exposure on *arrrested* expiration
✗ *Never* forcibly abduct the humerus
✗ Lateral – failure to abduct the arm results in humerus superimposed on the scapula

Radiological Assessment

✓ AP – the whole of the scapula *must* be included
✓ AP – lateral border should be free from the rib cage
✓ #s – usually the result of a direct crush-type injury
✓ Lateral – scapula blade *must* be clear of the rib cage
✗ Humerus should not superimpose the region of interest

AP

- Patient may be supine or erect facing the x-ray tube
- The body is very slightly rotated onto the affected side by approximately 30°
- Arm is abducted from the body and supinated

Collimation

To include: SUPERIORLY: Clavicle

INFERIORLY: Inferior angle of the scapula

LATERALLY: Soft tissues

MEDIALLY: Sternoclavicular joint

Lateral

- Patient may be prone or erect facing the Bucky with the affected shoulder in close contact
- The trunk is rotated so that the blade of the scapula is perpendicular to the Bucky
- The affected arm is abducted away from the body

Collimation

To include: SUPERIORLY: Acromioclavicular joint

INFERIORLY: Inferior angle of the scapula

LATERALLY: Soft tissue borders

MEDIALLY: Lateral rib cage

Notes:

Projection: AP and AP Weight-bearing

Film/Screen:

☐ Bucky

Cassette Size:

☐ Grid

Centring Point:

Suggested: To the palpable acromioclavicular joint
HORIZONTAL CENTRAL RAY

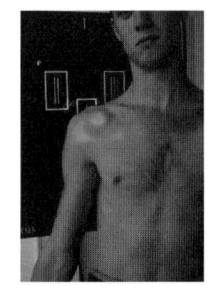
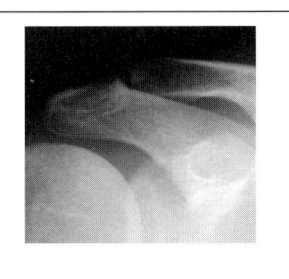
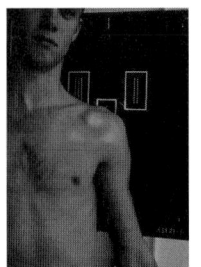
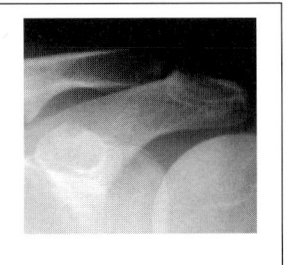

Points to Consider

Technique

✓ Two exposures – centre to each acromioclavicular joint in turn
✓ Exposure on arrested respiration
✓ Repeat examination with patient holding weights
✓ Patient must hold weights in both hands for at least 3 min before examination – allows gravity effect to take place
✗ *Do not* use one exposure with open collimation for both joints on one radiograph – consider dose to thyroid

Radiological Assessment

✓ Both radiographs should be comparable
✓ Normal size of joint space less than 10 mm in adult
✓ Clearly identify which are the weight-bearing radiographs
✓ Possible subluxation – clavicle will lift and separate from the acromion due to a tear in the acromioclavicular joint capsule
✗ Unsure of appearance – normally inferior aspect of the acromion and clavicle should be in a straight line

AP and AP Weight-bearing

- Patient erect facing the x-ray tube
- Arms are placed down by the side of the trunk and are relaxed
- The posterior aspect of the shoulder under examination is in contact with the cassette
- Patient's trunk is rotated approximately 10° to the side under examination
- Both acromioclavicular joints are taken for comparison

Collimation

- Precise collimation to include the acromioclavicular joint

Notes:

Projection: **PA**

Film/Screen:

☐ Bucky

Cassette Size:

☐ Grid

Centring Point:

Suggested: To the centre of the clavicle

HORIZONTAL CENTRAL RAY

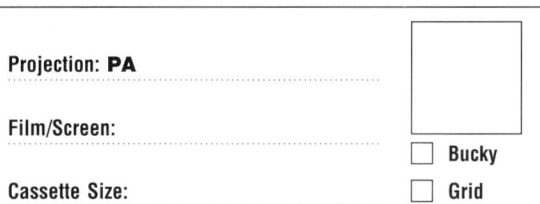
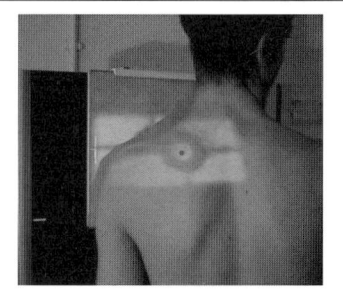
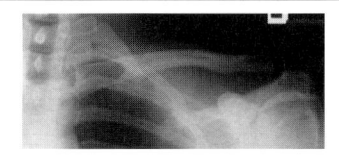

Projection: **Inferosuperior**

Film/Screen:

☐ Bucky

Cassette Size:

☐ Grid

Centring Point:

Suggested: To the centre of the clavicle

CENTRAL RAY 20° CEPHALAD

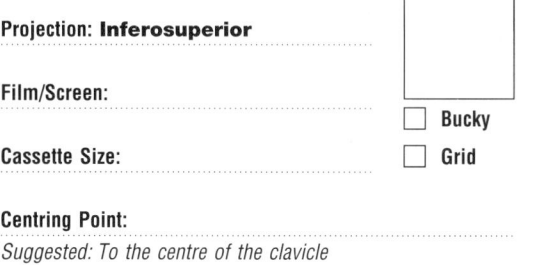
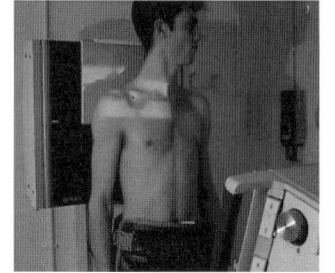
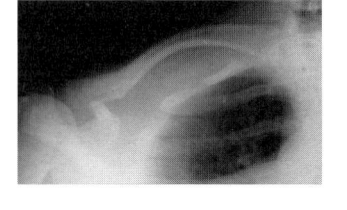

Points to Consider

Technique

✓ PA – increased definition is due to decreased object film distance
✓ Exposure on *arrested* respiration

✓ Inferosuperior – ensure the clavicle is not projected off the cassette

Radiological Assessment

✓ Clavicle #s are often comminuted and easy to detect
✓ Majority of #s involve the middle third
✓ *Must* include the medial end of the clavicle
✓ Inferosuperior – clavicle should be demonstrated clear of any superimposed shadows

PA

- Patient can be prone or erect facing the cassette
- The affected shoulder is rotated slightly to bring the clavicle in close contact with the cassette
- The patient's head is rotated away from the side being examined
- Arms are placed down by the patient's side

Collimation

To include the whole of the clavicle

Inferosuperior

- Patient can be supine or erect facing the x-ray tube
- The patient's shoulder is in close contact with the cassette
- The patient's head is rotated away from the side being examined
- Arms are placed down by the patient's side
- The cassette is displaced superiorly

Collimation

To include the whole of the clavicle

Notes:

Projection:

Film/Screen:

☐ **Bucky**

Cassette Size:

☐ **Grid**

Centring Point:

Notes:

Projection:

Film/Screen:

☐ **Bucky**

Cassette Size:

☐ **Grid**

Centring Point:

Notes:

Projection: ....

Film/Screen: ....

☐ **Bucky**

Cassette Size: ....

☐ **Grid**

Centring Point: ....

Notes:

....

....

....

....

....

....

....

....

....

....

Projection: ....

Film/Screen: ....

☐ **Bucky**

Cassette Size: ....

☐ **Grid**

Centring Point: ....

Notes:

....

....

....

....

....

....

....

....

....

....

Projection:

Film/Screen:

☐ Bucky

Cassette Size:

☐ Grid

Centring Point:

Notes:

Projection:

Film/Screen:

☐ Bucky

Cassette Size:

☐ Grid

Centring Point:

Notes:

Projection:

Film/Screen:

☐ **Bucky**

Cassette Size:

☐ **Grid**

Centring Point:

Notes:

Projection:

Film/Screen:

☐ **Bucky**

Cassette Size:

☐ **Grid**

Centring Point:

Notes:

Projection:

Film/Screen:

☐ **Bucky**

Cassette Size:

☐ **Grid**

Centring Point:

Notes:

Projection:

Film/Screen:

☐ **Bucky**

Cassette Size:

☐ **Grid**

Centring Point:

Notes:

Thoracic Cage

Projection: Right or Left Posterior Obliques

Film/Screen:

□ Bucky

Cassette Size:

□ Grid

Centring Point:

Suggested: In the mid-clavicular line of the side under examination – at level of the midpoint of the sternal body

HORIZONTAL CENTRAL RAY

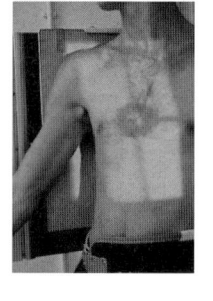
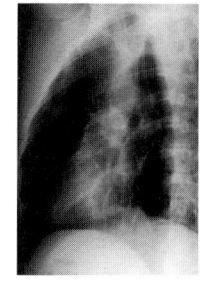

Projection: Lower Ribs – AP

Film/Screen:

□ Bucky

Cassette Size:

□ Grid

Centring Point:

Suggested: To a point in the midline midway between the xiphisternum and the lower costal margin

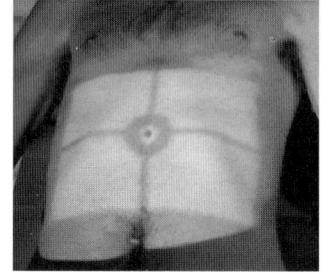
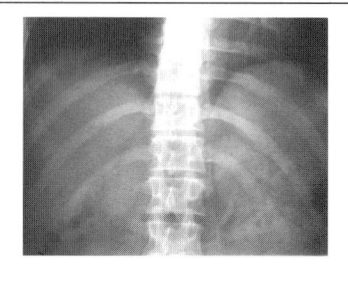

Points to Consider

Technique

✗ Trauma – oblique ribs not always necessary – rarely changes management of the patient

✓ Oblique – exposure on arrested full inspiration

✓ Oblique – patient erect – better with inspiration

✓ AP – exposure on arrested expiration to show the maximum number of ribs below the diaphragm

Radiological Assessment

✓ Check each rib for # – it is rare to see displacement due to the numerous attached muscles

✗ Oblique – ribs away from cassette will be foreshortened

✓ Oblique – posterior rib articulations seen well on the raised side

✓ #s of ribs will unite spontaneously – treatment is limited

✓ Look for metastatic deposits – associated with rib destruction

Right or Left Posterior Obliques

- Patient supine or erect, facing the x-ray tube
- Body rotated approximately 45° onto the affected side
- Arms are abducted away from the trunk

Collimation

To include: SUPERIORLY: First rib
              INFERIORLY: Diaphragms
              LATERALLY: Rib cage

Lower Ribs – AP

- Patient lies supine on the x-ray table
- Shoulders and anterior superior iliac spines (ASIS) equidistant from the table top

Collimation

To include: SUPERIORLY: Diaphragms
              INFERIORLY: Lower costal margin
              LATERALLY: Rib cage and abdominal wall

Notes:

Projection: Lateral

Film/Screen:

☐ Bucky

Cassette Size:

☐ Grid

Centring Point:

Suggested: To a point 3 cm below the sternal angle

HORIZONTAL CENTRAL RAY
FFD 150 cm

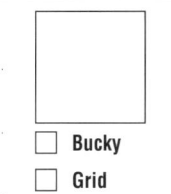
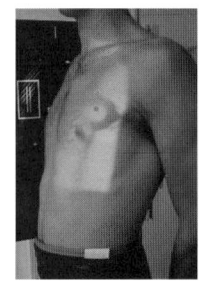
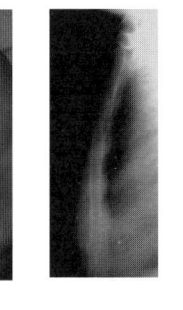

Projection: Anterior Oblique (RAO)

Film/Screen:

☐ Bucky

Cassette Size:

☐ Grid

Centring Point:

Suggested: To a point 8 cm lateral to the palpable fifth thoracic vertebra on the side furthest from the cassette

HORIZONTAL CENTRAL RAY

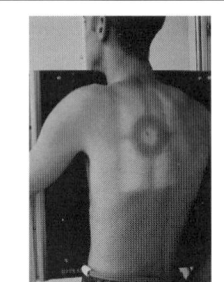
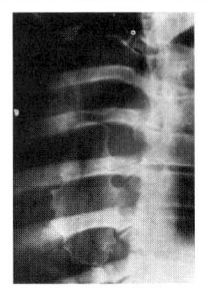

Points to Consider

Technique

✓ A grid or Bucky is essential for both projections
✓ Lateral – exposure on arrested full inspiration
✓ Lateral – greater FFD of 150 cm will decrease magnification
✓ Oblique – patient allowed to breath gently during exposure
✓ Right anterior oblique – cardiac shadow will help visualise the sternum

Radiological Assessment

✓ *Must* include from the sternoclavicular joint to xiphisternum
✗ Sternum *must* not be overpenetrated
✓ Gentle breathing will blur the rib shadows
✗ Obliquity – the spine and sternum *must* not be superimposed
✗ Over-rotation – sternum outside cardiac shadow

Lateral

- Patient erect
- Median sagittal plane is parallel to the erect Bucky
- Patient's shoulders are rotated posteriorly
- Arms placed behind the trunk and shoulders and gently pulled back

Collimation

To include: SUPERIORLY: Acromioclavicular joints
                      INFERIORLY: Xiphisternum
                      ANTERIORLY: Anterior soft tissues
                      POSTERIORLY: Posterior sternum

Anterior Oblique (RAO)

- Patient erect facing the cassette
- The trunk is rotated approximately 30° so that the right side of the body is in contact with the erect Bucky
- The arms are placed around the erect Bucky to maintain stability

Collimation

To include: SUPERIORLY: Acromioclavicular joints
                      INFERIORLY: Xiphisternum
                      LATERALLY: Costal cartilage

Notes:

Projection: Left and Right Anterior Obliques

Film/Screen:

☐ Bucky

Cassette Size:

☐ Grid

Centring Point:

*Suggested: To a point 10 cm lateral to the palpable fourth thoracic vertebra on the side **away** from the Bucky*

HORIZONTAL CENTRAL RAY

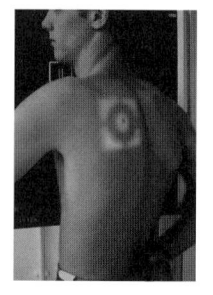 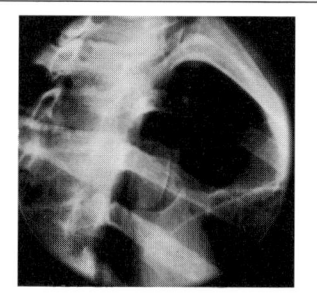

Projection: Lateral

Film/Screen:

☐ Bucky

Cassette Size:

☐ Grid

Centring Point:

Suggested: To the palpable sternoclavicular joints

HORIZONTAL CENTRAL RAY

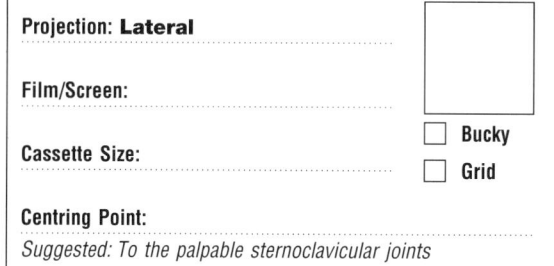 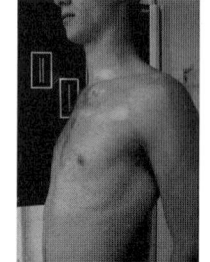 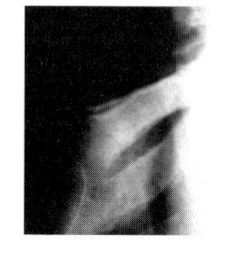

Points to Consider

Technique

✓ Oblique – joint closest to cassette is the joint being examined
✓ Oblique – exposure on gentle respiration
✓ Grid or Bucky *must* be used for both projections
✓ Lateral – a wedge filter will reduce scatter

Radiological Assessment

✓ Oblique – the joint should be seen clear of the spine
✓ Oblique – right and left joints *must* be comparable
✓ Lateral – dislocation and subluxation of the joint is possible – look for superimposition of joints

Left and Right Anterior Obliques

- Patient erect and facing the erect Bucky
- The patient is then rotated to each side in turn by approximately 45°
- Shoulders are relaxed and hands hold onto the erect Bucky to maintain stability

Collimation

- Precise collimation to include the sternoclavicular joints

Lateral

- Patient stands erect with a shoulder against the Bucky
- Patient adjusted so that the median sagittal plane is parallel to the Bucky
- Hands are clasped and arms and shoulders are pulled well back

Collimation

- Precise collimation to include the sternoclavicular joints

Notes:

Projection:

Film/Screen:

☐ Bucky

Cassette Size:

☐ Grid

Centring Point:

Notes:

Projection:

Film/Screen:

☐ Bucky

Cassette Size:

☐ Grid

Centring Point:

Notes:

Projection:

Film/Screen:

☐ Bucky

Cassette Size:

☐ Grid

Centring Point:

Notes:

Projection:

Film/Screen:

☐ Bucky

Cassette Size:

☐ Grid

Centring Point:

Notes:

Projection:

Film/Screen:

☐ Bucky

Cassette Size:

☐ Grid

Centring Point:

Notes:

Projection:

Film/Screen:

☐ Bucky

Cassette Size:

☐ Grid

Centring Point:

Notes:

Projection:

Film/Screen:

☐ Bucky

Cassette Size:

☐ Grid

Centring Point:

Notes:

Projection:

Film/Screen:

☐ Bucky

Cassette Size:

☐ Grid

Centring Point:

Notes:

Projection:

Film/Screen:

□ **Bucky**

Cassette Size:

□ **Grid**

Centring Point:

Notes:

Projection:

Film/Screen:

□ **Bucky**

Cassette Size:

□ **Grid**

Centring Point:

Notes:

Respiratory System

Lung Fields

Trachea–Thoracic Inlet

Projection: PA

Film/Screen:

☐ Bucky

Cassette Size:

☐ Grid

Centring Point:

Suggested: To the palpable sixth thoracic vertebra

HORIZONTAL CENTRAL RAY ANGLED 5° CAUDAD
FFD 180 cm

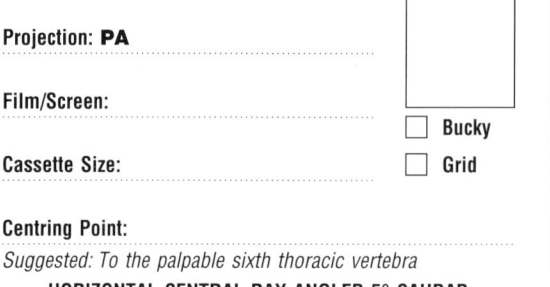
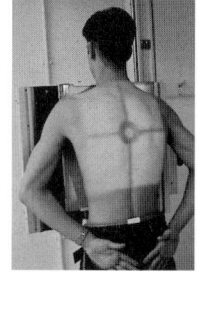
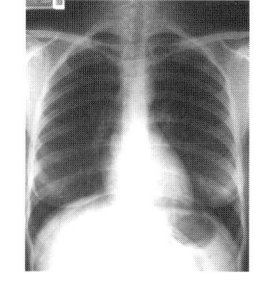

Projection: Lateral

Film/Screen:

☐ Bucky

Cassette Size:

☐ Grid

Centring Point:

Suggested: Mid-axillary line at the level sixth thoracic vertebra

HORIZONTAL CENTRAL RAY
FFD 180 cm

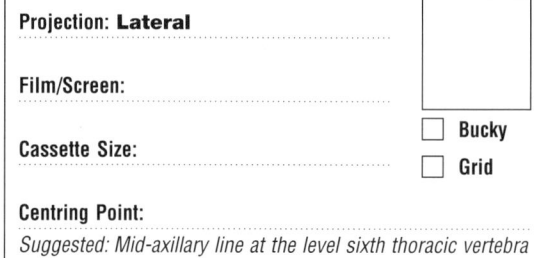
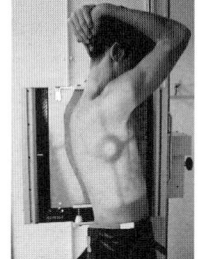
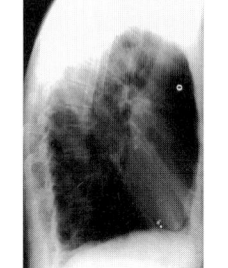

Points to Consider

Technique

- ✓ PA – radiograph *must* be taken on full inspiration
- ✓ PA – possible pneumothorax – radiograph taken on full expiration
- ✓ Make sure the scapulae are clear of the lung fields
- ✗ If the patient cannot place their hands on hips – turn the hands internally and place the arms around the cassette

Radiological Assessment

- ✓ Poor inspiration may mimic cardiac enlargement
- ✓ Small pneumothorax best seen on an expiration radiograph
- ✓ Full inspiration – right 8–9 posterior ribs are just clear of the diaphragm
- ✓ Haemoptysis – look for evidence of lung cancer or tuberculosis
- ✓ Breathlessness – look for heart failure or collapse of lobes

PA

- Patient facing the cassette with the chin extended
- The trunk is adjusted so that the median sagittal plane is perpendicular to the cassette
- The feet are parted to maintain stability
- The dorsal aspect of the hands are placed behind and below the hips and the elbows are brought forwards
- Shoulders are relaxed and rotated forwards until they are in contact with the cassette

Collimation

To include: SUPERIORLY: Apices
INFERIORLY: Costopherenic angles
LATERALLY: Soft tissue borders

Lateral

- Patient is rotated to bring the lung under examination in contact with the cassette
- Median sagittal plane is parallel to the cassette
- The patient's arms are folded over the head or can be raised to rest on a suitable support

Collimation

To include: SUPERIORLY: Apices
INFERIORLY: Costopherenic angles
ANTERIORLY: Sternum and anterior ribs
POSTERIORLY: Posterior rib cage

Notes:

Projection: Apices

Film/Screen:

☐ Bucky

Cassette Size:

☐ Grid

Centring Point:

Suggested: To the sternal angle

HORIZONTAL CENTRAL RAY

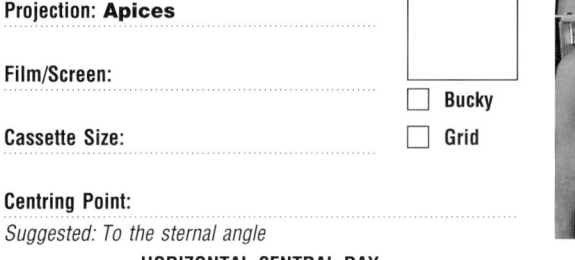
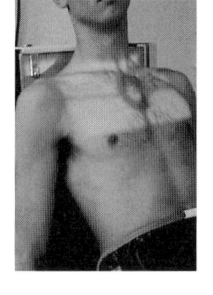
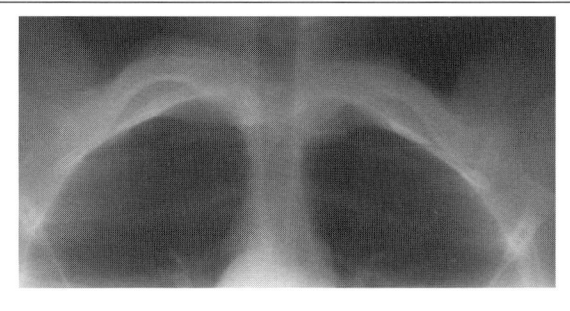

Projection: Lordotic

Film/Screen:

☐ Bucky

Cassette Size:

☐ Grid

Centring Point:

Suggested: To the palpable sixth thoracic vertebra

HORIZONTAL CENTRAL RAY

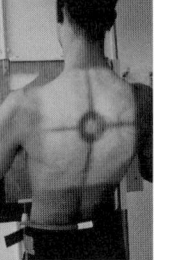
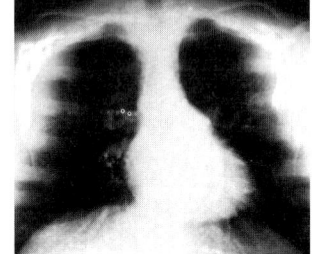

Points to Consider

Technique

✓ Apices – use if an opacity is obscured by ribs or clavicular shadows
✓ Apices – ensure both shoulders are level and touching the cassette
✓ Apices – if patient cannot lean back angle the tube 30° cephalad
✓ Both projections – exposure on arrested inspiration
✓ Lordotic – to demonstrate a right middle lobe collapse or an interlobar pleural effusion

Radiological Assessment

✓ The clavicles *must* be projected clear of the apices
✗ Apices – if clavicles are superimposed upon lung fields there is not enough angulation
✓ Lordotic – the middle lobe fissure should be horizontal
✓ Haemoptysis – look for evidence of lung cancer or tuberculosis
✓ Check the heart outline – an ill-defined right heart border may be the result of a middle lobe consolidation

Apices

- Patient seated and facing the x-ray tube with the back a short distance from the cassette
- The trunk is then carefully reclined so that the coronal plane is approximately 30–40° to the cassette

Collimation

To include: SUPERIORLY: Apices
INFERIORLY: Upper lung fields
LATERALLY: Rib cage

Lordotic

- Patient is positioned as for a routine PA chest examination
- The hands securely clasp the erect Bucky or cassette stand
- Patient leans backwards towards the x-ray tube by approximately 30–40°

Collimation

To include: SUPERIORLY: Apices
INFERIORLY: Diaphragms
LATERALLY: Rib cage

Notes:

Projection: AP

Film/Screen:

☐ Bucky

Cassette Size:

☐ Grid

Centring Point:

Suggested: To the sternal notch

HORIZONTAL CENTRAL RAY

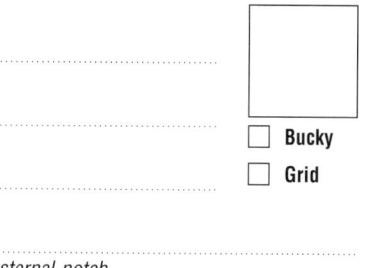
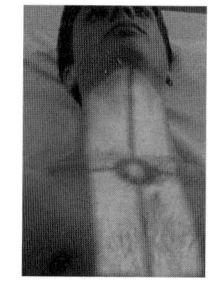
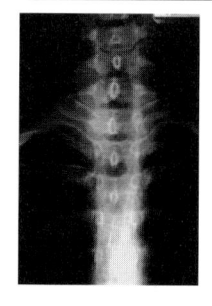

Projection: Lateral

Film/Screen:

☐ Bucky

Cassette Size:

☐ Grid

Centring Point:

Suggested: Just posterior to the sternal notch

HORIZONTAL CENTRAL RAY
FFD 150 cm

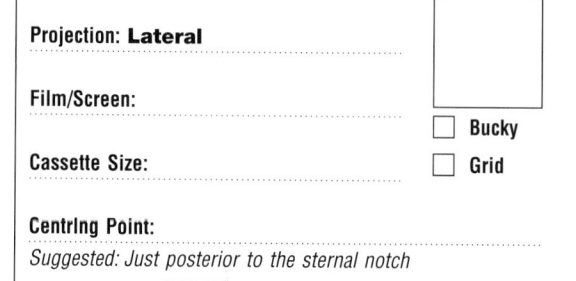
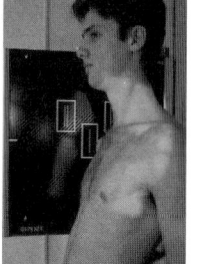
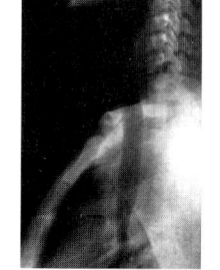

Points to Consider

Technique

✓ AP – patient can be erect or supine, but supine results in greater immobilisation
✓ Lateral – patient can be standing or seated
✓ Lateral – if patient standing, weight *must* be equally distributed
✓ Exposure on full *inspiration*

Radiological Assessment

✓ AP – must include from mid-cervical to mid-thoracic region
✓ Lateral – must include from mid-cervical to mid-thoracic region
✗ Shoulders *must* not superimpose the trachea
✓ AP and lateral – trachea should be demonstrated when filled with air

AP

- Patient supine on the x-ray table
- Shoulders equidistant from the table top
- Median sagittal plane perpendicular
- The chin is raised slightly

Collimation

To include: SUPERIORLY: Body of fourth cervical vertebra

INFERIORLY: Bifurcation of trachea (fourth thoracic vertebra)

LATERALLY: To include the spinous processes

Lateral

- Patient erect with a shoulder in contact with the erect Bucky
- Median sagittal plane is parallel to the Bucky
- Arms are placed behind the trunk and the hands clasped together
- The shoulders are rotated posteriorly as far as possible to bring the thorax forwards

Collimation

To include: ANTERIORLY: Manubrium of sternum

POSTERIORLY: Thoracic spine

SUPERIORLY: Body of fourth cervical vertebra

INFERIORLY: Bifurcation of trachea (fourth thoracic vertebra)

Notes:

Projection: ....

Film/Screen: ....

☐ Bucky

Cassette Size: ....

☐ Grid

Centring Point: ....

Notes: ....

....

....

....

....

....

....

....

....

Projection: ....

Film/Screen: ....

☐ Bucky

Cassette Size: ....

☐ Grid

Centring Point: ....

Notes: ....

....

....

....

....

....

....

....

....

Projection:

Film/Screen:

☐ Bucky

Cassette Size:

☐ Grid

Centring Point:

Notes:

Projection:

Film/Screen:

☐ Bucky

Cassette Size:

☐ Grid

Centring Point:

Notes:

Projection:

Film/Screen:

☐ Bucky

Cassette Size: ☐ Grid

Centring Point:

Notes:

Projection:

Film/Screen:

☐ Bucky

Cassette Size: ☐ Grid

Centring Point:

Notes:

Projection:
....

Film/Screen:
....

☐ Bucky

Cassette Size:
....

☐ Grid

Centring Point:
....

Notes:
....
....
....
....
....
....
....
....

Projection:
....

Film/Screen:
....

☐ Bucky

Cassette Size:
....

☐ Grid

Centring Point:
....

Notes:
....
....
....
....
....
....
....
....

Projection:

Film/Screen:

☐ Bucky

Cassette Size:

☐ Grid

Centring Point:

Notes:

Projection:

Film/Screen:

☐ Bucky

Cassette Size:

☐ Grid

Centring Point:

Notes:

Abdominal Contents

Projection: AP Supine

Film/Screen:

☐ Bucky

Cassette Size:

☐ Grid

Centring Point:

Suggested: In the midline at the level of iliac crests

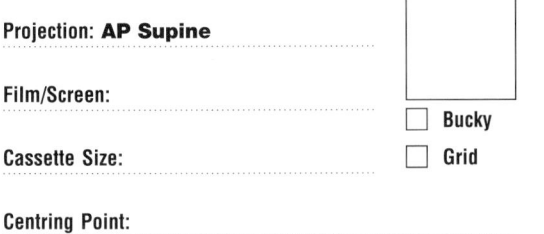

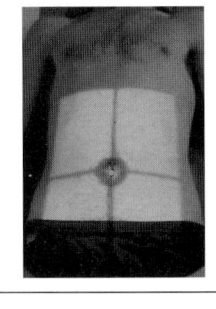

Projection: AP Erect

Film/Screen:

☐ Bucky

Cassette Size:

☐ Grid

Centring Point:

Suggested: In the midline at the level of lower costal margin

HORIZONTAL CENTRAL RAY

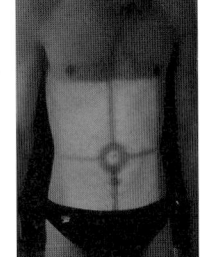
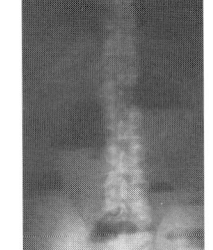

Points to Consider

Technique

✓ Acute abdomen – *must* include an *erect* chest radiograph
✓ Exposure – usually on arrested expiration
✓ Place pads under the knees to aid comfort for the patient
✓ Use gonad protection for male patients
✗ Erect abdomen – adds little diagnostic information – possibly use other modalities – possibly ultrasound first, then consider CT

Radiological Assessment

✓ Check the size of organs – a knowledge of anatomy is essential
✓ Symphysis pubis *must* be included on the radiograph
✓ Pneumoperitoneum – commonest cause is a perforated peptic ulcer
✓ Normal small bowel gas pattern should *not* exceed 2.5 cm
✓ Acute abdomen – check lower ribs and lumbar transverse processes if #s present – consider injury to liver, spleen or kidney

AP Supine

- Patient lies supine upon the x-ray table
- The median sagittal plane is perpendicular and the anterior superior iliac spines (ASIS) are equidistant to the table top
- A pad is placed under the knees for support

Collimation

To include: SUPERIORLY: Diaphragm

INFERIORLY: Symphysis pubis

LATERALLY: Soft tissue borders

AP Erect

- Patient is erect with the back leaning against the upright Bucky
- The median sagittal plane is perpendicular and the ASIS are equidistant to the erect Bucky
- Immobilisation bands can be applied to support the patient in this position

Collimation

To include: SUPERIORLY: Diaphragm

INFERIORLY: ASIS

LATERALLY: Soft tissue borders

Notes:

Projection: Left Lateral Decubitus

Film/Screen:

☐ **Bucky**

Cassette Size:

☐ **Grid**

Centring Point:

Suggested: In the midline at the level of iliac crests

HORIZONTAL CENTRAL RAY

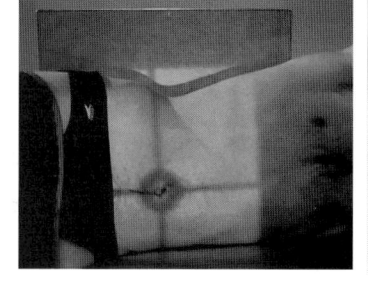
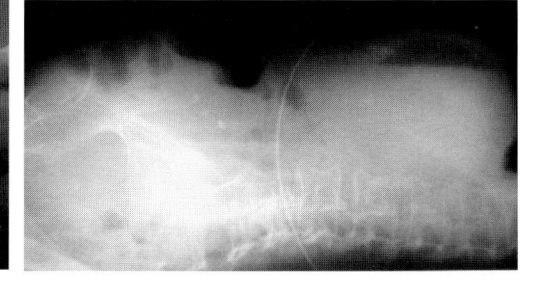

Points to Consider

Technique

✓ Useful alternative to the erect if the patient is immobile

✓ Acute abdomen – position patient for at least 5 min before making an exposure – enables free gas to rise and redistribute

✓ Vertical gridded cassette – position as close to abdomen as possible

✓ *Right* marker on upper cassette – anatomically correct

Radiological Assessment

✓ Will demonstrate the whole of left hemidiaphragm and part of right hemidiaphragm – free gas will collect at this point

✓ Exposure should demonstrate soft tissue of abdominal wall

✓ Remember chest radiograph – chest disease can mimic an acute abdomen

✗ Overpenetration for bony anatomy is less important

Left Lateral Decubitus

- Patient lies on the left side
- The elbows and arms are flexed and placed by the side of the head
- The median sagittal plane is parallel to the table top
- Hips and knees are slightly flexed to maintain stability

Collimation

To include: SUPERIORLY: Diaphragm
                     INFERIORLY: ASIS
                     LATERALLY: Lateral abdominal walls
                     (contrast studies *must* include the rectum)

Notes:

Projection: AP Supine – KUB

Film/Screen:

☐ Bucky

Cassette Size:

☐ Grid

Centring Point:
Suggested: In the midline at level of iliac crests and adjusted to include the symphysis pubis on the cassette

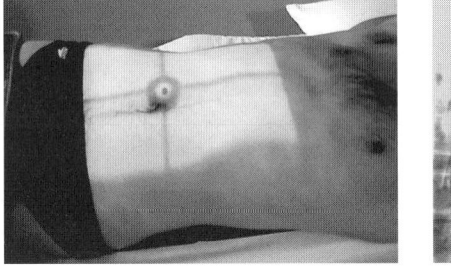
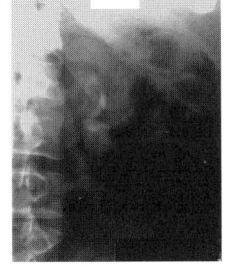

Projection: Kidney/Ureter Posterior Obliques

Film/Screen:

☐ Bucky

Cassette Size:

☐ Grid

Centring Point:
Suggested: In the mid-clavicular line – on the raised side at the level of the lower costal margin

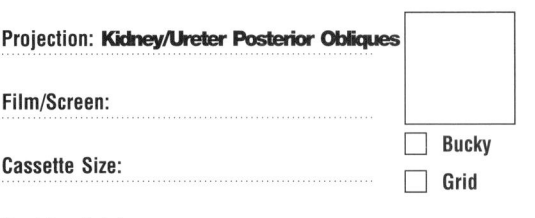

Points to Consider

Technique

✓ Patient should have a low residue diet and a laxative 48 hours before the examination

✓ AP – the symphysis pubis *must* be included on the radiograph

✓ AP – exposure in full inspiration is so all urinary tract is visualised

✓ Use gonad protection for male patients

✓ Renal colic – a limited IVU is highly accurate in confirming the diagnosis

Radiological Assessment

✓ Check that the upper poles of the kidneys are included

✗ *Do not* confuse renal stones and pelvic phleboliths

✓ Approximately 85% of renal stones are radiopaque

✓ Pelvic phleboliths have a round radiopaque halo surrounding a small lucent centre

✓ Oblique – kidney closer to the cassette seen in profile, kidney away from the cassette seen *en face*

AP Supine – KUB

- Patient lies supine upon the x-ray table
- The median sagittal plane is perpendicular and the ASIS are equidistant to the table top
- A pad is placed under the knees for support

Collimation

To include: SUPERIORLY: Upper pole of kidney
INFERIORLY: Symphysis pubis
LATERALLY: Both kidneys

Kidney/Ureter Posterior Obliques

- Patient lies supine upon the x-ray table
- The unaffected side of the trunk is raised approximately 20–30° and supported in this position with non-opaque pads
- Arms and elbows are flexed and placed at the side of the head
- Hips and knees are slightly flexed to maintain stability

Collimation

To include: Precise collimation to include both or a specific kidney

Notes:

Projection: AP Bladder

Film/Screen:

☐ Bucky

Cassette Size:

☐ Grid

Centring Point:

Suggested: In the midline 5 cm above the symphysis pubis

CENTRAL RAY 15° CAUDAD

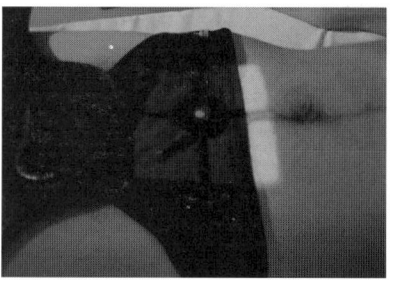

Projection: Bladder Posterior Obliques

Film/Screen:

☐ Bucky

Cassette Size:

☐ Grid

Centring Point:

Suggested: 2.5 cm above the symphysis pubis

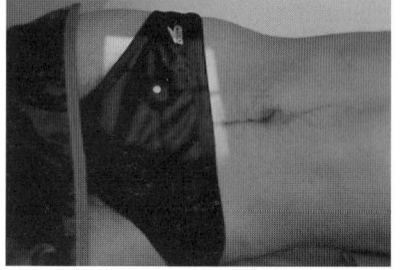
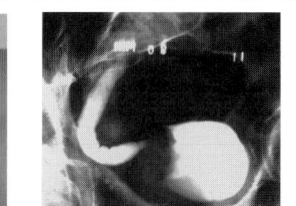

Points to Consider

Technique

✓ Symphysis pubis *must* be included on the radiograph
✓ Lower bowel preparation is an advantage
✓ Gonad protection for the male patient
✓ Raise affected side to demonstrate insertion of ureter into the bladder

Radiological Assessment

✓ Contrast media – will identify bladder retention or prolapse
✓ Oblique – will differentiate between calculus in the bladder and calculi outside the bladder
✓ Radiograph above contains contrast media to appreciate the size and position of the bladder

AP Bladder

- Patient lies supine upon the x-ray table
- The median sagittal plane is perpendicular and the ASIS are equidistant to the table top
- A pad is placed under the knees for support

Collimation

To include: SUPERIORLY: Sacrum
                     INFERIORLY: Symphysis pubis
                     LATERALLY: Pelvic brim

Bladder Posterior Obliques

- Patient lies supine upon the x-ray table
- The affected side of the trunk is raised approximately 30–40° and supported in this position with non-opaque pads
- Arms and elbows are flexed and placed at the side of the head
- Hips and knees are slightly flexed to maintain stability

Collimation

To include: SUPERIORLY: Sacrum
                     INFERIORLY: Symphysis pubis
                     LATERALLY: Pelvic brim

Notes:

Projection: ....

Film/Screen: ....

☐ Bucky

Cassette Size: ....

☐ Grid

Centring Point: ....

Notes:

....
....
....
....
....
....
....

Projection: ....

Film/Screen: ....

☐ Bucky

Cassette Size: ....

☐ Grid

Centring Point: ....

Notes:

....
....
....
....
....
....
....

Projection:

Film/Screen:

☐ **Bucky**

Cassette Size:

☐ **Grid**

Centring Point:

Notes:

Projection:

Film/Screen:

☐ **Bucky**

Cassette Size:

☐ **Grid**

Centring Point:

Notes:

Projection: ....

Film/Screen: ....

☐ **Bucky**

Cassette Size: ....

☐ **Grid**

Centring Point: ....

Notes:

....

....

....

....

....

....

....

....

....

Projection: ....

Film/Screen: ....

☐ **Bucky**

Cassette Size: ....

☐ **Grid**

Centring Point: ....

Notes:

....

....

....

....

....

....

....

....

....

Projection: ....

Film/Screen: ....

☐ Bucky

Cassette Size: ....

☐ Grid

Centring Point: ....

Notes:

Projection: ....

Film/Screen: ....

☐ Bucky

Cassette Size: ....

☐ Grid

Centring Point: ....

Notes:

Projection:

Film/Screen:

☐ Bucky

Cassette Size:

☐ Grid

Centring Point:

Notes:

Projection:

Film/Screen:

☐ Bucky

Cassette Size:

☐ Grid

Centring Point:

Notes:

Hip Joint, Upper Third of Femur and Pelvis

Both Hips
- AP   94
- Lateral (Frog)   94

Single Hip
- Lateral – Neck of Femur   96
- AP – Single Hip   96
- Lateral – Non-Trauma   98

Pelvis
- AP   100

Further Projections   **102**

Projection: **AP**

Film/Screen: ....

☐ Bucky

Cassette Size: ....

☐ Grid

Centring Point: ....

Suggested: *Midline 2.5 cm superior to the symphysis pubis*

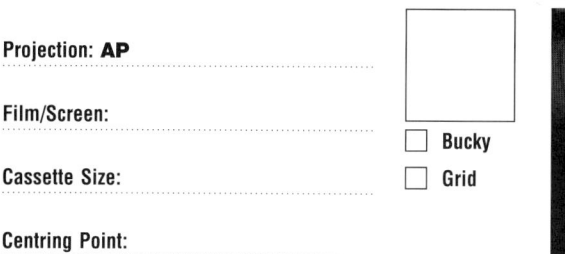 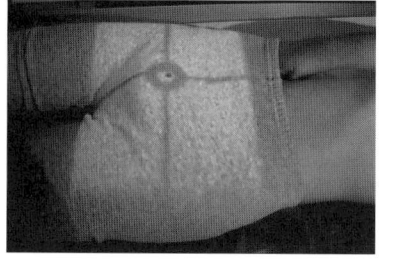 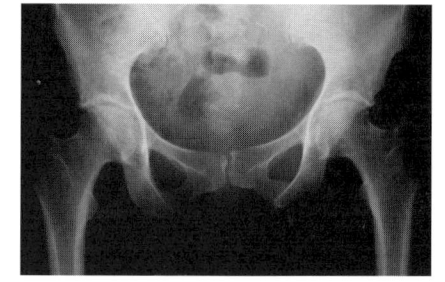

Projection: **Lateral (Frog)**

Film/Screen: ....

☐ Bucky

Cassette Size: ....

☐ Grid

Centring Point: ....

Suggested: *Midline 2.5 cm superior to the symphysis pubis*

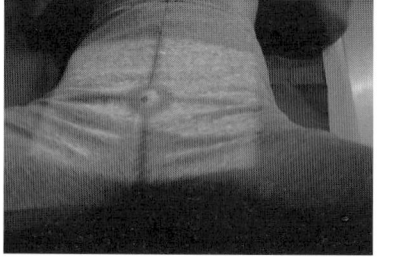 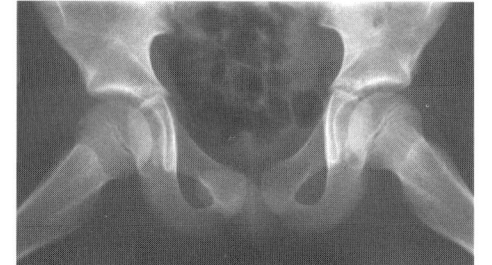

Points to Consider

Technique

✓ Both hips and femur should be symmetrical

✓ Trauma – *no* gonad protection is needed for first examination *only*

✓ Keep the hands away from the pelvis

✓ Place a small pad under the knees to ensure patient comfort

✗ *Do not* forcibly rotate the limb if possible fractured neck of femur

Radiological Assessment

✓ AP – allows comparison between both hips

✓ Femoral epiphysis present from 3 months to 18–20 years

✓ Break in cortical outline or interruption cortical pattern – #

✓ Perthes' disease – more common in boys and rare over 7 years of age

✓ Slipped epiphysis – more common in boys and rare under 8 years of age

AP

- Patient lies supine
- The anterior superior iliac spines (ASIS) are equidistant from the table top
- The heels are separated and the limbs rotated medially approximately 10° and supported by sandbags

Collimation

To include: SUPERIORLY: ASIS
                  INFERIORLY: Upper third of femur
                  LATERALLY: Ilium and soft tissues

Lateral (Frog)

- Patient lies supine
- The ASIS are equidistant from the table top
- Hips and knees are flexed
- The knees are separated and rotated laterally approximately 60° so that the plantar aspects of the feet are in contact with each other
- The patient is supported with sandbags and non-opaque pads

Collimation

To include: SUPERIORLY: ASIS
                  INFERIORLY: Upper femur
                  LATERALLY: Ilium and soft tissues

Notes:

Projection: **Lateral – Neck of Femur**

Film/Screen:

☐ Bucky

Cassette Size:

☐ Grid

Centring Point:

Suggested: So the central ray emerges at the level of the greater trochanter

HORIZONTAL CENTRAL RAY

PERPENDICULAR TO THE CASSETTE

Projection: **AP – Single Hip**

Film/Screen:

☐ Bucky

Cassette Size:

☐ Grid

Centring Point:

Suggested: 2.5 cm distally along a perpendicular bisector of a line joining the ASIS and the symphysis pubis

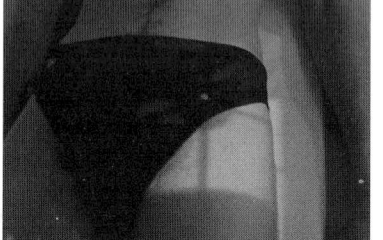
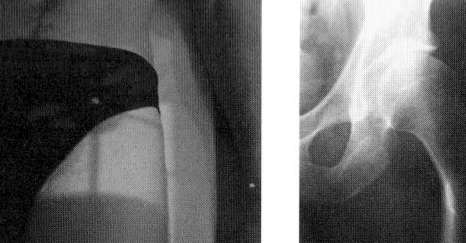
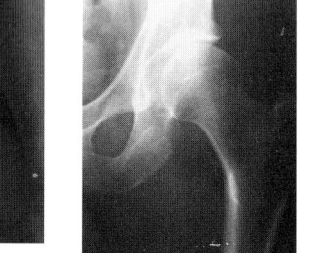

Points to Consider

Technique

✓ Lateral – ensure to maintain the FFD

✓ Lateral – the opposite limb *must* be securely supported

✓ Lateral – ensure the central ray is not directed at the control panel or a door

✓ Lateral – horizontal beam *must* be perpendicular to cassette

✗ Trauma – *never* forcibly rotate the affected limb

Radiological Assessment

✓ Look for any increased density – may be due to an impacted #

✓ Undisplaced fractured neck of femur – discontinuity in trabecular lines

✓ Complication of fractured neck of femur – avascular necrosis of femoral head

✓ A bright light may be required to view the image

✓ Positive # – a chest radiograph *will* be required

Lateral – Neck Of Femur

- Patient lies supine with the affected leg extended
- Rotate the limb so that the foot is vertical – care *must* be taken not to exacerbate the injury
- The opposite limb is raised so that the femur is in a vertical position
- The opposite knee is flexed and supported
- A gridded stationary cassette is positioned vertically with one edge placed against the patient's waist
- The cassette is adjusted so that it is parallel to the neck of femur and is supported in position with a 45° pad

Collimation

Precise collimation by the use of a cone or diaphragm to include the acetabulum and neck of femur

AP – Single Hip

- Patient lies supine with the affected hip in the centre of the table
- The pelvis is adjusted so that the ASIS are equidistant from the table top
- The affected limb is rotated so that the foot is vertical and supported

Collimation

To include the whole of the hip joint

Notes:

Projection: **Lateral (Non-trauma)**

Film/Screen:

☐ Bucky

Cassette Size:

☐ Grid

Centring Point:
Suggested: Directly to the femoral head

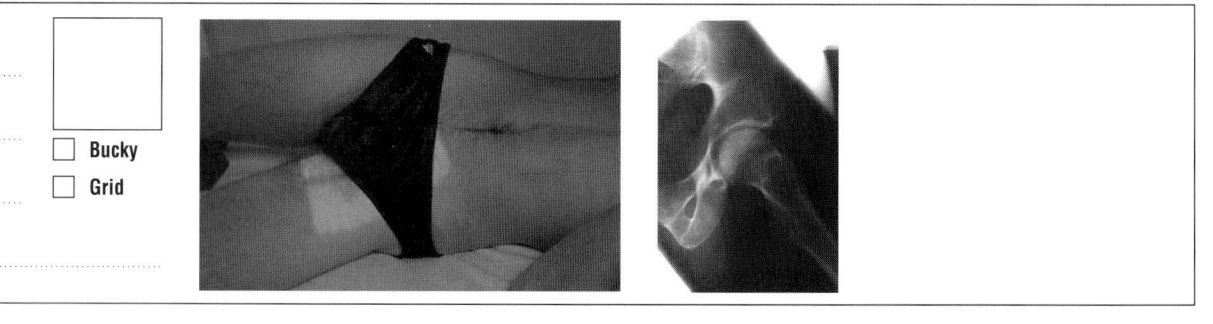

Points to Consider

Technique

✓ *Only* to be used when a # is not suspected
✓ Place a non-opaque pad under the knee for support
✓ Oblique the pelvis slightly to aid patient's comfort
✓ Care with exposure – especially if an automatic exposure device (AED) is used

Radiological Assessment

✓ Neck of femur should appear in the centre of the radiograph
✓ The greater trochanter should be superimposed over the neck of femur
✓ Lesser trochanter is seen on the medial aspect
✗ Over-rotation – the obturator foramen appears closed

Lateral (Non-trauma)

- Patient lies supine upon the x-ray table
- The joint under examination is adjusted so that it is central to the table
- The trunk is rotated approximately 45° onto the affected side
- The hip and knee of the side being examined are slightly flexed and the knee is in close contact with the table top
- The opposite limb is raised and supported in this position

Collimation

To include: PROXIMALLY: The acetabulum
DISTALLY: Upper shaft of femur
LATERALLY: Soft tissue borders
MEDIALLY: Obturator foramen

Notes:

Projection: AP

Film/Screen:

Cassette Size:

☐ Bucky

☐ Grid

Centring Point:

Suggested: Midline midway between the ASIS and the superior border of the symphysis pubis

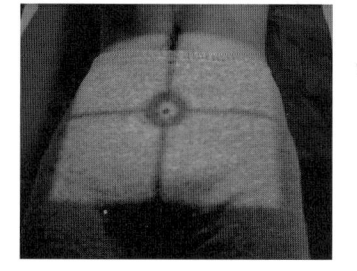

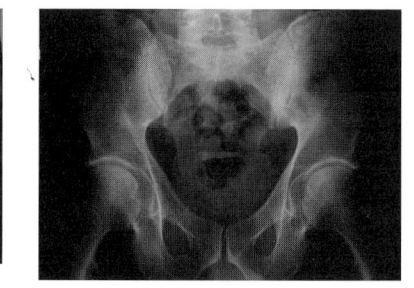

Points to Consider

Technique

✓ Rotate the legs approximately 15° medially and support
✓ Large patient – raise the FFD to 120 cm to reduce magnification, but care with exposure and dose
✗ Exposure – too high a mAs will blacken out the iliac fossa
✗ *Do not* place arms by side – they may appear on the radiograph

Radiological Assessment

✗ Foreshortened femoral neck – inadequate medial rotation
✓ Check obturator foramina are equal size and shape
✓ The whole of the pelvis *must* be included on the radiograph
✓ Check Shenton's line – any disruption is due to a fractured neck of femur
✗ *Do not* confuse epiphyseal lines with #s – iliac crest fuses late teens to early twenties

AP

- Patient lies supine in the centre of the table
- The ASIS must be equidistant from the table top
- Both knees are *very* slightly flexed and supported by non-opaque pads
- The heels are separated and the limbs are rotated internally until the toes are touching

Collimation

To include: SUPERIORLY: Body of fifth lumbar vertebra and iliac crests
INFERIORLY: Proximal femurs
LATERALLY: Soft tissue borders

Notes:

Projection:

Film/Screen:

☐ Bucky

Cassette Size:

☐ Grid

Centring Point:

Notes:

Projection:

Film/Screen:

☐ Bucky

Cassette Size:

☐ Grid

Centring Point:

Notes:

Projection:

Film/Screen:

☐ Bucky

Cassette Size:

☐ Grid

Centring Point:

Notes:

Projection:

Film/Screen:

☐ Bucky

Cassette Size:

☐ Grid

Centring Point:

Notes:

Projection:

Film/Screen:

☐ Bucky

Cassette Size:

☐ Grid

Centring Point:

Notes:

Projection:

Film/Screen:

☐ Bucky

Cassette Size:

☐ Grid

Centring Point:

Notes:

Lower Extremity

Projection: Dorsiplantar (AP)

Film/Screen:

☐ Bucky

Cassette Size:

☐ Grid

Centring Point:

Suggested: To the third metatarso-phalangeal joint

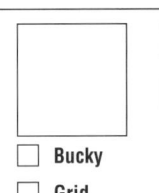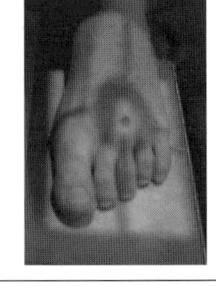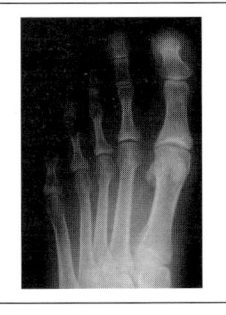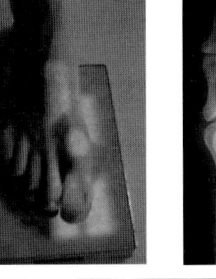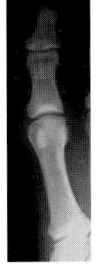

Projection: Dorsiplantar (AP Oblique)

Film/Screen:

☐ Bucky

Cassette Size:

☐ Grid

Centring Point:

Suggested: To the third metatarso-phalangeal joint

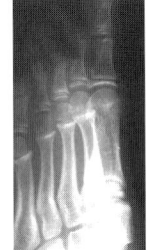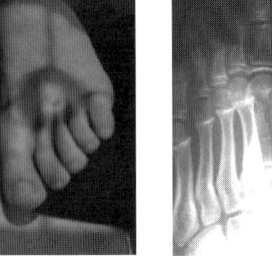

Points to Consider

Technique

✓ Always include the phalanges and distal metatarsals
✓ AP – hip, knee and foot on the same longitudinal plane
✓ Care with exposure – overpenetration of distal phalanges
✓ Try using an aluminium filter for the optimal exposure
✓ For the great toe – centre to proximal interphalangeal joint

Radiological Assessment

✓ Freiburg's infarction – osteochondritis of the second metatarsal head
✓ Osteomyelitis – soft tissue swelling and irregular depleted bone
✓ Trabeculae should be uniform or change gradually
✓ Extensive soft tissue swelling – severe injury or bone infection
✓ Phalanges and metatarsals of each toe should lie straight

Dorsiplantar (AP)

- Patient sitting with hips and knees flexed
- Affected foot is placed with the plantar aspect upon the cassette

Collimation

To include: PROXIMALLY: The metatarsals
DISTALLY: The phalanges
LATERALLY: Soft tissue borders
MEDIALLY: Soft tissue borders

Dorsiplantar (AP Oblique)

- Patient sitting with hips and knees flexed
- Affected foot is placed with the plantar aspect upon the cassette
- The leg is medially rotated so that the foot is at an angle of approximately 30–40° to the cassette
- A non-opaque pad is placed under the toes

Collimation

To include: PROXIMALLY: The metatarsals
DISTALLY: The phalanges
LATERALLY: Soft tissue borders
MEDIALLY: Soft tissue borders

Notes:

Projection: **Lateral**

Film/Screen:

☐ Bucky

Cassette Size:

☐ Grid

Centring Point:

Suggested: To the first metatarso-phalangeal joint

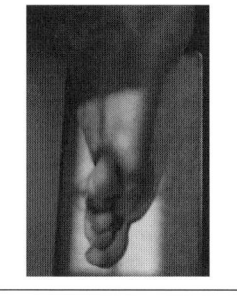
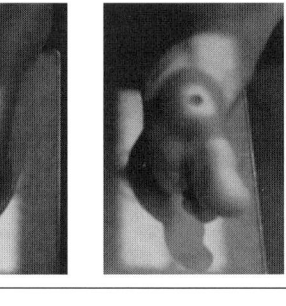
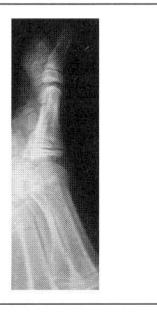

Points to Consider

Technique

✗ True lateral – limited value as the toes are superimposed
✓ To isolate a specific toe – use a non-opaque pad
✗ *Do not* forcibly separate the toes – exacerbates injury
✓ Slightly flex the knee to aid positioning and comfort
✓ Try raising the cassette upon a pad before positioning

Radiological Assessment

✓ Sesamoid bones of the great toe arise from two or more centres
✓ Failure to unite – may resemble an epiphyseal #
✓ Trabeculae should be uniform or change gradually
✗ Projection has limited value apart from assessing the extent of any displacement

Lateral

- Patient lies:
  - For the first, second and third toes – on the side opposite to that being examined
  - the medial side of the foot and leg under examination is placed in contact with the table top

  - For the fourth and fifth toes – on the side under examination
  - the lateral side of the foot and leg under examination is placed in contact with the table top

- The plantar aspect of the foot is at right angles to the cassette
- A pad is placed under the ankle to maintain the position

Collimation

To include: PROXIMALLY: The metatarsals
DISTALLY: The phalanges
LATERALLY: Soft tissue borders
MEDIALLY: Soft tissue borders

Notes:

Projection: Dorsiplantar (AP)

Film/Screen:

☐ Bucky

Cassette Size: ☐ Grid

Centring Point:
Suggested: To the cuboid-navicular joint

Projection: Dorsiplantar (AP Oblique)

Film/Screen:

☐ Bucky

Cassette Size: ☐ Grid

Centring Point:
Suggested: To the cuboid-navicular joint

Points to Consider

Technique

✓ Slight angulation of tube towards the ankle – this will open the articulations of the foot

✓ Oblique – metatarsals free from superimposition

✓ Consider using a wedge filter for optimum penetration

✓ Ensure knee is flexed to prevent the cassette from slipping

Radiological Assessment

✓ Lisfranc injury – # through base of second metatarsal and dislocation of third, fourth and fifth metatarsals

✓ Accessory ossification centre – base of fifth metatarsal – bone contours smooth and rounded with intact cortical margins

✓ Look for periosteal thickening – stress #

✓ Oblique – consider the anterior calcaneum for avulsion #s

Dorsiplantar (AP)

- Patient sitting with hips and knees flexed
- Affected foot is placed with the plantar aspect upon the cassette
- The leg can be supported by the opposite leg

Collimation

To include: PROXIMALLY: Head of talus
                 DISTALLY: The great toe
                 LATERALLY: Soft tissue borders
                 MEDIALLY: Soft tissue borders

Dorsiplantar (AP Oblique)

- Patient sitting with hips and knees flexed
- Affected foot is placed with the plantar aspect upon the cassette
- The leg is medially rotated so that the foot is at an angle of approximately 30–40° to the cassette
- A non-opaque pad is placed under the foot

Collimation

To include: PROXIMALLY: Head of talus
                 DISTALLY: The great toe
                 LATERALLY: Soft tissue borders
                 MEDIALLY: Soft tissue borders

Notes:

Projection: Lateral

Film/Screen:

☐ Bucky

Cassette Size:

☐ Grid

Centring Point:

Suggested: To the navicular-cuneiform joint

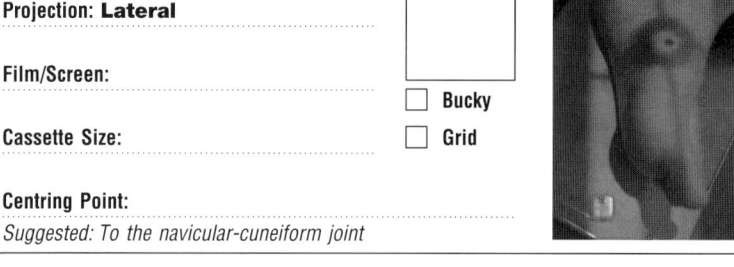

Points to Consider

Technique

✓ This projection is used when a foreign body is suspected or an additional projection for # or dislocation

✓ Lateral projection *must* include the whole of calcaneum

✗ *Do not* overpenetrate the calcaneum

✓ Place a pad under the knee to maintain the position

Radiological Assessment

✓ Check the alignment of the talonavicular and calcaneocuboid bones

✓ Look for breaks in the cortical bone or bony trabeculae

✓ Soft tissue overlying the calcaneum should be seen

✓ Possible # of calcaneum – consider Bohler's (see calcaneum)

Lateral

- Patient lies on the affected side
- Hips and knees are flexed
- The knee is supported so that the plantar aspect of the foot is at right angles to the cassette

Collimation

To include: PROXIMALLY: The calcaneum

DISTALLY: The great toe

LATERALLY: Soft tissue borders

Notes:

Projection: AP

Film/Screen:

☐ Bucky

Cassette Size:

☐ Grid

Centring Point:
Suggested: Midway between the malleoli

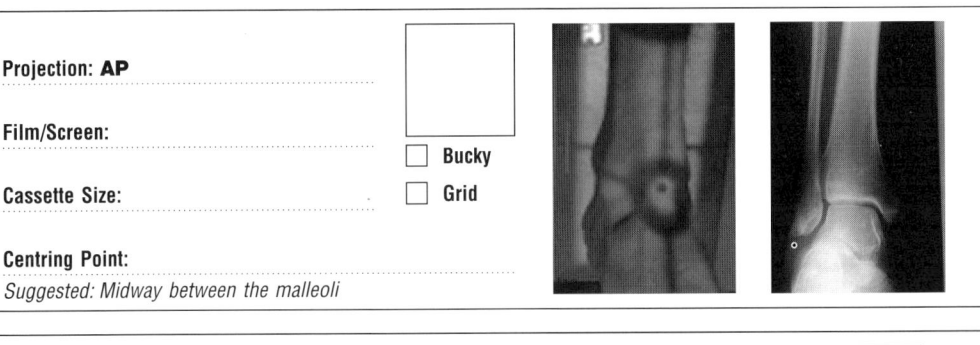

Projection: Lateral

Film/Screen:

☐ Bucky

Cassette Size:

☐ Grid

Centring Point:
Suggested: Midway between the malleoli

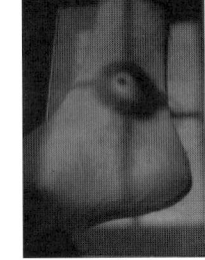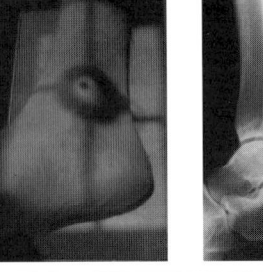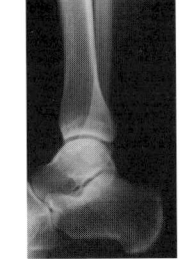

Points to Consider

Technique

✓ AP – ankle *must* be supported in dorsiflexion
✓ Include calcaneum and base of fifth metatarsal
✓ Slight medial rotation so the head of fibula will not overlap the talus
✗ Stress projections – only taken under medical supervision
✗ Lateral – over-rotation – fibula projected too far posteriorly

Radiological Assessment

✓ AP – widening of one side of joint space – positive injury
✓ Check fifth metatarsal – common site for #s
✓ Talus has a poor blood supply – fractured waist can result in necrosis
✓ Lateral – check calcaneum for # – the result of twisting injury
✓ Lateral – the malleoli should be superimposed

AP

- Patient seated with the ankle in dorsiflexion
- Limb rotated medially until the medial and lateral malleoli are equidistant from the cassette
- The ankle is supported by pads and sandbags

Collimation

To include: PROXIMALLY: Lower third of tibia

                DISTALLY: Proximal metatarsals

                LATERALLY: Soft tissue borders

                MEDIALLY: Soft tissue borders

Lateral

- The patient is turned onto the side under examination
- Ankle remains in dorsiflexion and the limb is rotated until the medial and lateral malleoli are superimposed vertically
- A small pad under the toes will aid positioning

Collimation

To include: PROXIMALLY: Lower third of tibia

                DISTALLY: Calcaneum and fifth metatarsal

                LATERALLY: Soft tissue borders

                MEDIALLY: Soft tissue borders

Notes:

Projection: **Lateral**

Film/Screen:

☐ Bucky

Cassette Size:

☐ Grid

Centring Point:
Suggested: Midway between the medial malleolus and plantar aspect of the heel

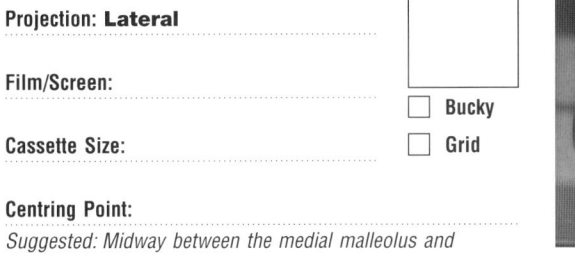
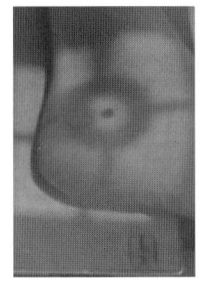
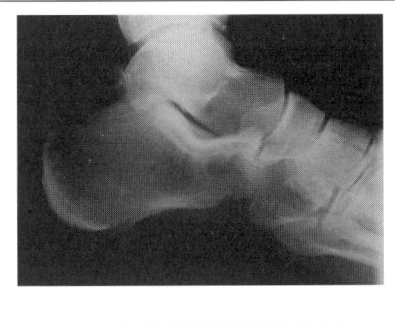

Projection: **Axial**

Film/Screen:

☐ Bucky

Cassette Size:

☐ Grid

Centring Point:
Suggested: To the plantar aspect of the heel at the level of the fifth metatarsal bone

CENTRAL RAY 40° CAUDAL

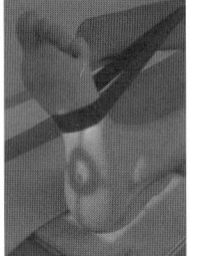
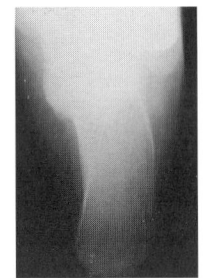

Points to Consider

Technique

✓ Axial – if both to be examined place a pad between heels
✓ Suspected calcaneal spur – lateral projection – both calcanea only
✓ Thoracolumbar # *must* be considered if a fall onto the feet
✓ Place a pad under the knee to prevent overrotation
✓ Axial – prepare equipment first – uncomfortable for patient

Radiological Assessment

✓ Suspected calcaneal # – *must* obtain an axial projection
✗ # of the anterior process is common – but poor visualisation of area
✓ Fall onto feet – associated # of upper lumbar spine (second lumbar vertebra)
✓ Bohler's angle – if # the angle is reduced to < 30°
✓ A sclerotic line may represent an impacted #

Lateral

- The patient lies on the side under examination
- The limb is adjusted so that the malleoli are superimposed
- A pad is placed under the knee to maintain position

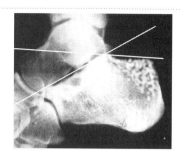

> Bohler's angle – assessed on lateral radiograph – measured by drawing a line from the posterior aspect of the calcaneum to its highest midpoint. The second line is drawn from this point to the highest anterior point. The angle is normally 30–40°

Collimation

To include: PROXIMALLY: Distal tibia/fibula
                     DISTALLY: Inferior calcaneum
                     MEDIALLY: Subtalar joints
                     LATERALLY: Soft tissue borders

Axial

- Patient seated with the limbs extended with the feet vertical
- The affected ankle is dorsiflexed with the aid of a bandage around the forefoot and held by the patient
- The foot is slightly internally rotated so that a line drawn down from the little toe falls to the centre of the calcaneum

Collimation

To include: SUPERIORLY: Subtalar joints
                     INFERIORLY: Calcaneal heel
                     LATERALLY: Soft tissue borders

Notes:

Projection: AP

Film/Screen:

☐ Bucky

Cassette Size:

☐ Grid

Centring Point:

Suggested: Midway between the ankle and knee joint

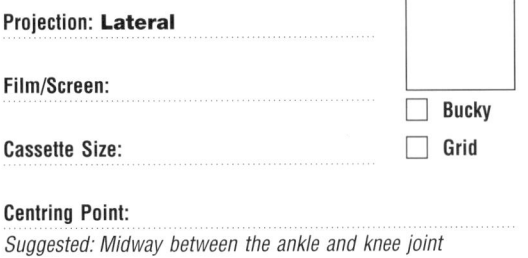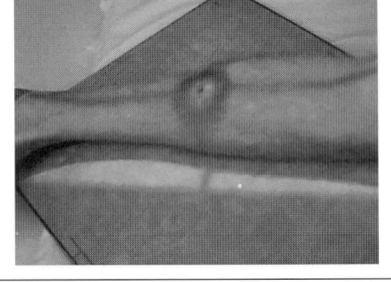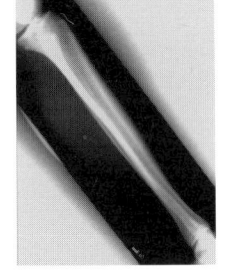

Projection: Lateral

Film/Screen:

☐ Bucky

Cassette Size:

☐ Grid

Centring Point:

Suggested: Midway between the ankle and knee joint

Points to Consider

Technique

✓ Plantar surface of foot should be perpendicular to cassette
✓ *Must* include the knee and the ankle joint
✓ *Remember* – a wet plaster cast needs more exposure
✓ Tibia and fibula should be separate apart from articular ends
✗ Avoid superimposition of calcaneum and distal malleolus
✓ Lateral – horizontal beam *must* be used for acute trauma

Radiological Assessment

✓ If # of the distal tibia – check proximal fibula for contrecoup #
✓ Look for subtle lucent # lines or discontinuity in trabeculae
✓ Toddler's # – child falls on one leg resulting in a spiral # of tibia – care is needed as the # may mimic vascular markings
✓ Tibia and fibula #s can compress vessels

AP

- Patient supine with the affected limb extended
- Ankle is dorsiflexed and the limb is rotated until the medial and lateral malleoli are superimposed
- The ankle is supported by pads and sandbags

Collimation

To include: PROXIMALLY: Knee joint
DISTALLY: Ankle joint
LATERALLY: Soft tissue borders
MEDIALLY: Soft tissue borders

Lateral

- The patient is turned onto the side under examination
- The hip and knee joint are slightly flexed
- Opposite limb is moved away and supported
- The ankle remains dorsiflexed and the medial and lateral malleoli are superimposed vertically

Collimation

To include: PROXIMALLY: Knee joint
DISTALLY: Ankle joint
LATERALLY: Soft tissue borders
MEDIALLY: Soft tissue borders

Notes:

Projection: AP

Film/Screen:

☐ Bucky

Cassette Size:

☐ Grid

Centring Point:
Suggested: 2.5 cm below the apex of the patella

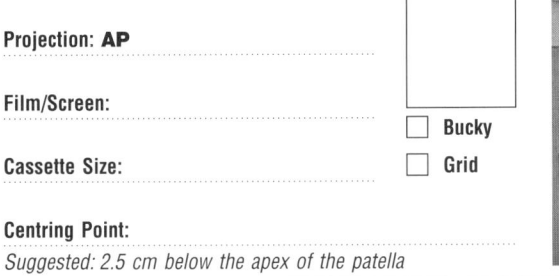
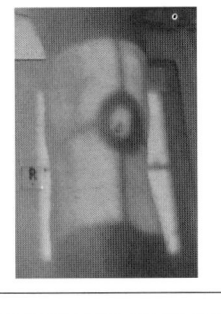
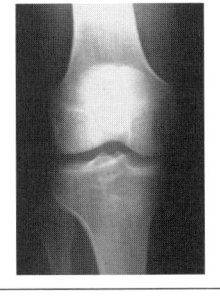

Projection: Lateral

Film/Screen:

☐ Bucky

Cassette Size:

☐ Grid

Centring Point:
Suggested: Over the superior border of the medial tibial condyle

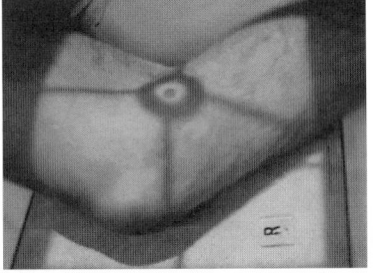
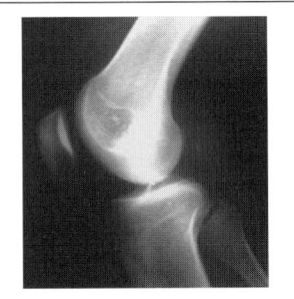

Points to Consider

Technique

✓ AP – medially rotate the lower leg 2–3°
✓ AP – to open the joint space try cephalad angle of 5°
✓ Lateral – the knee is flexed 30–40°
✓ Place a small pad under the ankle – stabilises the knee
✓ Lateral – for acute trauma you *must* use a horizontal beam

Radiological Assessment

✓ AP – the joint spaces should be open and equidistant
✓ AP – fibula head is partially superimposed by lateral condyle
✓ Lateral – patella should be seen in profile
✗ Head of fibula – if you see all the head there is over-rotation
✓ Look for an articular fat–fluid level – intra-articular #

AP

- Patient supine with the affected limb extended
- Rotate the limb slightly medially to centralise the patella between the femoral condyles
- Immobilise the limb with pads and sandbags

Collimation

To include: PROXIMALLY: Patella and distal femur
               DISTALLY: Proximal tibia and fibula
               LATERALLY: Soft tissue borders

Lateral

- The patient is turned onto the side under examination
- Hip and knee are slightly flexed
- The unaffected limb can lie behind the affected limb or be brought well forward and supported on pads and sandbags
- The limb is rotated until the patella is at 90° to the cassette
- Raise the foot on a pad to bring the tibia parallel to the table top

Collimation

To include: PROXIMALLY: Patella and distal femur
               DISTALLY: Proximal tibia and fibula
               LATERALLY: Soft tissue borders

Notes:

Projection: 90° Anterior Joint

Film/Screen:

☐ Bucky

Cassette Size:

☐ Grid

Centring Point:

Suggested: To the crease of the knee

CENTRAL RAY 90° TO AXIS OF TIBIA

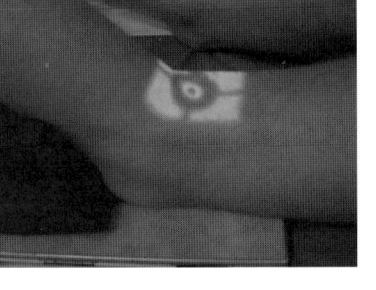

Projection: 110° Posterior Joint

Film/Screen:

☐ Bucky

Cassette Size:

☐ Grid

Centring Point:

Suggested: To the crease of the knee

CENTRAL RAY 110° TO AXIS OF TIBIA

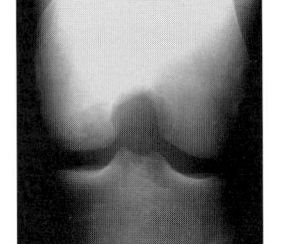
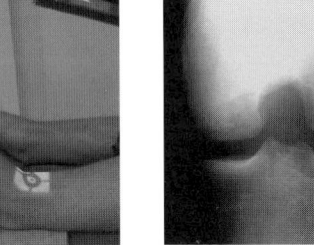
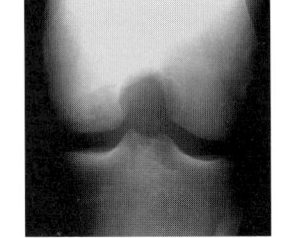

Points to Consider

Technique

✓ Anterior – ensure collimator face is parallel to the tibia
✓ Beam is angled away from the gonads
✓ Ensure the FFD remains at 100 cm
✓ A single anterior projection may be sufficient
✓ If the patella apex is seen in the fossa – flex the knee more

Radiological Assessment

✓ Useful for assessing #s of tibial spines and loose bodies
✓ Intra-articular bone fragments may indicate severe trauma and may be associated with cruciate ligament injury
✓ Two projections will be necessary to examine the whole joint
✗ Apex of the patella should not be seen within the fossa

90° Anterior Joint

- Patient prone on the x-ray table
- Patella should be in the centre of the femur
- Leg under examination is flexed to form an angle of approximately 60°
- The limb is supported by pads and sandbags
- Central ray perpendicular to the axis of the tibia

Collimation

Precise collimation to include the intercondylar fossa

110° Posterior Joint

- Patient prone on the x-ray table
- Patella should be in the centre of the femur
- Leg under examination is flexed to form an angle of approximately 60°
- The limb is supported by pads and sandbags
- Central ray angled 20° towards the femur

Collimation

Precise collimation to include the intercondylar fossa

Notes:

Projection: **Patella – Inferosuperior**

Film/Screen:

☐ Bucky

Cassette Size:

☐ Grid

Centring Point:

Suggested: To the apex of the patella

CENTRAL RAY ANGLED 15° UP FROM THE HORIZONTAL

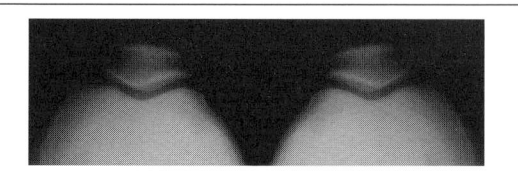

Points to Consider

Technique

✓ Place patient at the end of table – allows tube angulation
✗ Too much knee flexion – reduce femoropatellar joint space
✓ Gonad protection is *essential*
✗ Trauma – *do not* flex the knee – the patella may be fractured

Radiological Assessment

✓ May demonstrate vertical #s – not seen on basic projections
✓ Severe muscle spasm can cause a transverse #
✓ Bipartite patella is normal – not to be confused with a #
    Look for the margins, which will be well-defined and sclerotic

Patella – Inferosuperior (Skyline Projection)

- The patient is seated with the leg under examination flexed to form an angle of approximately 120°
- Knee supported upon pads and sandbags
- The knee is slightly medially rotated to centralise the patella between the femoral condyles
- A cassette is placed on the anterior aspect of the thigh and is angled down 15° from the vertical
- The cassette is supported in position with non-opaque pads

Collimation

- Precise collimation to include the patella and femoropatellar joint space

Notes:

Projection: AP

Film/Screen:

☐ Bucky

Cassette Size:

☐ Grid

Centring Point:
Suggested: Midway between the hip and the knee joint

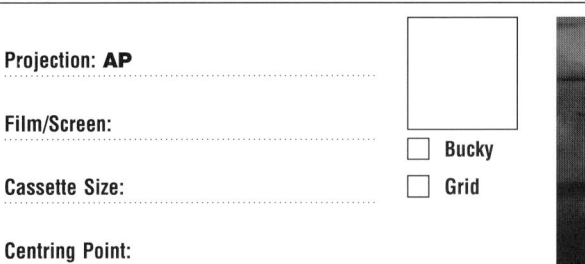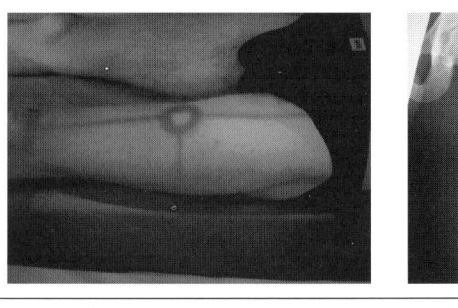

Projection: Lateral

Film/Screen:

☐ Bucky

Cassette Size:

☐ Grid

Centring Point:
Suggested: Midway between the hip and the knee joint

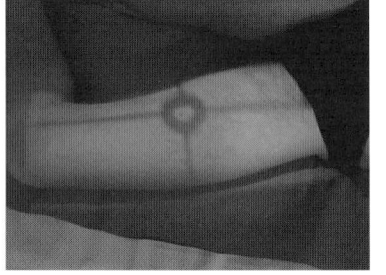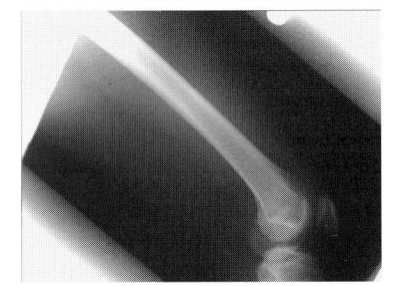

Points to Consider

Technique

✓ AP – extreme care when rotating the limb

✓ Where possible include whole femur on one radiograph

✓ Use gonad shielding – take care not to occlude area of interest

✗ Divergent beam – take care not to project hip or knee off cassette

✗ The lateral is *not* recommended if there may be a #

Radiological Assessment

✓ #ed shaft of femur – the result of considerable force

✓ Look for limb shortening and displacement

✓ Fracture causes considerable loss of blood – consider patient in shock

✓ # completely intra-articular – the bones may not unite

✓ Symptoms of a fractured pubic ramus can mimic those of a #ed femoral neck

AP

- Patient supine with the leg under examination extended
- Where possible gently rotate the limb medially to centralise the patella between the femoral condyles
- Immobilise with pads and sandbags to maintain position

Collimation

To include: PROXIMALLY: Hip joint
DISTALLY: Knee joint
LATERALLY: Soft tissue borders
MEDIALLY: Soft tissue borders

Lateral

- Patient turns onto the side under examination with the hip and knee slightly flexed
- The pelvis is slightly rotated away from the leg under examination to separate the two thighs and visualise the upper femur
- The affected limb is adjusted so that the femoral condyles are superimposed
- Immobilise with pads and sandbags to maintain position

Collimation

To include: PROXIMALLY: Hip joint
DISTALLY: Knee joint
LATERALLY: Soft tissue borders
MEDIALLY: Soft tissue borders

Notes:

Projection: Lateral – Horizontal Beam

Film/Screen:

☐ **Bucky**

Cassette Size:

☐ **Grid**

Centring Point:

Suggested: Midway between the hip and knee joint

HORIZONTAL CENTRAL RAY

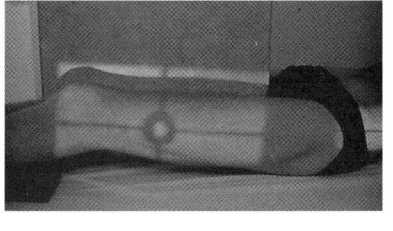
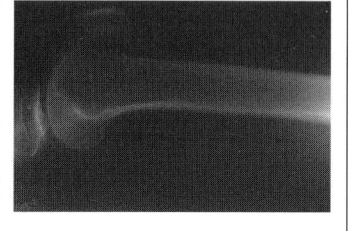

Points to Consider

Technique

✓ Use if there may be a fractured femur or patient cannot turn onto their side
✓ For upper femur – cassette on lateral side of the thigh
✓ For lower femur – cassette against medial side of the thigh
✓ Use gonad shielding – take care not to occlude area of interest
✗ *Do not* rotate the limb – this will exacerbate the injury

Radiological Assessment

✓ Check for any break in the cortical outline
✓ Remember symptoms of a fractured pubic ramus can mimic those of a fractured neck of femur
✓ Femoral condylar #s can be displaced or undisplaced
✓ Severe comminuted condylar #s may be associated with a spiral # of the distal femur

Lateral – Horizontal Beam

- Patient supine
- Leg under examination is extended
- Rotate the limb to centralise the patella over the femur
- The opposite limb is raised upon a suitable support and is immobilised

Collimation

To include: PROXIMALLY: Upper femur

DISTALLY: Knee joint

LATERALLY: Soft tissue borders

MEDIALLY: Soft tissue borders

Notes:

Projection:

Film/Screen:

☐ Bucky

Cassette Size:

☐ Grid

Centring Point:

Notes:

Projection:

Film/Screen:

☐ Bucky

Cassette Size:

☐ Grid

Centring Point:

Notes:

Projection:
....

Film/Screen:
....

Cassette Size:
....

☐ Bucky

☐ Grid

Centring Point:
....

Notes:
....
....
....
....
....
....
....

Projection:
....

Film/Screen:
....

Cassette Size:
....

☐ Bucky

☐ Grid

Centring Point:
....

Notes:
....
....
....
....
....
....
....

Projection:

Film/Screen:

☐ Bucky

Cassette Size:

☐ Grid

Centring Point:

Notes:

Projection:

Film/Screen:

☐ Bucky

Cassette Size:

☐ Grid

Centring Point:

Notes:

Vertebral Column

Projection: AP C1–C3

Film/Screen:

☐ Bucky

Cassette Size:

☐ Grid

Centring Point:
Suggested: To the lower border of the incisors – directly to the open mouth

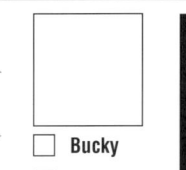
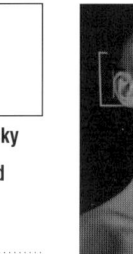
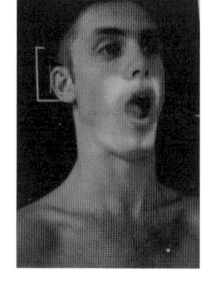
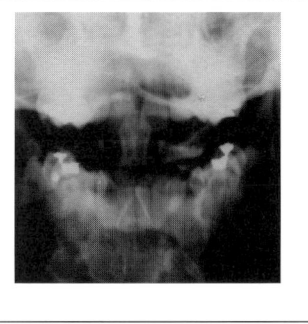

Projection: AP C3–C7

Film/Screen:

☐ Bucky

Cassette Size:

☐ Grid

Centring Point:
Suggested: To the sternal notch – then angle the central ray cranially to the thyroid cartilage

CENTRAL RAY APPROXIMATELY 15° CRANIALLY

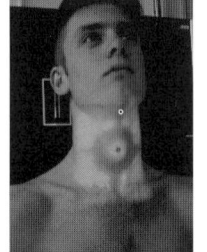
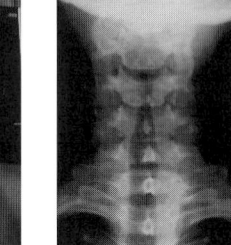
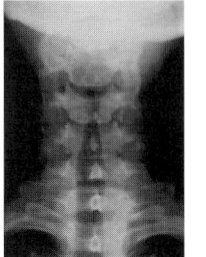

Points to Consider

Technique

- ✓ Remember to set the exposure before positioning
- ✓ AP C1–C3 – adjust patient so that occipital bone and lower edge of upper incisors are superimposed
- ✗ AP C1–C3 – patient may overextend the head when opening the mouth
- ✓ AP – mental region of mandible should be superimposed over the occiput

Radiological Assessment

- ✓ Check that each intervertebral joint space is consistent
- ✓ AP C1–C3 – the odontoid process *must* be clear of the occipital bone
- ✓ All vertebral bodies should be rectangular – any variation may be due to trauma
- ✓ AP – ensure C3–T1 are visualised – C1–C3 may be obscured

AP C1–C3

- Patient erect or supine
- Median saggital plane 90° to the cassette
- Patient's neck is extended until the upper occlusal plane is perpendicular to the table top
- The patient is then asked to open the mouth as wide as possible

Collimation

To include: SUPERIORLY: Upper C1
INFERIORLY: Body C3
LATERALLY : Transverse processes

AP C3–C7

- Patient erect or supine
- Median saggital plane 90° to the cassette
- The patient's neck is extended until the angle of the mouth and the tragus of the ear are perpendicular to the table top

Collimation

To include: SUPERIORLY: Lower border of mandible
INFERIORLY: Body T1
LATERALLY: Transverse processes

Notes:

Projection: **Lateral**

Film/Screen:

Cassette Size:

☐ Bucky
☐ Grid

Centring Point:
Suggested: 2.5 cm behind and 5 cm below the angle of the mandible

HORIZONTAL CENTRAL RAY
FFD 180 cm

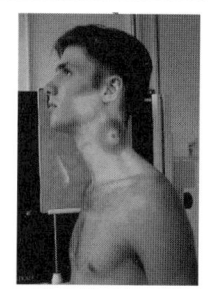
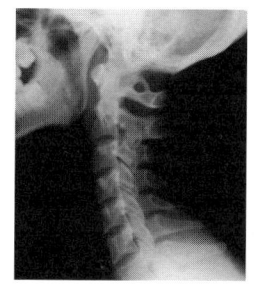

Projection: **Anterior Obliques**

Film/Screen:

Cassette Size:

☐ Bucky
☐ Grid

Centring Point:
Suggested: To the middle of the cervical spine

CENTRAL RAY 15° CAUDAL
FFD 180 cm

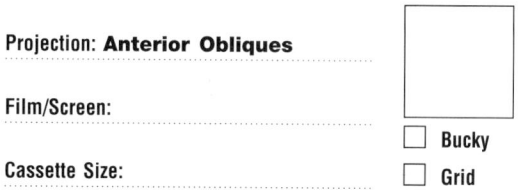
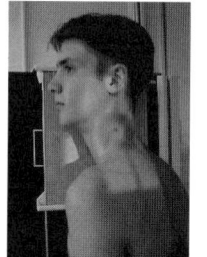
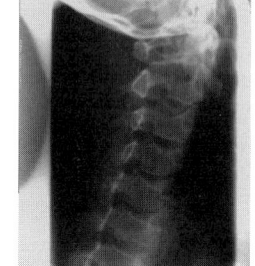

Points to Consider

Technique

✓ Acute trauma – use horizontal beam – *do not* adjust head
✓ Exposure made on arrested expiration
✓ *Must* include C7 on the radiograph
✓ Oblique – extend the head back to avoid superimposition of the mandible

Radiological Assessment

✓ Anterior displacement over 3.5 mm – ligaments torn
✓ Vertebral bodies C3–T1 should be the same size – a disparity of 2 mm may be due to a compression #
✓ Check all seven vertebrae are seen on the radiograph
✓ Oblique – demonstrates intervertebral foramina closest to the film (right anterior oblique – right foramina; left anterior oblique – left foramina)

Lateral

- Patient in the erect position with the shoulder against the cassette
- Median sagittal plane parallel to the cassette
- The patient's shoulders should be relaxed and arms are placed down and slightly behind the trunk
- The feet are separated to aid stability
- The patient's chin is raised and extended slightly forwards so that the mandible does not obscure the spine

Collimation

To include: SUPERIORLY: EAM
INFERIORLY: Body T1
LATERALLY: Soft tissue borders

Anterior Obliques – Both sides for comparison

- Patient erect facing a vertical Bucky
- The trunk is then rotated 45° to each side in turn
- The patient's head is rotated so that the median sagittal plane is parallel to the Bucky

Collimation

To include: SUPERIORLY: EAM
INFERIORLY: Body T1
LATERALLY: Soft tissue borders

Notes:

Projection: Swimmer's

Film/Screen:

☐ Bucky

Cassette Size:

☐ Grid

Centring Point:

Suggested: To a level just above the shoulder remote from the cassette

HORIZONTAL CENTRAL RAY

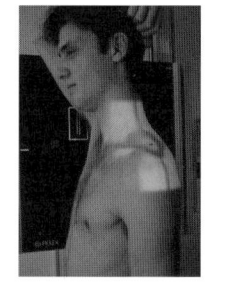
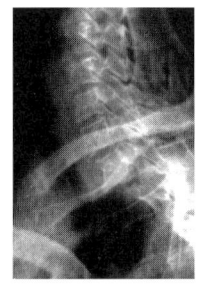

Points to Consider

Technique

✓ Remember to set the exposure before positioning
✓ Exposure *must* penetrate the shoulder region
✗ *Do not* rotate the thorax unless an oblique projection is required
✓ Exposure on *arrested* respiration

Radiological Assessment

✓ Check that each intervertebral joint space is consistent
✓ Shoulders should be seen separated from each other
✓ All vertebral bodies should be rectangular – any variation may be due to trauma
✓ *Must* include from C5 to T5

Swimmer's

- Patient erect
- A shoulder is placed against the erect Bucky
- Arm nearest the cassette is raised and folded over the head
- Arm furthest from the cassette is depressed as far as possible
- Median sagittal plane is parallel to the cassette

Collimation

To include: SUPERIORLY: Body C5
INFERIORLY: Body T5
ANTERIORLY: Anterior clavicles
POSTERIORLY: Posterior ribs

Notes:

Projection: AP

Film/Screen:

Cassette Size:

☐ Bucky
☐ Grid

Centring Point:
Suggested: To a point 5 cm below the suprasternal notch

 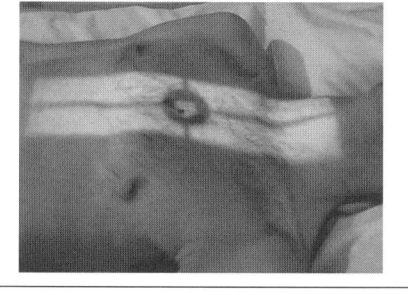

Projection: Lateral

Film/Screen:

Cassette Size:

☐ Bucky
☐ Grid

Centring Point:
Suggested: To a point 5 cm anterior to the palpable sixth spinous process

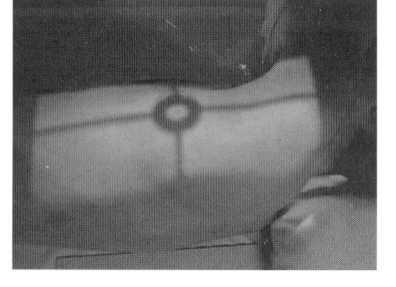 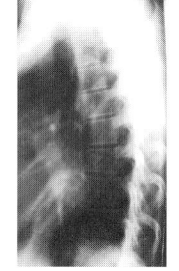

Points to Consider

Technique

✓ AP – use a wedge filter to prevent the upper thoracic vertebrae being overpenetrated
✓ Flex the knees to aid the patient's comfort
✓ AP – exposure on arrested inspiration
✓ Lateral – a long exposure with gentle breathing to blur the lung fields and ribs

Radiological Assessment

✓ AP – abnormal soft tissue enlargement around the spine is a positive indication of trauma or infection
✓ Check all pedicles are present and intact
✓ The vertebral bodies should be the same height – anteriorly and posteriorly
✓ Lateral – upper spine difficult to visualise due to shoulders. A swimmer's projection may be required – CT is better

AP

- Patient supine
- Median sagittal plane perpendicular to the cassette
- A small pillow supports the head
- Patient's arms are placed down by the side

Collimation

To include: SUPERIORLY: Body of C7
INFERIORLY: Body of L1
LATERALLY: Transverse processes and soft tissues

Lateral

- Patient lying on the side
- Median sagittal plane and the spine are parallel to the table top
- The arms are raised and placed onto the pillow
- The knees are flexed and a soft pad is placed between them for comfort

Collimation

To include: SUPERIORLY: Upper thoracic spine
INFERIORLY: Body of L1
ANTERIORLY: Vertebral bodies
POSTERIORLY: Posterior rib cage

Notes:

Projection: AP

Film/Screen:

☐ Bucky

Cassette Size:

☐ Grid

Centring Point:

Suggested: Midline at the level of lower costal margin

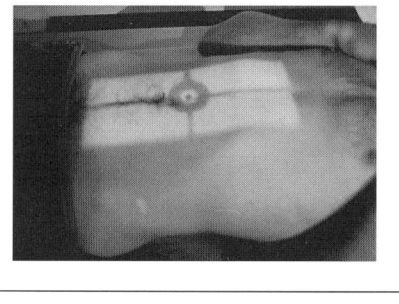
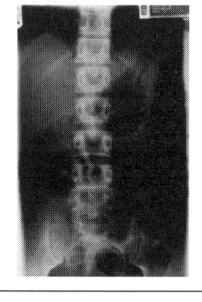

Projection: Lateral

Film/Screen:

☐ Bucky

Cassette Size:

☐ Grid

Centring Point:

Suggested: 8–10 cm anterior to the third lumbar spinous process at the level of the lower costal margin

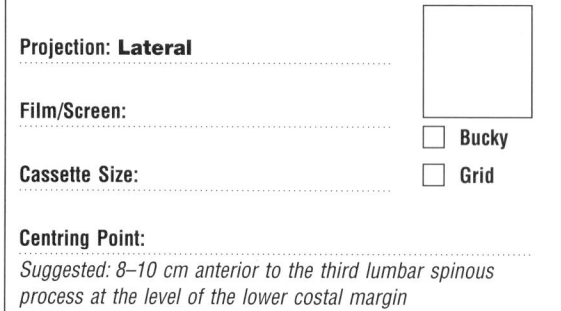
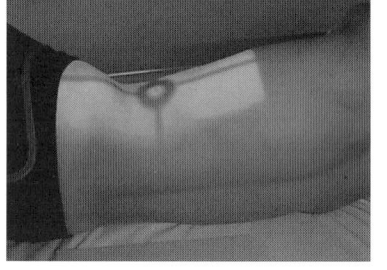
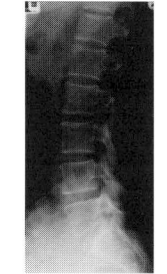

Points to Consider

Technique

✓ AP – reduce lumbar lordosis – flex knees and support

✓ AP – ensure sacroiliac joints included on the radiograph

✓ AP and lateral – exposure on arrested *expiration* – diaphragm should be above L1 – or try breathing technique to blur bowel shadows

✓ Lateral – non-opaque pad under the waist so spine is parallel to the table top

✓ Use gonad shield – but take care not to obscure the area of interest

Radiological Assessment

✓ AP – distance between pedicles gradually widens from L1 to L5

✓ AP – *must* inspect the transverse processes for #

✓ Check soft tissues changes – may indicate underlying pathology – renal stones mimic skeletal back pain

✓ Lateral – vertebral bodies should be same height anteriorly and posteriorly

✓ Any loss of height or wedging suggests a possible compression #

AP

- Patient supine
- Median sagittal plane perpendicular to the table top and the anterior superior iliac spines (ASIS) are equidistant
- The hips and knees are flexed and supported with pads
- Patient's arms are placed across the upper thorax or away from the body

Collimation

To include: SUPERIORLY: T12

INFERIORLY: Sacroiliac joints

(Some imaging centres require visualisation of the kidneys due to the possibility of referred pain from kidney pathology)

LATERALLY: Sacroiliac joints

Lateral

- Patient lying on side
- Median sagittal plane and the spine are parallel to the table top
- The arms are raised and placed onto the pillow
- The knees are flexed and a soft pad is placed between them for comfort

Collimation

To include: SUPERIORLY: T12

INFERIORLY: L5 – sacral junction

ANTERIORLY: Vertebral bodies (possibly kidneys)

POSTERIORLY: Spinous processes

Notes:

Projection: **Lumbosacral Junction (L5–S1)**

Film/Screen:

☐ Bucky

Cassette Size:

☐ Grid

Centring Point:

Suggested: 8 cm anterior to the fifth lumbar spinous process

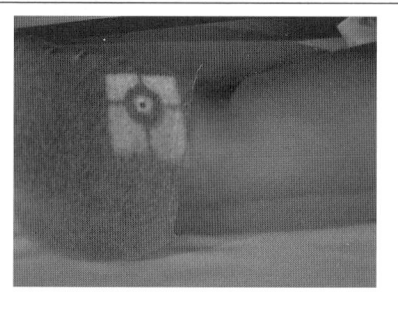
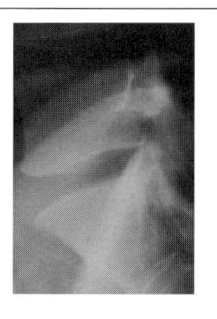

Projection: **AP Obliques**

Film/Screen:

☐ Bucky

Cassette Size:

☐ Grid

Centring Point:

Suggested: To the midclavicular line on the raised side at the level of lower costal margin

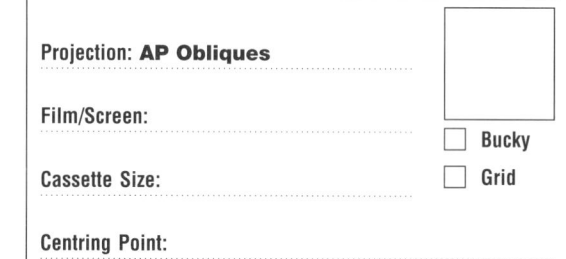
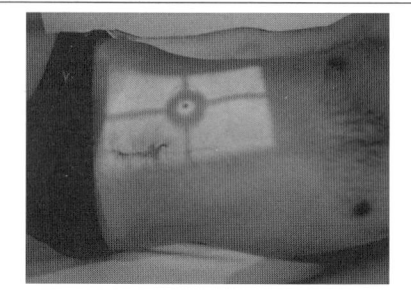
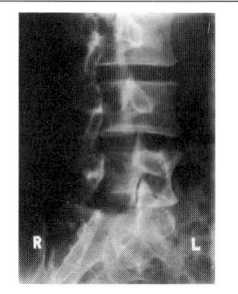

Points to Consider

Technique

✓ *Do not* proceed until you have examined the lateral
✓ L5–S1 – a 5° caudal angulation may open the disc space
✓ L5–S1 – collimation important to reduce scattered radiation
✓ Lateral – place a non-opaque pad under the waist to bring the spine parallel to the table top

Radiological Assessment

✓ The disc space at L5–S1 – usually smaller than at L4–L5
✓ The joint space *must* be visualised open
✓ Obliques – suspected spondylolisthesis – a defect in pars articularis – look for a collar around the Scotty dog's neck!
✓ Obliques – will demonstrate superior and inferior articular processes and the zygopophyseal joints of the side nearest the cassette

Lumbosacral Junction (L5–S1)

- Patient lying on side
- Median sagittal plane and the spine are parallel to the table top
- The arms are raised and placed onto the pillow
- The knees are flexed and a soft pad is placed between them for comfort
- Posterior superior iliac spines (PSIS) are perpendicular to the table top

Collimation

To include: SUPERIORLY: L5
INFERIORLY: Sacral segment
ANTERIORLY: Anterior lumbar bodies
POSTERIORLY: Spinous processes

AP Obliques

- Patient supine
- The trunk is rotated 45° to either side in turn
- The hips and knees are flexed and supported in position

Collimation

To include: SUPERIORLY: L1
INFERIORLY: Upper sacral segment
LATERALLY: Spinal column

Notes:

Projection: AP

Film/Screen:

☐ Bucky

Cassette Size:

☐ Grid

Centring Point:
Suggested: Midline 5 cm above superior border of symphysis pubis

CRANIAL – CENTRAL RAY: 10° MALE : 20° FEMALE

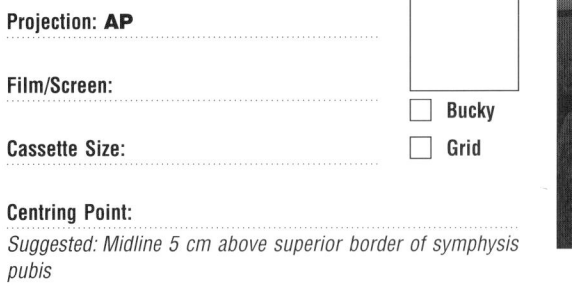
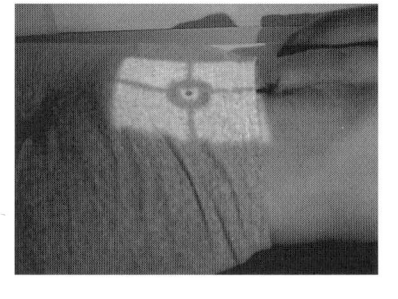
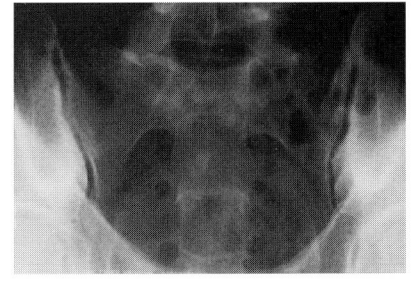

Projection: Lateral

Film/Screen:

☐ Bucky

Cassette Size:

☐ Grid

Centring Point:
Suggested: Midway between the PSIS and the palpable coccyx

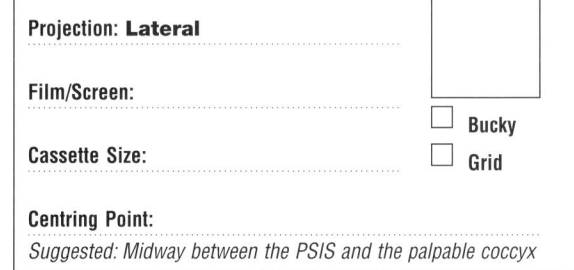
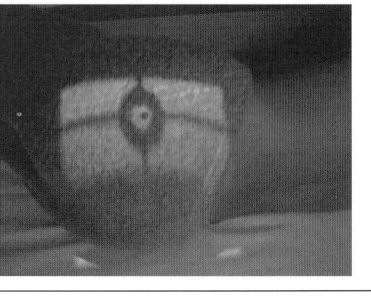
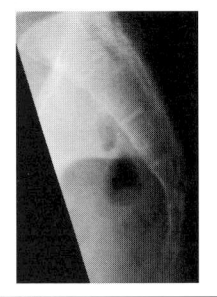

Points to Consider

Technique

✓ AP – lower bowel preparation is an advantage
✓ AP – central ray will differ between males and females
✓ Lateral – place lead or rubber around the sacrum to reduce scattered radiation
✓ Lateral – place a non-opaque pad under the waist

Radiological Assessment

✓ *Must* demonstrate the sacrum and sacroiliac joints
✓ Obturator foramina will appear wide open
✓ Symphysis will appear broadened depending upon tube angle
✓ Lateral – *must* include the L5–S1 joint space on the radiograph

AP

- Patient supine
- Median sagittal plane perpendicular to the table top and ASIS equidistant
- Hips and knees are flexed and supported in position

Collimation

To include: SUPERIORLY: L5–S1 joint space
INFERIORLY: Coccyx
LATERALLY: Sacroiliac joints

Lateral

- Patient lies on the side
- Median sagittal plane parallel to the table top
- Hips and knees are flexed
- PSIS are perpendicular to the table top

Collimation

To include: SUPERIORLY: L5–S1 joint space
INFERIORLY: Coccyx
ANTERIORLY: Sacral promontory and coccyx
POSTERIORLY: Sacral spinous tubercles

Notes:

Projection: AP

Film/Screen:

☐ Bucky

Cassette Size:

☐ Grid

Centring Point:
Suggested: Midline 2.5 cm superior to the symphysis pubis

CENTRAL RAY 15° CAUDAD

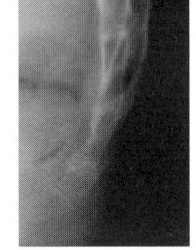

Projection: Lateral

Film/Screen:

☐ Bucky

Cassette Size:

☐ Grid

Centring Point:
Suggested: Directly over the palpable coccyx

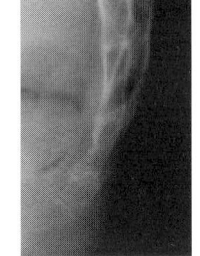

Points to Consider

Technique

✓ Bowel preparation may be necessary for optimal visualisation
✓ If patient cannot tolerate lying supine – try prone position
✓ Place a pad under the knees for patient comfort
✗ Care with the exposure – *do not* overpenetrate – exposure will depend upon the degree of collimation used

Radiological Assessment

✓ AP – check that the amount of angulation has corrected the natural curvature of the coccyx
✗ PA – not ideal because of increased object to film distance (OFD) – if used check that the angle of the central ray is cephalic
✓ AP – the obturator foramina will appear to be almost closed

AP

- Patient supine
- Median sagittal plane perpendicular to the table top and the ASIS are equidistant
- Knees are flexed and supported with pads
- Patient's arms are placed across the upper thorax

Lateral

- Patient lying on the side
- Median sagittal plane and the spine are parallel to the table top
- Hips and knees are flexed
- PSIS are perpendicular to the table top
- The arms are raised and placed level with the head

Collimation

- Precise to the area of interest – use a cone if available

Notes:

Projection:

Film/Screen:

☐ Bucky

Cassette Size:

☐ Grid

Centring Point:

Notes:

Projection:

Film/Screen:

☐ Bucky

Cassette Size:

☐ Grid

Centring Point:

Notes:

Projection: ....

Film/Screen: ....

☐ Bucky

Cassette Size: ....

☐ Grid

Centring Point: ....

Notes:
....
....
....
....
....
....
....
....

Projection: ....

Film/Screen: ....

☐ Bucky

Cassette Size: ....

☐ Grid

Centring Point: ....

Notes:
....
....
....
....
....
....
....
....

Projection:

Film/Screen:

☐ Bucky

Cassette Size:

☐ Grid

Centring Point:

Notes:

Projection:

Film/Screen:

☐ Bucky

Cassette Size:

☐ Grid

Centring Point:

Notes:

The Skull

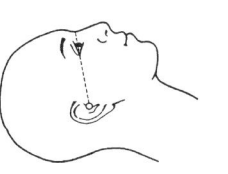

ORBITOMEATAL BASELINE
Line joins the outer canthus of the eye to the midpoint of the external auditory meatus.

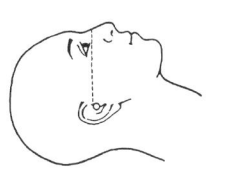

ANTHROPOLOGICAL BASELINE
Line joins the infraorbital margin to the superior border of the external auditory meatus.
The difference in angles between the *orbitomeatal baseline* and the *anthropological baseline* is 10°.

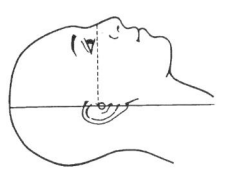

AURICULAR LINE
Line passes perpendicular to the anthropological baseline through the centre of the external auditory meatus.

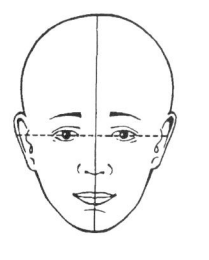

INTERPUPILLARY LINE
Line joins the centre of the two orbits and is perpendicular to the median sagittal plane.

Notes:

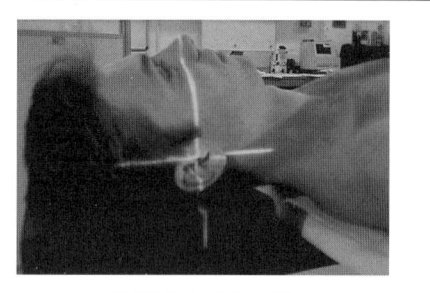

REFERENCE POSITION

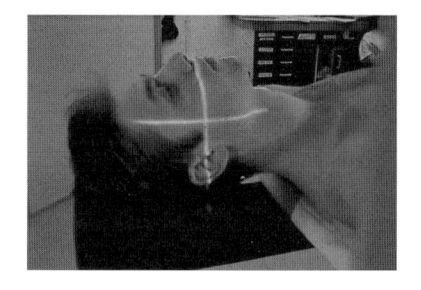

*FACIAL BONES
REFERENCE POSITION*

✓ *Total* immobilisation of the patient is essential

✓ Patient can be examined erect or supine – easier to immobilise when supine

✓ Overexposure can be tolerated more than underexposure

✓ Dulac technique is positioning patient so that the area of interest is in the centre of a sphere – *isocentre*

✗ Unsure of your position – move tube 180° to check the other side

✓ Up to 50% reduction in dose can be achieved

✓ Radiation protection – use cones and collimators to limit the beam – *most* important – to avoid the need for repeats

✓ Some radiographs may appear different – due to decrease in distortion and true representation of the patient

✓ Skull #s – linear is most common – stellate is star shaped. Depressed – detached fragment and may be comminuted

✓ Where possible the patient should remain in a comfortable position – different projections achieved by moving the tube

Planes

- Median sagittal plane = Vertical
- Anthropological plane = Vertical
- Auricular plane = Horizontal

Reference Position

- Patient supine
- Head resting on non-opaque pad over the head support

Tube Column

- Tube and vertical arm is set to 0° so that it is perpendicular to the table top
- Sagittal light beam should coincide with median sagittal plane and the transverse light beam with the anthropological plane
- Horizontal beam *must* pass through auditory canals and coincide with auricular plane
- Velcro band placed across the forehead to maintain this position

Main Movements

1. Above (Vent: Ventral) Below (Dors: Dorsal)
   - Degree of displacement in relation to the auricular plane
     e.g. Vent 4 cm = tube *raised* 4 cm *above* the *auricular* plane
     Dors 4 cm = tube *lowered* 4 cm *below* the *auricular* plane
2. Right and Left
   - Degree of displacement in relation to the median sagittal plane
     e.g. Moving the patient to the left brings the right half of the skull into the isocentre
3. Cranial and Caudal
   - Patient displacement in relation to the anthropological plane

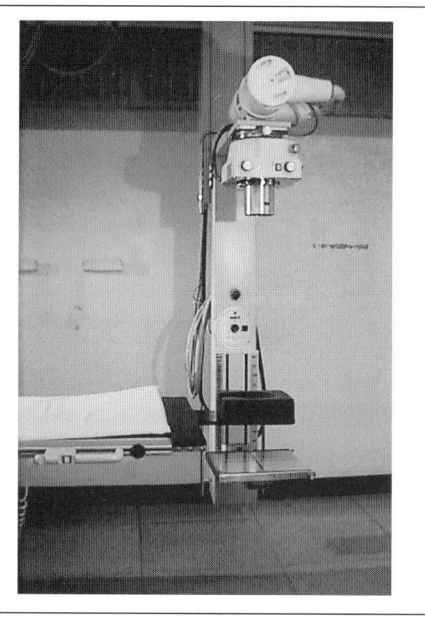
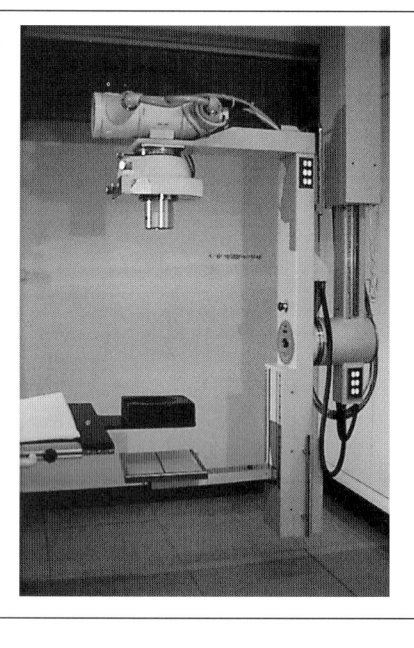

Reminder

Lateral Position

Tube positioned lateral to the patient so that the tube can be rotated cephalad or caudad along the long axis of the table and patient

Medial Position

Tube positioned so that the column is at the vertex of the skull so that the tube can be angled to either side of the head

Basic Equipment Positions

1. Lateral – L
   - Tube arm and vertical arm at 0°
   - The 'C' arm at the side of the patient's head
   - Used to set the reference position and examination area
2. Medial – M
   - The 'C' arm supporting the tube is parallel to the median sagittal plane
   - X-ray tube is able to be rotated laterally to either side of the patient's head
   - Used to rotate the tube and for lateral projections

Magnification

   - Should be kept the same for all projections (1, 2)

Notes:

Projection: Occipitofrontal

Film/Screen:

Cassette:

Central Ray: Directed 10° CAUDAD
ENTRY POINT: Midline between parietal bones
EXIT POINT: Nasion

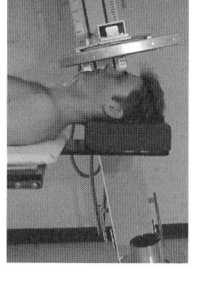
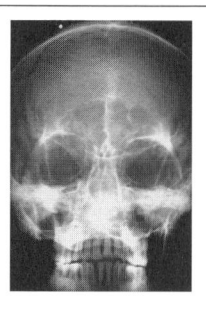

Projection: Pineal

Film/Screen:

Cassette:

Central Ray: Directed 25° CEPHALAD
ENTRY POINT: 2 cm above external occipital protuberance
EXIT POINT: 4 cm above the glabella

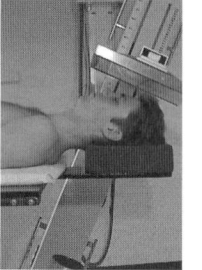
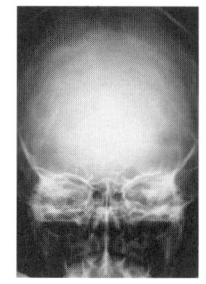

Occipitofrontal

✓ Visualise – anterior vault – frontal sinuses – facial bones
✓ Correct position:
  • measure outer orbit to the lateral vault on both sides
  • petrous ridge should be level with or better just below the lower orbital margin
✗ If petrous ridge is below lower orbital margin the angle is too great – if it appears within the orbits the angle is too small

Pineal

✓ Visualise – the pineal gland's position within the vault
✓ Correct position:
  • distance from the outer orbital margin symmetrical both sides
  • petrous ridges and orbital margins should be superimposed and anterior clinoid processes should be at the same level
✗ If petrous ridge is below orbital margin the angle is too small – if it appears above the orbits the angle is too great

Occipitofrontal

    TUBE COLUMN BASE POSITION: Lateral, with x-ray tube beneath the patient
    PATIENT DISPLACEMENT: Caudad 4 cm (brings nasion and frontal structures to the isocentre)

Pineal

    TUBE COLUMN BASE POSITION: Lateral, with x-ray tube beneath the patient
    PATIENT DISPLACEMENT: Caudad 4 cm (to bring the pineal gland to the isocentre)

Notes:

Projection: **Half-Axial**

Film/Screen:

Cassette:

Central Ray: **Directed 40° CEPHALAD**
ENTRY POINT: Midline through foramen magnum
EXIT POINT: Midline 6 cm above glabella

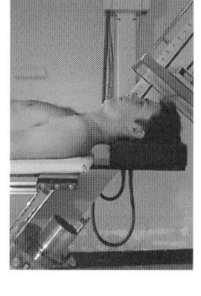

Projection: **Lateral**

Film/Screen:

Cassette:

Central Ray: **Horizontal**
ENTRY POINT: 4 cm above the anthropological baseline in the auricular plane
EXIT POINT: Corresponds to opposite side

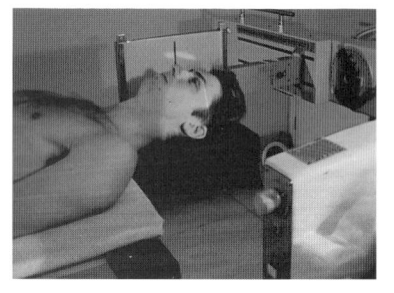 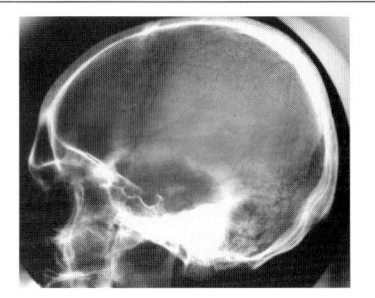

Half-Axial

✓ Visualise – occiput – foramen magnum – lambdoid suture
✓ Correct position:
  • not easy to assess – middle of foramen magnum should be equidistant to the outer skull on both sides – posterior clinoid processes seen within the foramen magnum
✗ Too little angle – foramen magnum will not be seen

Lateral

✓ Visualise – whole of the vault – some facial bones – mandible
✓ Correct position:
  • superimposed is the anterior cranial fossa – middle fossa – external auditory meatus (EAM)
  • posterior rami of the mandible
✗ If EAM is separated the head is rotated – if the anterior cranial fossa is separated the head is tilted

Half-Axial

       TUBE COLUMN BASE POSITION: Lateral, with x-ray tube beneath the patient
       PATIENT DISPLACEMENT: Caudad 4 cm

Lateral

Horizontal beam is imperative
       TUBE COLUMN BASE POSITION: Medial, tube at the side of the patient's head so the central ray is horizontal
       PATIENT DISPLACEMENT: Caudad 4 cm

Notes:

Projection: Occipitomental 15°

Film/Screen:

Cassette:

Central Ray: Directed 15° CAUDAD
ENTRY POINT: The occipital bone
EXIT POINT: Upper incisor teeth

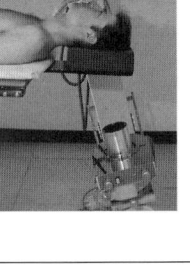

Projection: Occipitomental 30°

Film/Screen:

Cassette:

Central Ray: Directed 30° CAUDAD
ENTRY POINT: The occipital bone
EXIT POINT: Upper incisor teeth

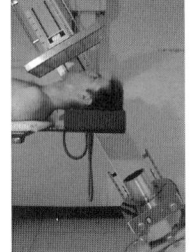
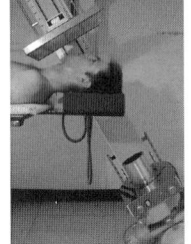

Occipitomental 15°

- ✓ Visualise – maxilla – zygoma – lower orbital margin
- ✓ Correct position:
  - petrous bone just below the apex of the maxillary sinuses
  - distance from outer orbital margin symmetrical both sides
- ✓ Erect technique for blow out # of the floor of the orbit

Occipitomental 30°

- ✓ Visualise – orbital floor – zygomatic arch
- ✓ Correct position:
  - petrous bone level with the body of the mandible
  - distance from outer orbital margin symmetrical both sides
- ✓ Erect technique for blow out # of the floor of the orbit

Occipitomental 15°

TUBE COLUMN BASE POSITION:	Lateral, with x-ray tube beneath the patient
TUBE DISPLACEMENT:	6 cm above the auricular plane
PATIENT POSITION:	Patient's anthropological baseline is raised 30°

Occipitomental 30°

TUBE COLUMN BASE POSITION:	Lateral, with x-ray tube beneath the patient
TUBE DISPLACEMENT:	6 cm above the auricular plane
PATIENT POSITION:	Patient's anthropological baseline is raised 30°

Notes:

Projection: Lateral

Film/Screen:

Cassette:

Central Ray: Horizontal Beam
ENTRY POINT: Along the anthropological baseline to the level of the outer canthus of the eye
EXIT POINT: Corresponding opposite side

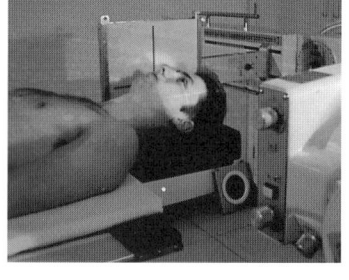
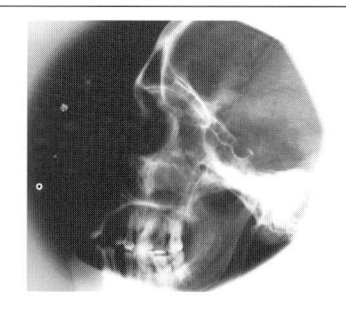

Lateral

✓ Visualise – amount of displacement of facial bones
✓ Correct position:
  • anterior cranial fossa should be superimposed
  • heads of mandible superimposed
✗ Suspected cervical injury – *do not* proceed with facial bone examination until medical officer consents

✓ Nasal bone injury – should be diagnosed clinically – routine radiography is unnecessary – possibly an occipitomental for displacement *only*
✓ Check for foreign bodies
✓ Examine soft tissues for swelling using a bright light

Lateral

TUBE COLUMN BASE POSITION: Medial, with x-ray tube horizontal
TUBE DISPLACEMENT: 6 cm above the auricular plane
PATIENT POSITION: Patient returned to the reference position

Notes:

Projection: Occipitomental

Film/Screen:

Cassette:

Central Ray: Horizontal Beam
ENTRY POINT: The occipital bone
EXIT POINT: Upper incisor teeth

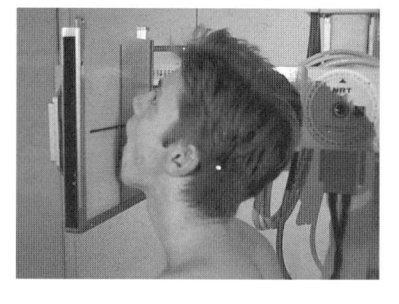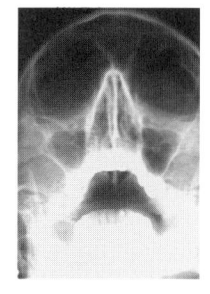

Projection: Lateral

Film/Screen:

Cassette:

Central Ray: Horizontal Beam
*ENTRY POINT: 2 cm behind the outer canthus of the eye,
along the anthropological baseline*
EXIT POINT: Corresponding opposite side

Occipitomental

✓ Visualise – maxillary sinus – sphenoid sinus through open mouth and ethmoidal sinuses
✓ Correct position:
  • petrous bones *must* be below the maxillary antra
  • foramen ovale should be seen on each side
✗ Difficulty immobilising the patient – isocentric technique

Lateral

✓ Visualise – all the paranasal sinuses – superimposed
✓ Correct position:
  • anterior cranial fossa superimposed
  • heads of mandible superimposed
✓ *Both* projections – patient should be in the *erect* position

Occipitomental

TUBE COLUMN BASE POSITION: Medial, with x-ray tube horizontal

PATIENT POSITION: Patient's anthropological baseline is raised 35° from the horizontal (orbitomeatal 45°)

Patient opens mouth before exposure

Lateral

TUBE COLUMN BASE POSITION: Medial, with x-ray tube horizontal

PATIENT POSITION: Patient's head rotated to the affected side in a lateral position

Notes:

Projection: Occipitofrontal

Film/Screen:

Cassette:

Central Ray: Horizontal Beam
ENTRY POINT: The occipital bone
EXIT POINT: Nasion

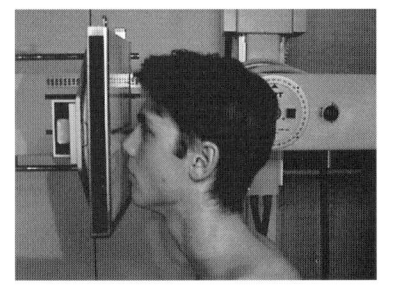
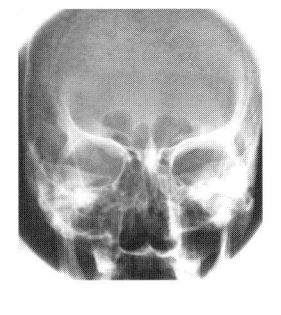

Projection: Modified Occipitofrontal

Film/Screen:

Cassette:

Central Ray: Directed 10° CEPHALAD
ENTRY POINT: The occipital bone
EXIT POINT: Nasion

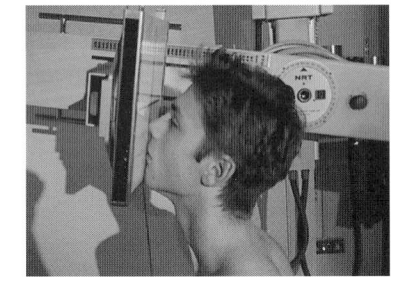

Occipitofrontal

✓ Visualise – frontal sinus – ethmoidal sinuses
✓ Correct position:
  • innominate line to outer orbit should be equidistant
  • petrous ridge seen just below the lower orbital margin
✓ Position suitable if the patient can remain immobile

Modified Occipitofrontal

✓ Visualise – frontal sinus – ethmoidal sinuses
✓ Correct position:
  • innominate line to outer orbit should be equidistant
  • petrous ridge seen just below the lower orbital margin
✓ Position suitable if patient has difficulty in remaining still

Occipitofrontal **Horizontal Central Ray**

TUBE COLUMN BASE POSITION: Medial, with x-ray tube horizontal
PATIENT POSITION: Patient's anthropological baseline is raised 10° from the horizontal

Modified Occipitofrontal **Angled Beam – For patient stability**

TUBE COLUMN BASE POSITION: Medial, with x-ray tube horizontal
PATIENT POSITION: Patient's anthropological baseline is raised 30° from the horizontal

Notes:

Projection:

Film/Screen:

Cassette Size:

Centring Point:

Notes:

Projection:

Film/Screen:

Cassette Size:

Centring Point:

Notes:

Projection:

Film/Screen:

Cassette Size:

Centring Point:

Notes:

Projection:

Film/Screen:

Cassette Size:

Centring Point:

Notes:

Projection:

Film/Screen:

Cassette Size:

Centring Point:

Notes:

Projection:

Film/Screen:

Cassette Size:

Centring Point:

Notes:

Appendix

Location	Projection	Exposure	Notes

Location	Projection	Exposure	Notes

Location	Projection	Exposure	Notes

Location	Projection	Exposure	Notes

Location	Projection	Exposure	Notes

Location	Projection	Exposure	Notes

Theatre

Location	Examination	Exposure	Notes

Location	Examination	Exposure	Notes

Location	Examination	Exposure	Notes

Location	Examination	Exposure	Notes

Location	Examination	Exposure	Notes

Location	Examination	Exposure	Notes

Examination: ....

Radiologist	Film sequence	Cassette size	Notes

Examination:			
Radiologist	Film sequence	Cassette size	Notes

Examination: ....

Radiologist	Film sequence	Cassette size	Notes

Examination:			
Radiologist	Film sequence	Cassette size	Notes

Examination:			
Radiologist	Film sequence	Cassette size	Notes

Examination:			
Radiologist	Film sequence	Cassette size	Notes

Examination: ....

Radiologist	Film sequence	Cassette size	Notes

Examination:			
Radiologist	Film sequence	Cassette size	Notes

Examination: ....

Radiologist	Film sequence	Cassette size	Notes

Examination:			
Radiologist	Film sequence	Cassette size	Notes

Examination:			
Radiologist	Film sequence	Cassette size	Notes

Examination:			
Radiologist	Film sequence	Cassette size	Notes

Examination: ....

Radiologist	Film sequence	Cassette size	Notes

Examination:			
Radiologist	Film sequence	Cassette size	Notes

	Examination:		
Radiologist	Film sequence	Cassette size	Notes

	Examination:		
Radiologist	Film sequence	Cassette size	Notes

Examination: ....

Radiologist	Film sequence	Cassette size	Notes

Examination:			
Radiologist	Film sequence	Cassette size	Notes

Non-accidental injury

Projection	Cassette size	Exposure	Notes

NB: Requires two radiographers
Letters/markers should be present on radiographs – no crunch markers!

Myeloma

Projection	Cassette size	Exposure	Notes

Renal			
Projection	Cassette size	Exposure	Notes

Projection	Cassette size	Exposure	Notes

Abortion	Natural or artificial expulsion from uterus
Abscess	Localised collection of pus
Achalasia	Obstruction due to non-relaxant muscular sphincter
Achondroplasia	Dwarfism due to the failure of endochondral ossification
Acoustic neuroma	Benign tumour of the eighth cranial nerve
Acromegaly	Overgrowth of soft and bony structures, result of pituitary tumour
Addison's disease	Chronic adrenal cortical failure associated with adults
Adenoma	Benign tumour of glandular tissues
Adhesions	Fibrous tissue bands due to inflammation or surgery
Akathisia	The inability to sit still associated with Parkinson's disease
Albuminuria	Albumin found in the urine
Alopecia	Baldness
Alport's syndrome	Albuminuria associated with deafness and eye lesions
Aluminosis	Lung fibrosis due to inhalation of metallic dust
Amenorrhoea	Absence of menstrual periods
Anencephaly	Congenital absence of cranial vault and brain
Aneurysm	Localised distension of an artery or duct
Angioma	Benign tumour associated with blood vessels
Ankylosing spondylitis	Arthritis of the spine resulting in fusion of the vertebrae
Ankylosis	Immobilisation of a joint
Antepartum	Before delivery
Aortic regurgitation	Blood backflow through the aortic valve of the heart
Aortic stenosis	Narrowing of the aortic valve
Arachnodactyly	Abnormally long fingers or toes
Areflexia	Absence of reflexes
Arteriosclerosis	Hardening of the arteries with narrowing of the lumen
Arthrodesis	Surgical fusion of a joint
Asbestosis	Lung disease due to exposure to dust (asbestos)
Ascites	Excess fluid in the peritoneum
Asthenia	Generalised and nonspecific weakness
Astrocytoma	A cranial tumour – the commonest form of glioma
Atelectasis	Collapse or non-expansion of the lungs
Atheroma	Fatty degeneration of inner linings of blood vessels
Atherosclerosis	Arterial disease with atheroma
Atresia	Failure of normal lumen to develop in hollow organs
Atrophy	Abnormal reduction in the size of tissues
Auricular fibrillation	Abnormality in the rhythm of heart beat
Avulsion	The forcible tearing away of bone fragments
Benign	Non-malignant, simple tumour
Bennett's fracture	Fracture of the base of the thumb involving the joint
Brachycephaly	A short high skull associated with premature suture closure
Bright's disease	Kidney disease, a form of nephritis
Bronchiectasis	Dilatation of the bronchi, often associated with infection
Bursa	Pocket-like structure containing a small quantity of fluid
Bursitis	Inflammation of a bursa
Calculus	A stone
Callus	Tempory bone formed during the process of healing
Carcinoma	A malignant tumour of epithelial origin
Carcinomatosis	Diffuse spread of carcinoma
Carditis	Inflammation of the heart
Cellulitis	Spreading infection of connective tissue
Cholecystectomy	Surgical removal of the gallbladder
Cholecystitis	Inflammation of the gallbladder
Cholelithiasis	Formation of stones within the gallbladder or ducts
Chondroma	A benign tumour of cartilage
Chondromalacia patellae	Juvenile osteoarthritis-like condition of the knee
Chordoma	Rare locally malignant tumour of the skull or sacral region
Claudication	Deficient blood supply, intermittent pain on exertion
Coarctation	Congenital narrowing in the thoracic aorta
Coeliac disease	Malabsorption and gluten sensitivity associated with loss of villi
Colostrum	High protein milk produced in the first days of lactation
Congenital	Present at birth

Congestion	Accumulation of fluid in the body tissues
Consolidation	Solidification of exudate, usually in the lungs
Contusion	Bruising
Coxa vara	Congenital deformity of the neck of femur
Craniostenosis	Premature closure of cranial sutures
Crepitus	The sound and feel of a fracture or surfaces rubbing together
Crohn's disease	Chronic nonspecific inflammation of any part of intestine
Croup	Infant cough with dyspnoea due to mucosal swelling
Cushing's syndrome	Effect of excess adrenal corticosteroids
Cyanosis	Bluish skin caused by insufficient oxygenation
Cyst	Hollow sac containing fluid or semi-solid material
Dacryoadenitis	Inflammation of the lacrimal glands
Degloving	Traumatic detachment of the skin from underlying tissues
Dermoid cyst	Cystic structure containing fluid and semi-solid material
Dextrocardia	The siting of the heart on the right side of the thorax
Diabetes mellitus	High blood sugar due to a deficiency of insulin
Diaphysis	The shaft of a long bone
Dislocation	Displacement of the bones that form a joint
Diverticulitis	Inflammation of the diverticulae of the bowel
Diverticulosis	Presence of numerous diverticula in the bowel
Diverticulum	Abnormal outpouching arising from a hollow organ
Ductus arteriosus patent	Failure of the ductus arteriosus to close after birth
Dysmenorrhoea	Painful menstrual periods
Dyspnoea	Difficulty in breathing
Dyspepsia	Indigestion
Dysphagia	Difficulty in swallowing
Dysphasia	Speech defect due to cerebral cortical mechanisms
Dysplasia	Abnormality of growth
Dystrophy	Abnormal bone growth associated with poor nutrition
Dysuria	Difficult and or painful micturition

Ectopic pregnancy	Fetus formed outside the uterus
Effusion	Formation of fluid within a body cavity
Embolism	Obstruction of blood flow by a blood clot or other matter
Emphysema	Excessive size of lung alveoli due to prolonged stress
Empyema	Abscess containing pus within an enclosed cavity
Encephalitis	Inflammation of the brain
Enchondroma	Benign tumour of cartilage growing within bone
Endocarditis	Inflammation of the endocardium of the heart
Enteritis	Regional inflammation of the intestine
Enuresis	Urinary incontinence
Epilepsy	Episodic disorder of brain function producing a fit
Epistaxis	Nose bleed
Epithelioma	Tumour derived from epithelial cells
Ewing's sarcoma	Small cell carcinoma affecting juvenile bones
Exacerbation	Increase in severity
Exostosis	Outgrowth of bone
Fibrillation	Rapid and irregular movements of muscle fibres
Fibroid	Simple tumour of the uterus
Fistula	Abnormal communication between organs
Flail chest	Multiple rib fractures producing paradoxical movement of the chest wall
Freiberg's disease	Aseptic necrosis of metatarsal head, usually the second
Galeazzi's fracture	Fracture of radius with dislocation of radial head
Gangrene	Tissue necrosis due to lack of blood supply
Glioma	General term for tumour of nervous system
Glycosuria	Sugar in the urine
Goitre	Enlargement of the thyroid
Gout	Disease due to excess uric acid in the blood
Grand mal	Epilepsy with classical epileptic fits
Gravid	Pregnant woman
Greenstick fracture	Partial fracture or bending of children's bones
Guillain-Barré syndrome	Acute disorder with loss of conduction in peripheral nerves associated with respiratory difficulty

Haemangioma	Tumour of vascular tissues
Haematemesis	Vomiting of blood
Haematuria	Blood in the urine
Haemoptysis	Coughing-up of blood
Hallux valgus	Deviation of the big toe towards the other toes
Hemiplegia	Paralysis of one side of the body
Hepatitis	Inflammation of the liver
Hernia	Abnormal protrusion of tissue through any orifice
Hiatus hernia	Protrusion of abdominal organ through the diaphragm
Hirschsprung's disease	Congenital absence of muscle layer in the colon
Hodgkin's disease	Disease of the lymphatic system
Hydatid cyst	Cyst formed by infestation of a tapeworm
Hydrocephalus	Excess cerebrospinal fluid within the skull vault
Hydronephrosis	Enlargement of the kidney due to obstruction
Hydropneumothorax	The presence of fluid and air in the pleural cavity
Hydrothorax	The presence of fluid in the pleural cavity
Hyperglycaemia	Excessive sugar in the bloodstream
Hypernephroma	Carcinoma of the renal parenchyma
Hyperplasia	Tissue enlargement, without neoplasia
Hypertension	Abnormal high blood pressure
Hypertrophy	Enlargement of an organ through increase in tissue
Hypoplasia	Underdevelopment
Idiopathic	A disease of unknown origin
Ileitis	Inflammation of the ileum
Ileostomy	Artificial opening of the ileum onto the abdominal wall
Ileus	Intestinal obstruction
Infarction	Death of cells due to termination of blood supply
Inflammation	A local reaction of the body's cells to damage or infection
Intussusception	Obstruction in infants due to invagination of part of gut into a lower segment
Ischaemia	Local inadequacy of blood supply
Jaundice	Yellowing of skin due to excessive bilirubin in the blood
Kienböck's disease	Aseptic necrosis of lunate bone
Klippel–Feil syndrome	Congenital short neck with fusion of vertebrae
Köhler's disease	Aseptic necrosis of navicular bone
Kyphosis	Excessive backward convexity of the spine
Laminectomy	Surgical approach to the cord by removal of lamina
Lesion	Any injury or damage to tissue
Leukaemia	Malignant disease of blood, excessive production of white cells
Lipoma	Benign tumour developing from fat cells
Lordosis	Excessive forward convexity of the spine
Lumbago	Local pain arising from the lumbar spine
Lymphoma	Tumour of the lymphoid tissues
Malaise	A general feeling of being unwell
Malignant	Life-threatening tumour producing secondary effects
Mastectomy	Surgical removal of the breast
Mastoidectomy	Sugical operation on the mastoid air cells
Meckel's diverticulum	Outpouching of ileal wall, rudimentary remains of a duct
Megacolon	Dilation of the colon associated with constipation
Melaena	Faeces blackened by blood
Melanoma	Tumour of melanocytes, which are pigment-producing cells in the skin
Menière's disease	Disease of the inner ear associated with tinnitus and vertigo
Meninges	Membranes covering the brain and spinal cord
Meningioma	Generally benign tumour of the meninges
Meningitis	Inflammation of the meninges
Meningocoele	Congenital herniation of meninges through the skull or cord
Menorrhagia	Excessive loss of blood during menstrual periods
Meniscectomy	Surgical removal of cartilage from the knee joint
Multigravida	Woman with one or more previous pregnancies
Multipara	Woman who has given birth to one or more children
Mumps	An acute infection of the parotid salivary gland
Myasthenia gravis	Disease associated with voluntary muscle weakness

Myeloma	Tumour of bone marrow, characterised by multiple tumours
Myocarditis	Inflammation of the myocardium
Myositis ossificans	Ossification of a haematoma over bone following trauma
Naevus	A birth mark or mole on the skin
Necrosis	Death of an organ or tissue within a living body
Neoplasm	A tumour that can be benign or malignant
Nephrectomy	The surgical removal of a kidney
Nephritis	Inflammation of the kidney
Nephrostomy	Surgical drainage of the kidney
Neuralgia	Pain arising from the nervous system
Neuroblastoma	Malignant tumour in children arising from adrenal medulla
Neurofibroma	Benign tumour arising from the fibrous sheath of a nerve
Oedema	Increase in fluid within the tissues
Oesophageal varices	Dilated veins of the lower oesophagus associated with portal hypertension
Osgood–Schlatter disease	Osteochondritis of the tibial tubercle
Osteitis	Inflammation of bone
Osteoarthritis	Chronic degenerative arthritis
Osetochondroma	Benign tumour composed of bone and cartilage
Osteoclastoma	Bone tumour associated with long bone ends in young adults
Osteogenesis imperfecta	Defect of bone formation, with fragile easily fractured bones
Osteoma	Benign bone tumour associated with the skull or facial bones
Osteomalacia	Defective calcifaction of bone due to vitamin D deficiency
Osteomyelitis	Inflammation of bone
Osteoporosis	Loss of bone tissue with inadequate new replacement
Otalgia	Pain in the ear

Otitis media	Inflammation of the middle ear
Otorrhoea	A discharge from the ear
Paget's disease	Chronic disease of bone associated with softening and deformity
Pancreatitis	Inflammation of the pancreas
Papilloedema	Swelling of the optic disc due to raised intracranial pressure
Papilloma	Benign tumour with a vascular core
Paralytic ileus	Intestinal obstruction due to cessation of peristalsis
Paraplegia	Paralysis of both lower limbs
Parkinson's disease	A degenerative disease associated with tremor and rigidity
Pericardial effusion	Effusion between the two layers of the pericardium
Pericarditis	Inflammation of the pericardium
Peritonitis	Inflammation of the peritoneum
Perthes' disease	Asceptic necrosis of the femoral head epithesis
Petit mal	Epilepsy without major fits
Phlebitis	Inflammation of a vein
Phlebolith	Calcified thrombus within a vein
Placenta praevia	Placenta in an abnormal position
Pleural effusion	Fluid in the pleural cavity
Pleurisy	Inflammation of the pleura
Pneumoconiosis	Lung disease resulting from inhaled dust particles
Pneumonectomy	Surgical removal of a lung
Pneumoperitoneum	The presence of air or gas in the peritoneum
Pneumothorax	The presence of air in the pleural cavity
Poliomyelitis	Inflammation of the grey matter of the spinal cord associated with the poliovirus
Polycythaemia	Increase in the number of red blood cells in the blood
Polydactyly	Congenital presence of extra digits
Polyp	A protuberance of tissue on a stalk
Polyuria	Excessive production of urine
Pott's fracture	Fracture of the lower end of the tibia and fibula
Poupart's ligament	Inguinal ligament
Primigravida	A women pregnant for the first time

Primipara	A woman who has borne her first child
Prolapse	Abnormal descent of a structure within or into a cavity
Prostatectomy	Surgical removal of the prostate gland
Psoriasis	Common skin disease associated with red scaly patches
Pyelonephritis	Inflammation of the pelvis and calyces of the kidney
Pyloric stenosis	A narrowing of the pyloric canal
Pyrexia	A raised temperature associated with a fever
Quadriplegia	Paralysis of all limbs
Rheumatic fever	An infection affecting the heart, valves and the joints
Rheumatoid arthritis	Chronic type of arthritis affecting a number of joints
Rhinorrhoea	Any fluid discharge from the nose
Rickets	Softening and deformity of bone associated with lack of vitamin D in childhood
Rugae	Coarse surface folding (i.e. stomach lining)
Salpingitis	Inflammation of the fallopian tubes
Sarcoidosis	Chronic inflammatory disease of unknown cause
Sarcoma	Malignant tumour arising from connective tissues
Scheurmann's disease	Aseptic necrosis of the vertebral bodies associated with adolescents
Sciatica	Pain along the path of the sciatic nerve
Schmorl's node	Bone erosion associated with prolapse of a degenerate intervertebral disc
Scoliosis	Excessive lateral curvature of the spine
Seminoma	Malignant tumour of the testis associated with younger men
Shingles	A viral disease (chickenpox) of the nervous system
Sinusitis	Inflammation of the nasal accessory sinuses
Spalding's sign	Overlapping of the skull bones indicating fetal death
Spina bifida	Failure of posterior neural arch of a vertebra to develop and unite
Splenomegaly	Enlargement of the spleen
Spondylolisthesis	Forward slipping of L4 or L5 vertebrae due to defect
Spondylosis	Osteoarthritis of the spine

Stenosis	Narrowing of a previously patent passage
Still's disease	Juvenile rheumatoid arthritis
Stricture	Narrowing of a passage
Syndrome	A group of signs and symptoms of disease
Tachycardia	Abnormal rapid heart beat
Tenosynovitis	Inflammation of a tendon sheath
Teratoma	Complex tumour composed of multiple tissues derived from ovary or testis
Tetraplegia	Paralysis of all limbs
Thoracoplasty	Surgical local collapse of the lung by removal of several ribs
Thoracotomy	Surgical opening into the thoracic cavity
Thrombosis	Formation of a clot within a blood vessel
Thrombus	A blood clot
Thyrotoxicosis	Disease associated with overactivity of the thyroid gland
Tinnitus	Noises or ringing in the ears
Torticollis	Twisting of the head to the side associated with spasm of the neck muscles
Ulcer	An open sore of skin or membrane
Uraemia	Symptoms associated with toxic substances in the bloodstream
Varices	Dilated veins
Vertigo	Giddiness
Vesical calculus	A bladder stone
Volvulus	Twisting of the bowel obstructing the lumen
Wegener's granuloma	Destructive lesion of nasopharynx - poor prognosis
Whiplash injury	Traumatic injury to cervical spine with acute flexion and extension
Wilms' tumour	A malignant kidney tumour associated with young children
Xerosis	Dryness, often associated with the skin

INDICATOR	SEX	AGE	RANGE	UNIT	COMMENTS
BLOOD UREA		<54	2.4–7.0	mmol/l	Normal dose intravenous urogram ineffective if urea above 10 mmol/l
		>54	2.5–8.4	mmol/l	
SERUM BILIRUBIN			3.0–20	µmol/l	Oral cholecystography ineffective if above 20 µmol/l
POTASSIUM			3.6–5.0	mmol/l	
SODIUM			135–150	mmol/l	
URIC ACID	MALE		250–520	µmol/l	
	FEMALE		165–400	µmol/l	
ERYTHROCYTE	MALE		0–9 mm	/hour	A raised E.S.R is usually an indication of disease
SEDIMENTATION RATE (E.S.R)	FEMALE		0–15 mm	/hour	
BLEEDING TIME			3.0–7.0	min	

CLOTTING TIME
  Capillary
  Venous
			
			5–7
			4–7
				
				min
				min	

BLOOD SUGAR (FASTING)			3.3–6.7	mmol/l	
CHOLESTEROL			< 6.0	mmol/l	
GLUCOSE			2.8–8.9	mmol/l	
CALCIUM			2.1–2.6	mmol/l	
CHLORIDE			95–108	mmol/l	
BICARBONATE			25–35	mmol/l	
CREATININE			45–120	µmol/l	
ALBUMIN			34–50	g/l	
GLOBULIN			16–37	g/l	

AAA	Abdominal Aortic Aneurysm
Ab	Abortion
ACL	Anterior Cruciate Ligament
ADE	Acute Demyelinating Encephalitis
ADH	Antidiuretic Hormone
ADI	Acceptable Daily Intake
ADR	Adverse Drug Reaction
AIDS	Acquired Immune Deficiency Syndrome
ALARA	As Low As Reasonably Achievable
ALLO	Atypical *Legionella*-like Organisms
AMI	Acute Myocardial Infarction
AML	Acute Myeloid Leukaemia
ARDS	Acute Respiratory Distress Syndrome
ASD	Atrial Septal Defect
ASHD	Arteriosclerotic Heart Disease
ATN	Acute Tubular Necrosis
AVB	Atrioventricular Block
AVH	Acute Viral Hepatitis
AVM	Arteriovenous Malformation
AVR	Aortic Valve Replacement
BBB	Bundle Branch Block
BEL	Breech, Extended Legs
BFL	Breech, Flexed Legs
BI	Bone Injury
BMR	Basal Metabolic Rate
BMT	Bone Marrow Transplant
BO	Bowels Open
BPD	Biparietal Diameter
BPI	Blood Pessure Index
bpm	beats per minute
BSR	Blood Sedimentation Rate
Ca	Carcinoma
CAD	Coronary Artery Disease

CBF	Cerebral Blood Flow
CBP	Chronic Back Pain
CCF	Congestive Cardiac Failure
CDH	Congenital Dislocation of Hip or Coronary Heart Disease
CHF	Congestive Heart Failure
CIBD	Chronic Inflammatory Bowel Disease
CJD	Creutzfeldt–Jakob Disease
COAD	Chronic Obstructive Airways Disease
COPD	Chronic Obstructive Pulmonary Disease
CPB	Cardiopulmonary Bypass
CPR	Cardiopulmonary Resuscitation
CVA	Cerebrovascular Accident
CVP	Central Venous Pressure
DM	Diabetes Mellitus
DOA	Dead On Arrrival
DVT	Deep Vein Thrombosis
DXRT	Deep X-ray Therapy
EMI	Elderly with Mental Illness
ERCP	Endoscopic Retrograde Cholangiography Pancreatography
ESR	Erythrocyte Sedimentation Rate
EUA	Examination Under Anaesthetic
FB	Foreign Body
FFD	Focus–Film Distance
FHR	Fetal Heart Rate
FMNF	Fetal Movements Not Felt
FNA	Fine Needle Aspiration
GBS	Guillain–Barré Syndrome
GHRF	Growth Hormone Releasing Factor
GHIF	Growth Hormone Inhibiting Factor
GOO	Gastric Outlet Obstruction

GIT	Gastrointestinal Tract		MVD	Mitral Valve Disease
GU	Gastric Ulcer		Mx	Mastectomy
HGH	Human Growth Hormone		NAD	Nil Abnormal Detected
HPC	History of Present Complaint		NAI	Non-Accidental Injury
HRT	Hormone Replacement Therapy		NAR	Nasal Airway Resistance
			NFS	No Fracture Seen
IBD	Inflammatory Bowel Disease		NG	New Growth
IBS	Irritable Bowel Syndrome		NND	Neonatal Death
ICP	Intracranial Pressure		NWB	Non-Weight Bearing
IAM	Internal Auditory Meatus			
IDDM	Insulin Dependent Diabetes Mellitus		OA	Osteoarthritis
IOP	Intraocular Pressure		OC	Oral Contraceptive
IPH	Intrapartum Haemorrhage		OE	On Examination
ISD	Interventricular Septal Defect		ORIF	Open Reduction Internal Fixation
IUCD	Intrauterine Contraceptive Device			
IUD	Intrauterine Death/Device		PCL	Posterior Cruciate Ligament
IVD	Intervertebral Disc		PDA	Patent Ductus Arteriosus
IOFB	Intraocular Foreign Body		PID	Prolapsed Intervertebral Disc
			PIH	Pregnancy-Induced Hypertension
JCA	Juvenile Chronic Arthritis		PNS	Post Nasal Space
			PR	Per Rectum
LAO	Left Anterior Oblique		PTB	Pulmonary Tuberculosis
LBP	Low Back Pain		PTE	Pulmonary Thromboembolism
LFT	Liver Function Test		PTRF	Post Transplant Renal Failure
LLL	Left Lower Lobe		PUO	Pyrexia of Unknown Origin
LLO	*Legionella*-like Organisms		PV	Per Vaginam
LMP	Last Menstrual Period		PWB	Partial Weight Bearing
LUL	Left Upper Lobe			
			RAS	Renal Artery Stenosis
MABP	Mean Arterial Blood Pressure		RB	Recurrent Bleed
MI	Myocardial Infarction		RBBB	Right Bundle Branch Block
MPAP	Mean Pulmonary Artery Pressure		RDS	Respiratory Distress Syndrome
MR	Mitral Regurgitation		RLL	Right Lower Lobe
MSU	Mid-Stream Urine		RPN	Renal Papillary Necrosis

RTA	Road Traffic Accident
RUL	Right Upper Lobe
SAH	Subarachnoid Haemorrhage
SDH	Subdural Haemorrhage
SIDS	Sudden Infant Death Syndrome (Cot Death)
SOL	Space Occupying Lesion
TBI	Total Body Irradiation
TKN	Total Knee Replacement
TOF	Tracheo-Oesophageal Fistula
TSS	Toxic Shock Syndrome

TURP	Transurethral Resection of Prostate
Tx	Transplant
URTI	Upper Respiratory Tract Infection
UTI	Urinary Tract Infection
VEB	Ventricular Ectopic Beats
VLBW	Very Low Birth Weight
WB	Weight Bearing
WBC	White Blood Cell
WG	Wegener's Granuloma

Adams J. C. (1987)	Outline of Fractures	9th edn., Churchill Livingstone, Edinburgh
Bryan G. (1982)	Johnson and Kennedy – *Radiographic Skeletal Anatomy*	2nd edn., Churchill Livingstone, Edinburgh
Haglar M. J. (1993)	*The Pocket Rad Tech*	W. B. Saunders Company, London
Kimber P. M. (1983)	*Radiography of the Head*	Churchill Livingstone, Edinburgh
Prime N. (1987)	*Introduction to Pathology for Radiographers*	Harper & Rowe, London
Raby N., Berman L., de Lacy G. (1995)	*Accident and Emergency Radiology – A Survival Guide*	W. B. Saunders Company, London
Stripp W. J., Murray R. O., Jacobson H. G. (1979)	*Clark's Positioning in Radiography*	11th edn., Aspen Publishers, Rockville MD